THE BIOLOGY OF

HYDRA

AND OF SOME OTHER

COELENTERATES:

1961

EDITED BY: HOWARD M. LENHOFF
W. FARNSWORTH LOOMIS

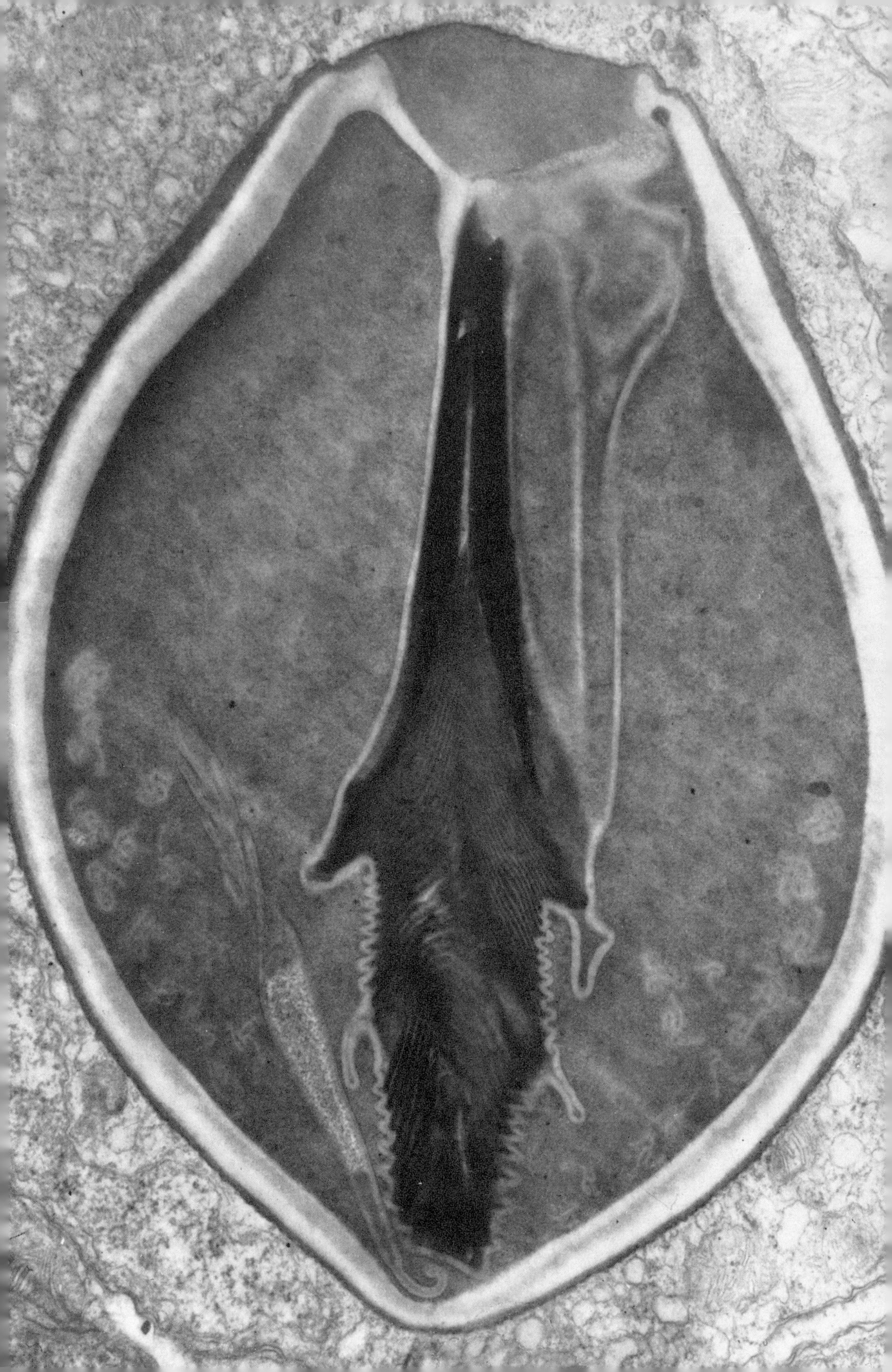

THE BIOLOGY OF
HYDRA
AND OF SOME OTHER COELENTERATES:
1961

Edited by

Howard M. Lenhoff
and
W. Farnsworth Loomis

UNIVERSITY OF MIAMI PRESS
CORAL GABLES, FLORIDA

Library of Congress Card Number 61-18157

Printed in the United States of America
by
Rose Printing Company
Tallahassee, Miami, Jacksonville, St. Augustine

Foreword

"Further, I discovered a little animal whose body was at times long, at times drawn up short, and to the middle of whose body . . . . a still lesser animalcule of the same make seemed to be fixed fast by its hinder end . . . [At that time the little animalcule] had only four very short little horns, yet after the lapse of sixteen hours I saw that its body and its horns had increased in bigness, and four hours later still I saw it had forsaken its mother."[1]

In this remarkable letter written on Christmas Day, 1702, Antony van Leeuwenhoek amazed members of the Royal Society by announcing a discovery of dual significance. While reporting the initial description of the organism which we now call hydra,[2] he also described the first instance of asexual reproduction ever observed in animals. Thus, from their very discovery hydra have served to reveal new biological phenomena.

More startling findings with hydra followed when, in 1744, Abraham Trembley published in his superb *Mémoires* an exposition of: the first controlled experiments on regeneration; the first successful animal grafting experiments; the first investigations of phototaxis in lower invertebrates; the first vital staining of tissues; and thorough proof of asexual reproduction by budding. Two centuries have passed since Trembley made these revolutionary discoveries, an interim during which research on hydra was sporadic, and hydra were relegated to a subsidiary role in classroom instruction. In the

---

[1] Letter 149, December 25, 1702. Quoted in *Antony van Leeuwenhoek and his "Little Animals,"* by Clifford Dobell, Dover Publs., N. Y., 1960, pp. 280-281.

[2] In this volume we have adopted, whenever possible, the following usages for purposes of uniformity and clarity: (a) *Hydra*, when referring to one or more specimens of this genus if the species has already been clearly indicated; (b) hydra, when referring to one or more specimens of the Hydridae in general, and when the species is not indicated; (c) hydras, when referring to a number of genera of the Hydridae.

last decade, however, a renaissance in the use of hydra as a laboratory animal has been in progress.

The return of hydra to their original status as laboratory animals is marked by the publication of *The Biology of Hydra : 1961.* This is the first book since Trembley's *Mémoires* devoted to original research reports dealing for the most part with hydra. The present volume is a record of a symposium on the *Physiology and Ultrastructure of Hydra and of some other Coelenterates* held March 29-31, 1961, at the Fairchild Tropical Gardens, Coral Gables, Florida.

In this symposium, North American workers representing many different fields of biology described their current work. They started with a discussion of the fine structure of hydra cells and mesoglea. Following a session devoted to the development, chemistry, and function of nematocysts, they considered the subjects of feeding and nutrition. Next, research on tissue culture, symbiosis, and calcification were discussed. A session concerning the various forces responsible for the patterns of colonial hydroids led, in turn, to a consideration of cellular differentiation and then of aging in both mortal and immortal coelenterate types. Appropriately, attention turned at last to regeneration and to new birth as seen in budding.

In organizing this symposium, the editors desired to bring about an integration of knowledge from a large variety of disciplines. Electron microscopists, naturalists, biochemists, and developmental biologists ordinarily do not read or publish in the same journals. The aim of the symposium was, therefore, to effect an *interdisciplinary* synthesis which might otherwise take years by normal channels. Accordingly, the discussions that followed each talk are included because they point out some of the many unsolved problems and therefore should prove of value in stimulating further investigations.

Much of the work presented at this symposium is in an early stage. At times we have thought that perhaps these results are too preliminary and should only be compiled after more data have been accumulated. The situation is analogous to constructing a new building. At times we might feel that all such work should proceed behind walls marked "Work in Progress. No Admittance." At other times we are intrigued with the very smell of sawdust and of wet paint. It is in this latter spirit that the volume was compiled, for these efforts, given time, may well show that hydra are particularly favorable material for the investigation of cellular and intercellular problems. History at least supports this view, because it was in hydroid material that asexual reproduction and regeneration were first discovered over two hundred years ago.

"I cut off the heads of the one that had seven, and after a few days I saw in it a prodigy scarcely inferior to the fabulous Hydre of Lernaea. It acquired seven new heads.... But here is something more than the legend dared to invent: the seven heads that I cut off from this Hydre, after being fed, became perfect animals...."[3]

W. FARNSWORTH LOOMIS, M.D.
Greenwich, Connecticut

HOWARD M. LENHOFF, Ph.D.
Miami, Florida

September 21, 1961

[3] Abraham Trembley, 1744. *Mémoires, pour servir à l'histoire d'un genre de polypes d'eau douce, à bras en forme de cornes.* Leide (Verbeek), p. 246. Quoted in *Abraham Trembley of Geneva*, John R. Baker, Arnold & Co., London, 1952, p. 34. (A complete translation, to be published, S. G. Lenhoff and H. M. Lenhoff, University of Miami Press.)

Front row: L. Muscatine, C. F. Lytle, R. L. Wood, E. D. Wangersky, C. M. Fulton, G. O. Mackie, C. Hand. Second row: R. Vishniac, G. B. Chapman, W. F. Loomis, H. M. Lenhoff, A. L. Loomis, D. M. Ross, S. Crowell, Y. F. Li, D. L. Claybrook, L. M. Passano. Third row: E. J. Martin, J. H. Phillips, E. S. Kline, G. F. Gauthier, E. Palincsar, D. B. Slautterback, B. Schuster, P. Lunger, A. Hess, P. Wangersky, J. H. Welsh, C. E. Lane, R. E. Eakin, B. L. Strehler, H. D. Park, R. Bryden, A. L. Burnett, T. F. Goreau, S. A. Wainwright, P. Broberg.

Participants

Barbara O. Alving
Eric Alving
Reza Bashey
Robert J. Boucek
B. Bourne
John Bovaird
Patricia Broberg
Robert R. Bryden
Stanley Burg
Allison Burnett
F. Gray Butcher
Edward L. Chambers
George B. Chapman
David L. Claybrook
Sears Crowell
Robert E. Eakin
Don W. Fawcett
Hector Fernandez
Bernard Fritzie
Chandler Fulton
Geraldine F. Gauthier
Lauren C. Gilman
Thomas Goreau
C. T. Grabowski
Cadet Hand
Arthur Hess
Ray M. Iverson
Edward Kline
A. R. Krall
Charles E. Lane
Edward Larson
W. Henry Leigh
Howard M. Lenhoff
Yu-Ying Fu Li
Alfred L. Loomis
W. Farnsworth Loomis
Philip Lunger
Charles F. Lytle
G. O. Mackie
A. G. Matoltsy
J. Marsh
Edgar J. Martin
N. Mason
Leonard Muscatine
Nancy L. Noble
Edward E. Palincsar
Helen D. Park
L. M. Passano
John H. Phillips
Earl R. Rich
Gordon C. Ring
D. M. Ross
K. Savard
Harriet Schapiro
David B. Slautterback
Daryl Stafford
Bernard L. Strehler
W. J. van Wagtendonk
Stephen A. Wainwright
Peter Wangersky
Eleanor D. Wangersky
John H. Welsh
Richard L. Wood
Edmund Zaharowicz

Acknowledgements

It is a pleasure to acknowledge all those who helped in this venture: Mr. Nixon Smiley, Director, and Mr. S. Kiem, Superintendent, of the Fairchild Tropical Gardens, for their special care in providing facilities conducive to discussion; Miss H. Schapiro, Mr. B. Fritzie, Mr. H. Fernandez, Mr. D. Stafford, and Mr. E. Zaharowicz, graduate students of the University of Miami, for their help throughout the symposium; Mr. R. Conklin of the Miami Seaquarium, for being a generous host to the participants and their families; Mrs. N. Jaffe, Mrs. E. Hirshhorn, Mr. J. Bovaird, and Mr. H. Reasor, who, in addition to their regular responsibilities, contributed in the preparation of the recorded discussions and of the index of this volume; Dr. B. Strehler, for his most helpful suggestions in expediting publication; Drs. L. Muscatine and E. L. Chambers, for their many suggestions; and Dr. R. J. Boucek of the Howard Hughes Medical Institute, for his encouragement and for providing facilities for arranging the symposium. Finally, we wish to express our deep thanks to every participant of the symposium for his cheerful cooperation in responding to our seemingly endless requests for corrected manuscripts, discussions, and galleys.

Contents

The Fine Structure of Cells in *Hydra*

Arthur Hess[1]
Department of Anatomy, Washington University School of Medicine, St. Louis, Missouri.

Hydra can be considered to have the following anatomical regions: tentacles, hypostome or mouth region, column or stomach, peduncle and basal disk. Sections of the column will serve most frequently to introduce the general histology of hydra. Then variations of the different body regions will be presented.

Hydra has in general two cellular layers, ectoderm or epidermis and endoderm or gastrodermis separated by a layer called mesoglea. The ectoderm is composed basically of epithelio-muscular cells and contains dispersed cnidoblasts or nematocyst-bearing cells and interstitial cells or undifferentiated cells. Gland cells occur in specialized regions. The endoderm contains gland cells, digestive cells and interstitial cells in its generalized areas. Cnidoblasts occur only rarely in the endoderm. The mesoglea is acellular.

Whole *Hydra oligactis* were fixed in an extended state in Dalton's fluid, a solution containing 1% osmium tetroxide, 1% potassium dichromate at a pH of 7.2 to 7.6 and 0.85% sodium chloride, in an ice bath for 15-45 minutes. Sometimes, the *Hydra* was divided into its various body regions; at other times, the animals were treated as a whole. They were then dehydrated in alcohol and embedded in methacrylate or araldite. Some sections were stained with lead acetate or potassium permanganate. They were photographed in the electron microscope.

---

[1]The author wishes to acknowledge the participation of Dr. A. I. Cohen and Mrs. Dorothy Sanderson in this study. The author's present address is Department of Physiology, University of Utah College of Medicine, Salt Lake City, Utah.

GENERAL HISTOLOGY

THE ECTODERM

Epithelio-muscular cells (Figs. 1, 3). Vacuolated cells are seen in the ectoderm. Their nuclei are large, of even granular texture, and contain prominent nucleoli. These cells have a few double membranes and many mitochondria in their cytoplasm. They frequently contain dense inclusions, which we have not as yet identified. Small vacuoles, in addition to the large ones, are present. Within these cells and accumulated at their base, closely packed bundles of fine fibrils arranged in parallel and running longitudinally with respect to the column axis are seen. The muscle system will be considered separately later.

These cells, frequently but not always, are the surface cells of *Hydra*. The surface of *Hydra* is covered by a granular material resting on two membranes (Fig. 6). One membrane obviously belongs to the surface cells, usually epithelio-muscular, but can be, at times, the cnidoblast. The other membrane apparently does not belong to a cell. A short varying distance separates the outer membrane of the surface cell and the membrane on which the granular material rests. *Hydra,* therefore, appears to be covered over most of its surface by this thin cuticular material.

Interstitial cells (Figs. 4, 5). Groups of small, rounded cells occur in the ectoderm. They are numerous in some areas and absent from others. These appear to be interstitial cells. They are characterized by having a very finely granular particulate cytoplasm with no double membranes. Mitochondria and a Golgi apparatus are present. Their nuclei are evenly granular with one or more prominent nucleoli. The cells are frequently very intimately related to each other and at times, the limiting membranes between two adjacent cells appear to be lacking and the cells appear to be syncytial (Fig. 5). Since these cells give rise to cnidoblasts, some interstitial cells can be seen with a few double membranes in their cytoplasm suggesting that they are beginning their differentiation. These cells can be seen at times adjacent to the muscle layer on the mesoglea.

Cnidoblasts (Figs. 3, 7-10). Cnidoblasts frequently occur in groups and can be found near the mesoglea or sometimes forming the surface cell of *Hydra.* These cells have mitochondria and a Golgi apparatus. However, it is the presence of the double membranes or endoplasmic reticulum which renders these cells distinctive. The cnidoblasts apparently are derived from interstitial cells. The cnidoblasts bearing very immature nematocysts have a series of vesicles (Fig. 7). As the nematocyst matures, these vesicles increase in amount and extent and apparently coalesce until the system of double membranes within the cell becomes quite elaborate and striking (Fig. 8). The nematocyst increases in size and displaces the nucleus. In cnidoblasts with well-developed nematocysts, the double membranes begin to decrease in amount (Fig. 9). In cnidocytes having what appear to be mature nematocysts, the double membrane system appears to have regressed and the cytoplasm of the cells is again granular with only a few strands of double membrane remaining (Fig. 10).

These cells are also apparently in syncytial relation to each other and frequently, the cell membranes between adjacent cnidoblasts can be seen to be lacking. Apparently the syncytium is no longer present after the nematocysts are mature and the cnidoblasts have completed their differentiation and are called cnidocytes. Each mature cnidocyte appears surrounded by a complete cell membrane in the tentacle, as will be shown later.

THE MESOGLEA

(Figs. 1, 15, 16, 19-21). The mesoglea presents a varying appearance in electron micrographs. It may appear fibrous or granular. Some of this variability may be due to the state of contraction or extension of the *Hydra* during fixation. No cells are present. Pieces of cytoplasm seen in the mesoglea can be seen to be connected to ectoderm or endoderm cells which are pushing into the mesoglea. These pieces of cytoplasm are surrounded by a cell membrane and thus strictly are outside the mesoglea.

The mesoglea is apparently not surrounded by its own limiting membrane. It penetrates between the cells of the ectoderm and endoderm (see especially Figs. 15 and 19), and granules, similar to those seen in the mesoglea, can be found in extracellular spaces between ectodermal and endodermal cells (Figs. 15, 19, 23, 25).

Thus, the constituent cells of *Hydra* can be considered as embedded in mesoglea and the mesoglea forms a supporting substance for the cells.

THE ENDODERM

Gland cells (Figs. 11, 12). The gland cell pours its secretion into the lumen to break down the food and make its products available for digestion. Essentially only one kind of gland cell has been found. This cell contains a series of large interlacing vacuoles, which most frequently appear light, but sometimes dark. Toward the base of the cell, the vacuoles frequently are smaller than in the portion of cell near the lumen. The cell appears to be undergoing a process of manufacture of the vacuoles starting toward the base. Thus, various vacuolar arrangements can be seen, but they are believed to be stages in the appearance of a single kind of gland cell. Between the vacuoles, some mitochondria and double membranes appear. Toward the base of the cell, the vacuoles are not present and the cytoplasm is filled with mitochondria and double membranes. It is probably here where the manufacture of the vacuolar contents, which will be secreted into the lumen, begins. The nucleus of the cell is toward its base. This cell apparently does not rest upon the mesoglea.

The digestive cell (Figs. 13-16). The digestive cell absorbs the food products after action of the gland cell. The digestive cell also undergoes cyclical changes according to the feeding activities of *Hydra* and also contains various inclusions depending on the kind of food and time of feeding. The cell can appear columnar and rather well organized or can contain huge vacuoles. It has a light cytoplasm with mitochondria and a Golgi apparatus. The surface of the digestive cell usually has a series of small cytoplasmic projections or villi extending into the lumen (Fig. 14). The digestive cells contain the endodermal muscle filaments at their base and rest upon the mesoglea (Figs. 15, 16).

Flagella (Fig. 18). Apparently both gland cell and digestive cell have flagella. It is difficult to determine exactly how many project from each cell. Two to four flagella are commonly seen. The flagella present the nine peripheral and two central longitudinal filaments characteristic of motile flagella in other animals. These flagella differ slightly from those of other organisms in that they possess a relatively thick membrane surrounding the filaments which frequently becomes separated from the filaments so that its relation to the filaments does not appear as intimate as the relatively thin membrane enclosing flagella elsewhere.

THE MUSCULAR SYSTEM

(Figs. 1, 15, 16, 17, 20, 21). The ectodermal muscle layer runs essentially longitudinally, while the endodermal layer is predominantly transversely oriented. The muscle filaments contained as a cell organelle in the base of the epithelio-muscular and digestive cells run parallel to each other, appear to be essentially of one kind, present no cross striation, and hence can be considered as smooth muscle filaments. The muscle fibers run along the mesoglea. They appear to be anchored to the mesoglea by small cytoplasmic extensions of the cells containing them (see especially Figs. 15 and 16). These extensions are frequently more numerous and robust on the ectodermal side and sometimes muscle filaments extend into these cytoplasmic attachment roots. The ectodermal muscle filaments in the cytoplasmic extensions of the base of one epithelio-muscular cell are very intimately related to the muscle filaments of an adjacent epithelio-muscular cell. The extensions of the cells can dovetail with each other in finger-like extensions or can overlap each other. However, the filaments do not pass from one cell to another. The filaments sometimes appear to insert on the cell membrane and when this happens in adjacent cells, an apparent thickening of the adjacent cell membranes occurs and a desmosome-like effect is produced (Fig. 17). The digestive cells usually do not undergo such an intimate arrangement and adjacent digestive cells are related to each other by relatively smooth membranes.

There are points along which the mesoglea appears very thin or interrupted and where the ectoderm and endodermal muscle filaments, or at least the membranes of the cells containing them, are practically in contiguity (Figs. 20, 21). Probably some very thin mesogleal substance intervenes between them since, as mentioned above, all the cells are probably embedded in mesoglea. These points of contact between the muscle layers are fairly frequent and occur in all areas investigated.

THE RELATIONS OF CELLS TO EACH OTHER

The special relationships of muscle cells and the fact that all cells appear embedded in mesoglea have already been discussed. However, there are other peculiar relations of cells that should be mentioned. By no means are the limiting membranes of the cells smooth. At times, a button or snap fastener arrangement can be seen where one cell evaginates a piece of cytoplasm to rest in an indentation of an adjacent cell (Fig. 2). This causes the frequent appearance of circular areas of cytoplasm located between cells. In addition, terminal bars are seen between some cells lining the lumen (Fig. 14) and between other cells near the mesoglea (Fig. 19).

NERVE CELLS AND FIBERS

No cell was found which could be called a nerve cell. As explained above, the small circles located between cells, which may sometimes form clusters and appear like bundles of nerve fibers (Figs. 15, 18, 21, 26), probably result from the peculiar formations of the cell borders. There is the possibility that nerve tissue of *Hydra* may appear different in the electron microscope from that of other organisms, and we are thus unable to identify nerve cells or fibers in our electron micrographs. However, if the absence of nerve tissue in *Hydra* can be accepted, one may perhaps go further and wonder if, indeed, *Hydra* needs any nerves. The epithelio-muscular cells containing the muscle filaments are on the surface of the animal and there can act as receptor cells to lead the impulse to its muscle filament organelles. The impulse of one ectodermal muscle fiber could easily be transmitted to muscle filaments in adjacent epithelio-muscular cells. Endodermal muscle could conduct an impulse from one cell to another in a similar manner. Lastly, the interaction of ectodermal and endodermal muscle could well be achieved through the points where mesoglea is practically absent and the two muscle layers are essentially in contact. The ordinary slow movement which *Hydra* performs could well be subserved by muscle to muscle transmission.

REGIONAL HISTOLOGY

The hypostome (Figs. 26, 27). The hypostome has a relatively low-lying ectoderm (Fig. 26). The endoderm is extremely well-developed (Fig. 27). The very large cells and dense accumulations of gland cells sometimes practically obliterate the lumen.

The peduncle. The endoderm of the peduncle is reduced in extent and gland cells are absent. The digestive cells consist of very vacuolated thin strands of cytoplasm. The ectoderm is similar to that already described. The epithelio-muscular cells of this region are characterized by having granules near their surface (see Fig. 30).

The basal disk (Fig. 29). The endoderm of this area is like that of the peduncle. The ectoderm is characterized by the presence of a type of gland cell which consists mostly of double membranes and has large granules, similar to those seen in the epithelio-muscular cells of the peduncle, but much larger. These granules of the gland cells of the ectoderm in this area are apparently the substance produced to cement *Hydra* to the substratum. The ectodermal cells of the pedal disk have small extensions of cytoplasm or villi on their surface. No granular and cuticular material is present on the surface of *Hydra* at this level.

The tentacle (Figs. 22, 24, 28). The tentacle arises at the level of the hypostome. Sections through this region reveal a gradual change of the cells with the tentacle compared to the hypostome having a reduced endoderm and ectoderm, reduced number of gland cells, increased vacuolation of digestive cells, increased number of cnidocytes, and perhaps better development of the muscle filaments in the epithelio-muscular cells. The endoderm-mesoglea interface at this level exhibits a characteristic scalloped appearance (Fig. 28).

The endoderm of the tentacle is severely reduced (Fig. 22). It consists of very thin wisps of cytoplasm of digestive cells enclosing huge vacuoles. The ectoderm is also very thin and has a series of bulges or ridges. At the height of each ridge are present the cnidocytes containing apparently mature nematocysts (Fig. 22). The cnidocytes can be surrounded by the cytoplasm of epithelio-muscular cells. Sometimes the cnidocytes rest on the muscle layer, in which case, epithelio-muscular cell cytoplasm is on three sides of them (Figs. 22, 24). At other times, the cnidocyte is the surface cell (Fig. 24). However, as far as we can determine, each cnidocyte is enclosed by a complete cell membrane, even when one cnidocyte abuts against another (Fig. 24). Hence, the syncytial relationship of cnidoblasts with immature nematocysts seen in the column has broken down during the maturation of these cells seen as cnidocytes in the tentacle. Frequently, muscle filaments are present in the cnidocyte (Fig. 24). At what stage of cnidoblast development these muscle filaments make their appearance is unknown.

The bud (Fig. 30). We have not studied the bud in detail, but we have noticed that the ectodermal cells of mother and bud fuse insensibly with the cuticular layer of the mother continuous over the surface of the bud. The portion of bud attaching to the mother *Hydra* looks essentially like the peduncle of the mother *Hydra* with very vacuolated endodermal digestive cells and ectodermal epithelio-muscular cells containing granules near their surface.

Pertinent literature is cited in:

HESS, A., A. I. COHEN, and E. A. ROBSON. 1957. Observations on the structure of hydra as seen with the electron and light microscopes. *Quart. J. Microscop. Sci. 98*: 315-326.

EXPLANATION OF PLATES

All photographs are electron micrographs of *Hydra*. The line on the photographs indicates 1 μ.

PLATE I. Fig. 1. Cross section of the ectoderm showing the epithelio-muscular cells with their nuclei (N), inclusion bodies (I) frequently found in these cells, the muscle filaments at the base of the epithelio-muscular cell forming the ectodermal muscular layer (E), and the vacuoles (V) in the cells. M is the mesoglea.

Fig. 2. The arrows point to the "snap-fastener" relationship between two cells in the ectoderm where a portion of cytoplasm of one cell evaginates and indents an adjacent cell.

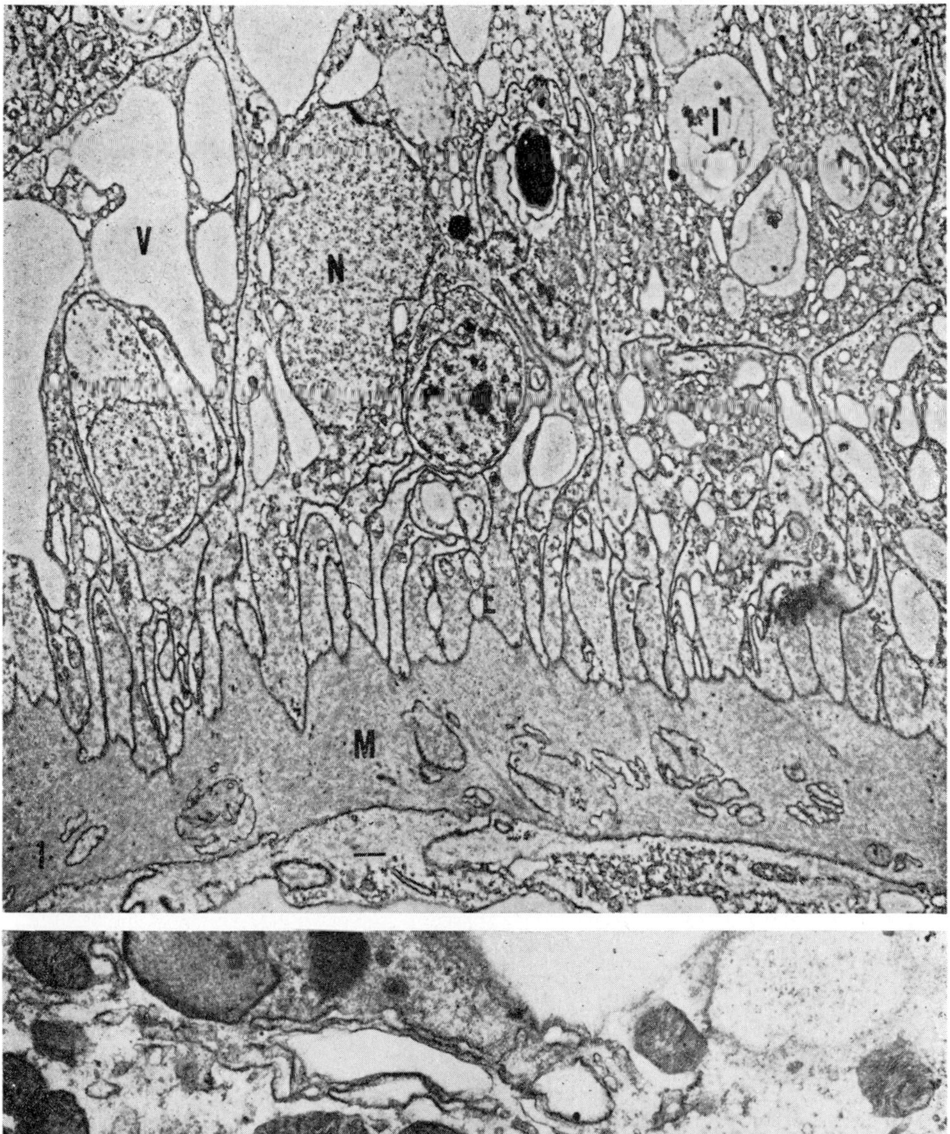

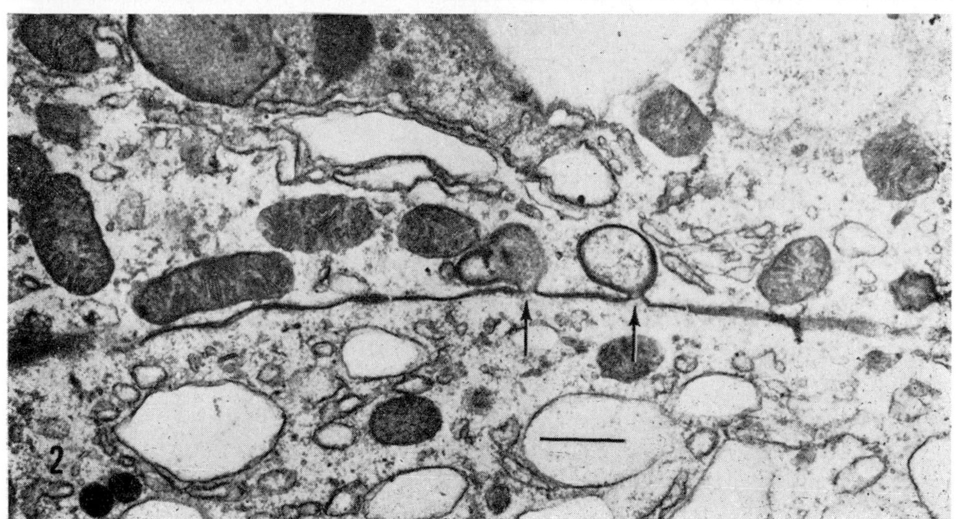
2

PLATE II. Fig. 3. Cross section of the ectoderm (surface of animal to to the left) showing epithelio-muscular cells (E), interstitial cells (I) and cnidoblasts (C), the latter in apparent syncytial relationship and having nematocysts and prominent double membranes.

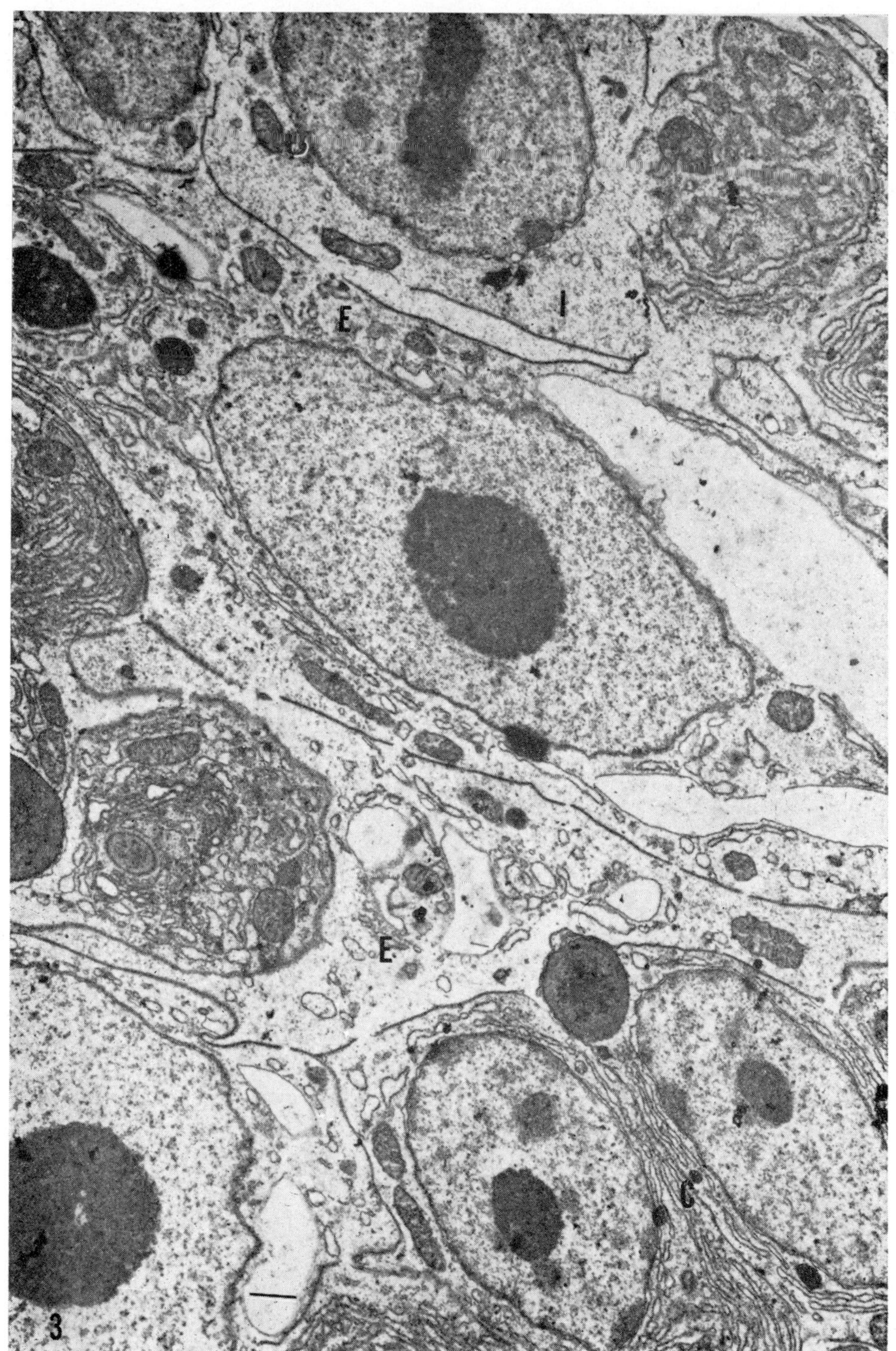
E
I
E
C
3

PLATE III. Fig. 4. An interstitial cell with its nucleus, granular cytoplasm, small mitochondria and a Golgi apparatus (G).

Fig. 5. The line, indicating the magnification, passes through an apparent cytoplasmic bridge between two adjacent interstitial cells.

Fig. 6. The surface of *Hydra* showing the cuticular substance resting on a membrane (Arrow # 1). Arrow # 2 shows another membrane, probably the limiting membrane of the surface cells.

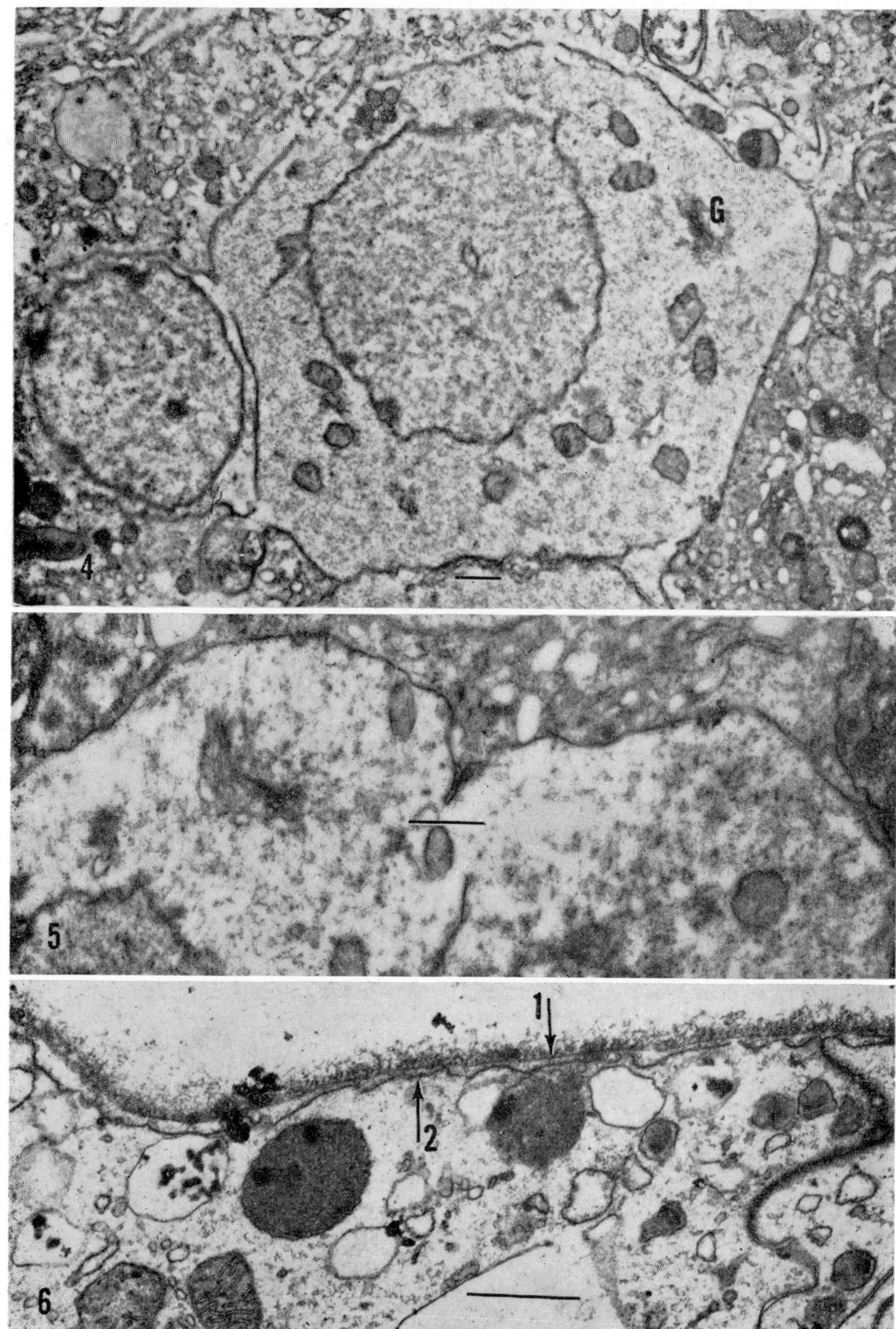
G
4
5
1
2
6

PLATE IV. Fig. 7. Cnidoblasts in syncytial relationship during the beginning of nematocyst development. Double membranes are present in the cytoplasm. See figures 8 to 10.

Fig. 8. Cnidoblasts in syncytial relationship at the height of nematocyst development. The double membranes in the cytoplasm have increased in amount and are very conspicuous in the cell.

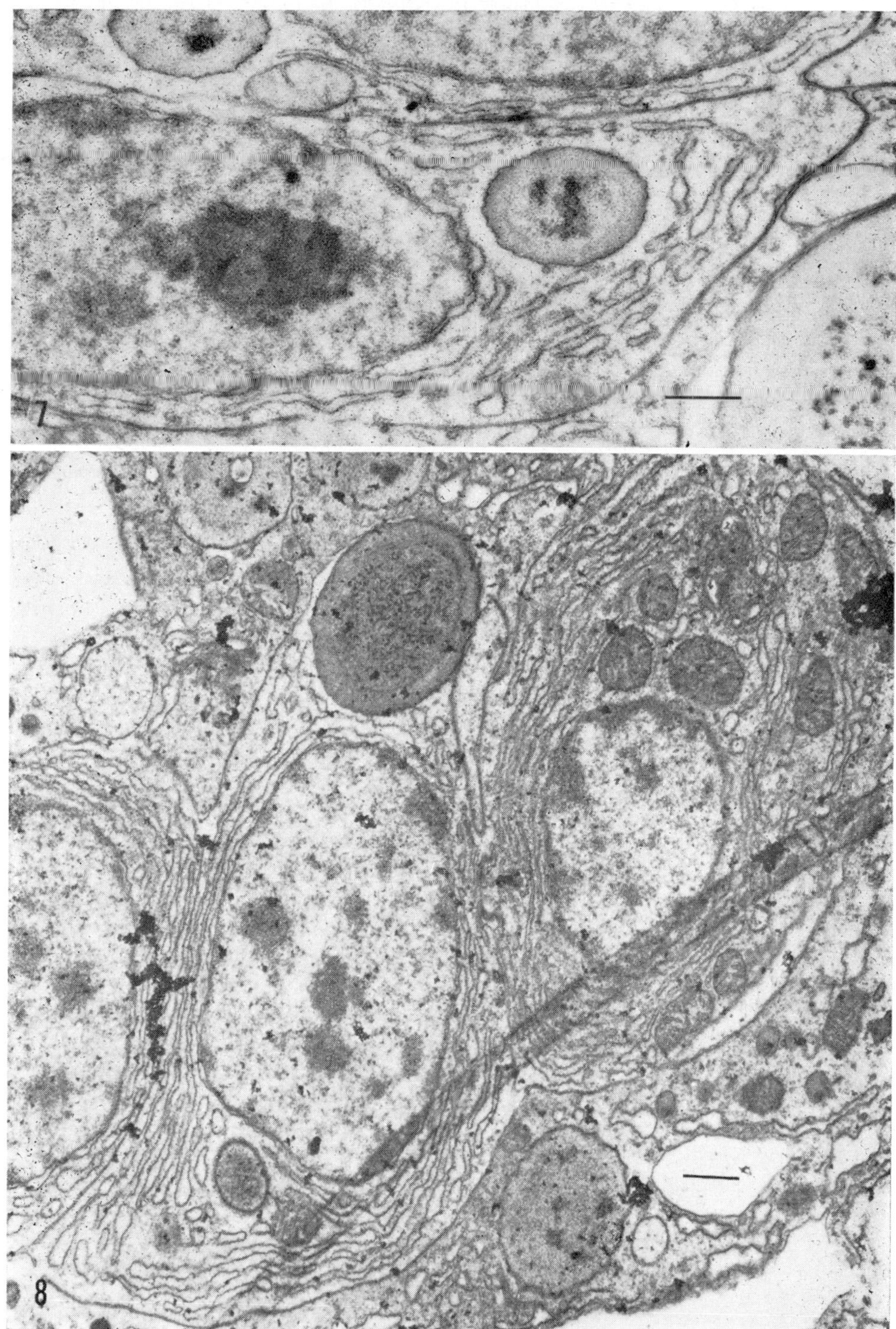
7
8

PLATE V. Fig. 9. Cnidoblast with a well-developed nematocyst. The double membranes are present, but are regressing in amount. See figure 8.

Fig. 10. Cnidocyte (mature cnidoblast) which contains a fully-developed nematocyst (not seen in figure). The double membranes in the cytoplasm are severely reduced in amount and only a few strands are left. G is a Golgi apparatus.

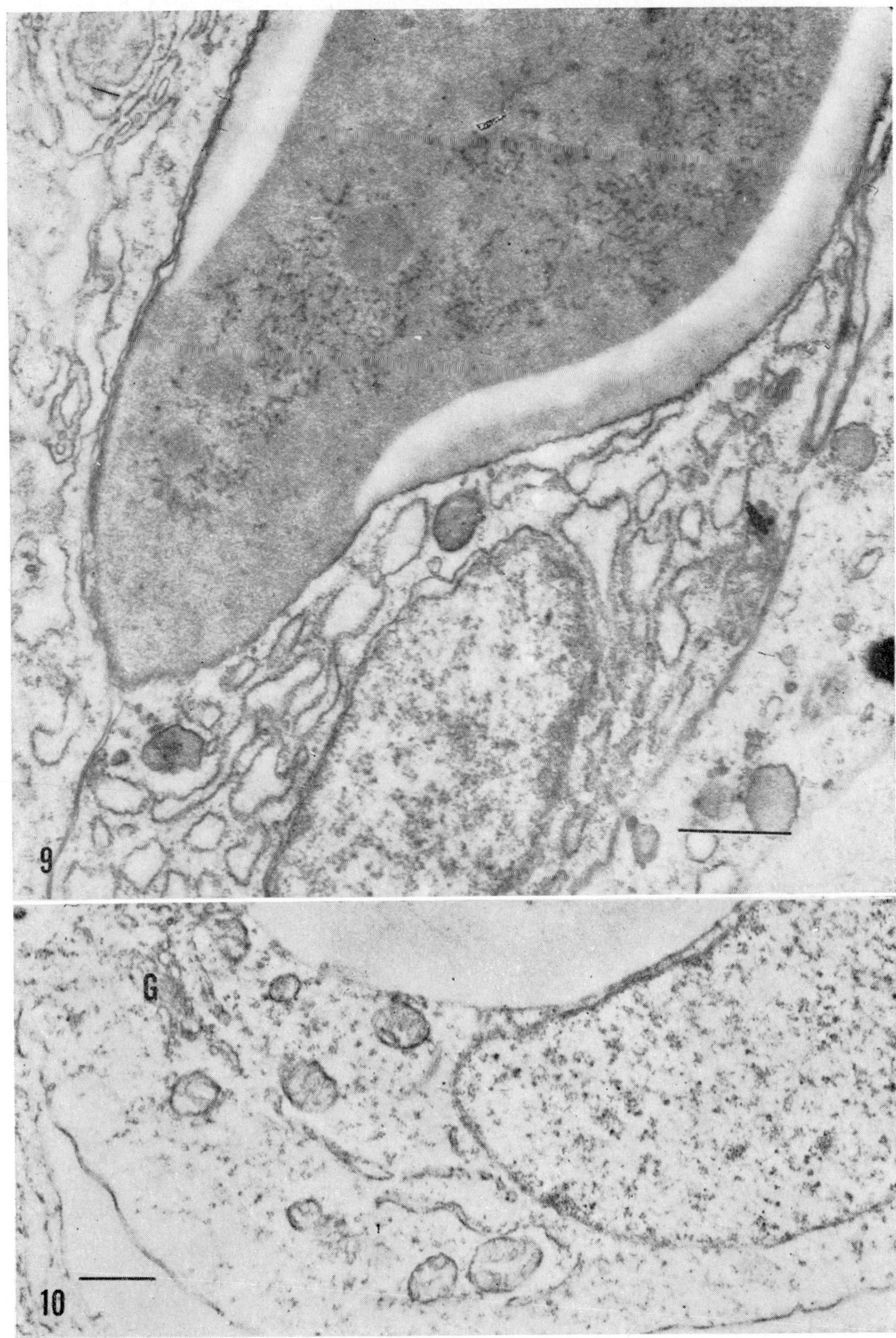
9
G
10

PLATE VI. Fig. 11. A gland cell with light vacuoles and concentrations of double membranes toward the base of the cell around its nucleus. The lumen is to the right.

Fig. 12. Dark vacuolar contents in another gland cell. Gland cells with dark vacuolar contents are seen only rarely.

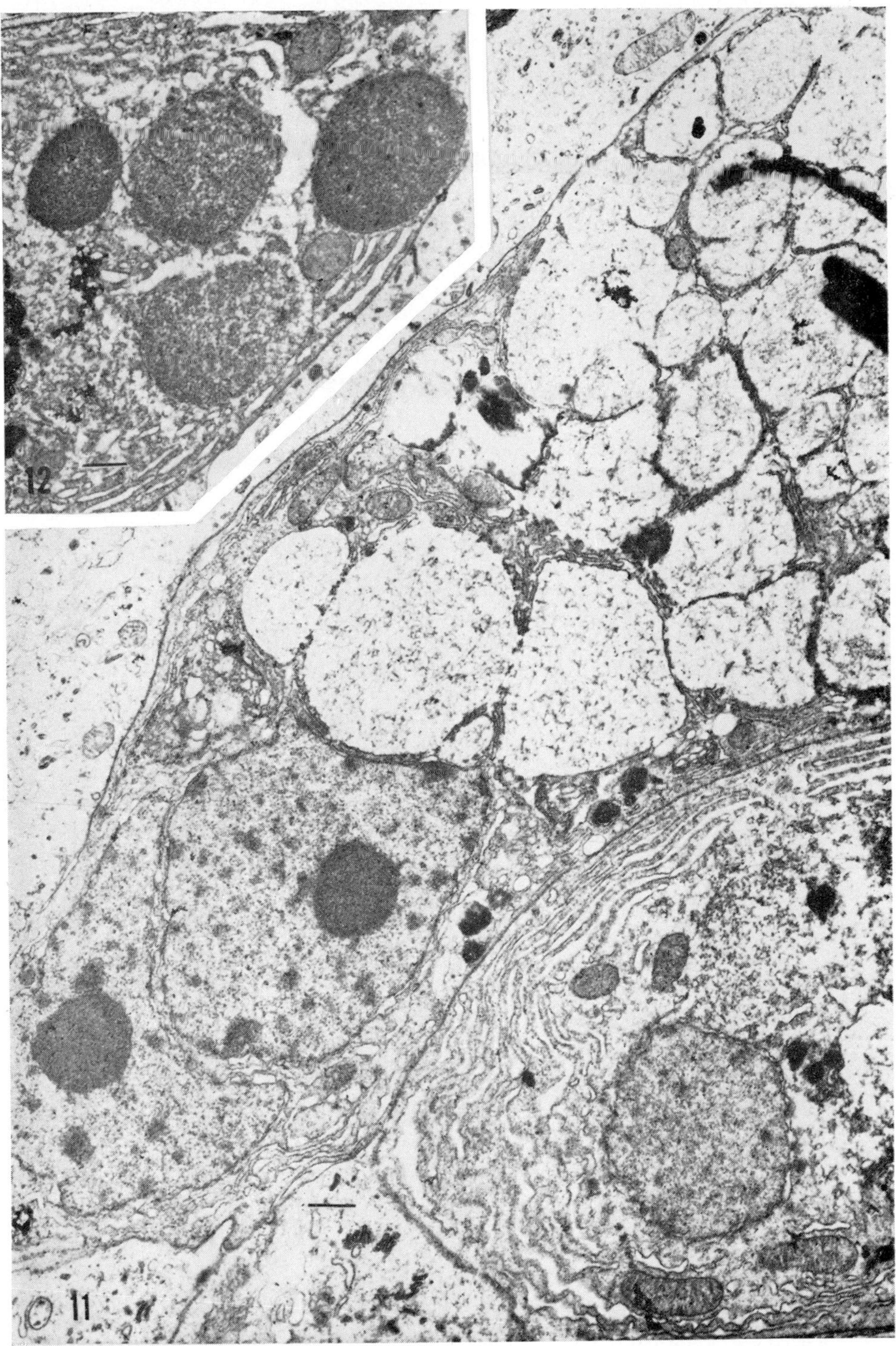
12
11

PLATE VII. Fig. 13. Digestive cells with relatively small vacuoles and large dark inclusion bodies, probably lipid. The nuclei of digestive cells and fairly light cytoplasm with mitochondria and some double membranes can also be seen.

Fig. 14. The surfaces of two digestive cells lining the lumen. The cells contain inclusion bodies. The cell membranes at the junction of the two cells near the lumen are rather dense for a short distance and resemble a terminal bar. Short tortuous process of cytoplasm extend into the lumen.

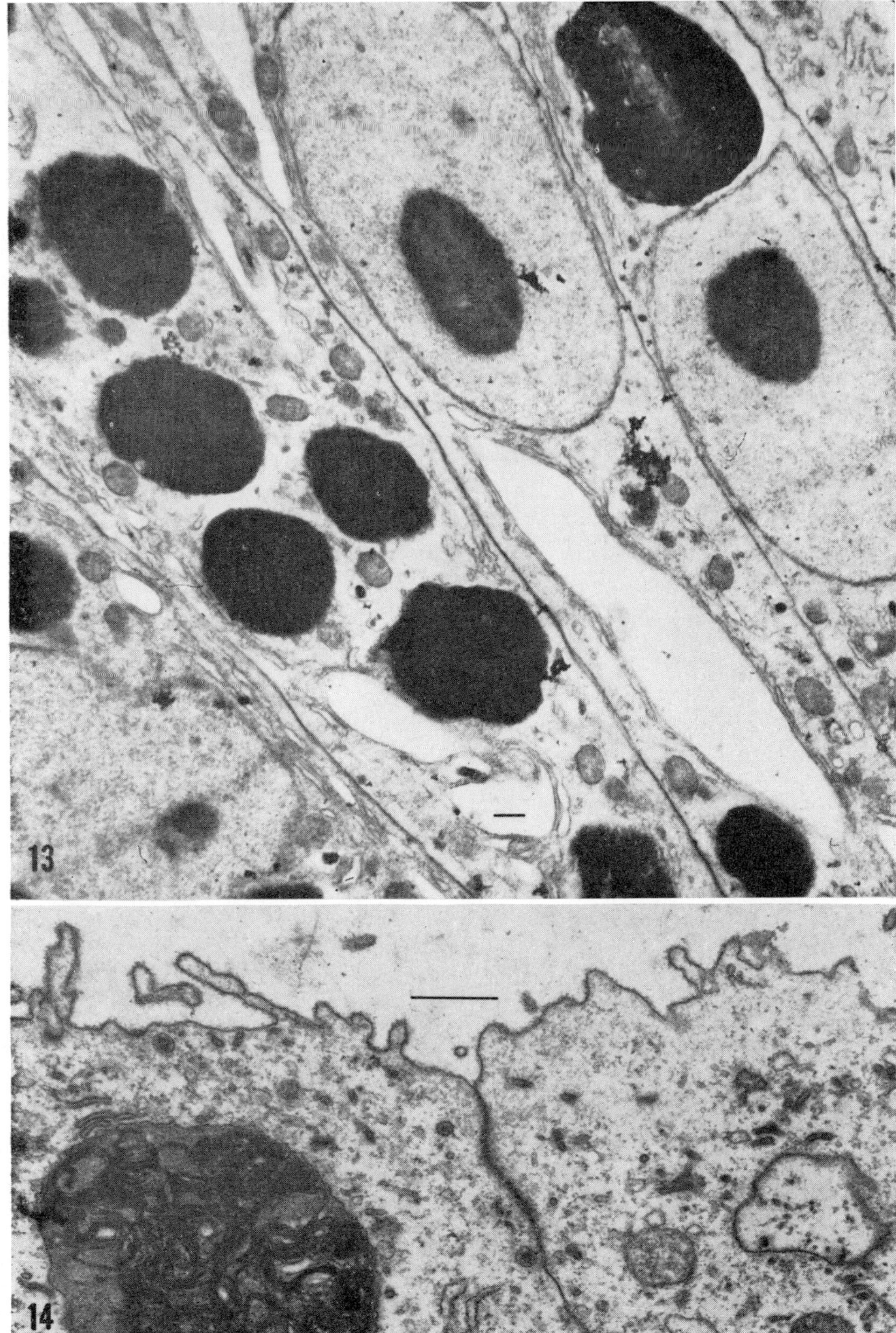
13
14

Plate VIII. Fig. 15. Sections showing the relations of ectoderm (EC), endoderm (EN) and mesoglea (M). The endoderm cells have muscle filaments in their base and send processes into the mesoglea. If the origin of the processes is missed in section, the processes appear to be lying as organelles or inclusions in the mesoglea. The mesoglea has no membrane around it. If the cell membranes of adjacent cells are traced for a short distance from the mesoglea, collections of granules, similar to those in the mesoglea, can be found in the extracellular space (arrow).

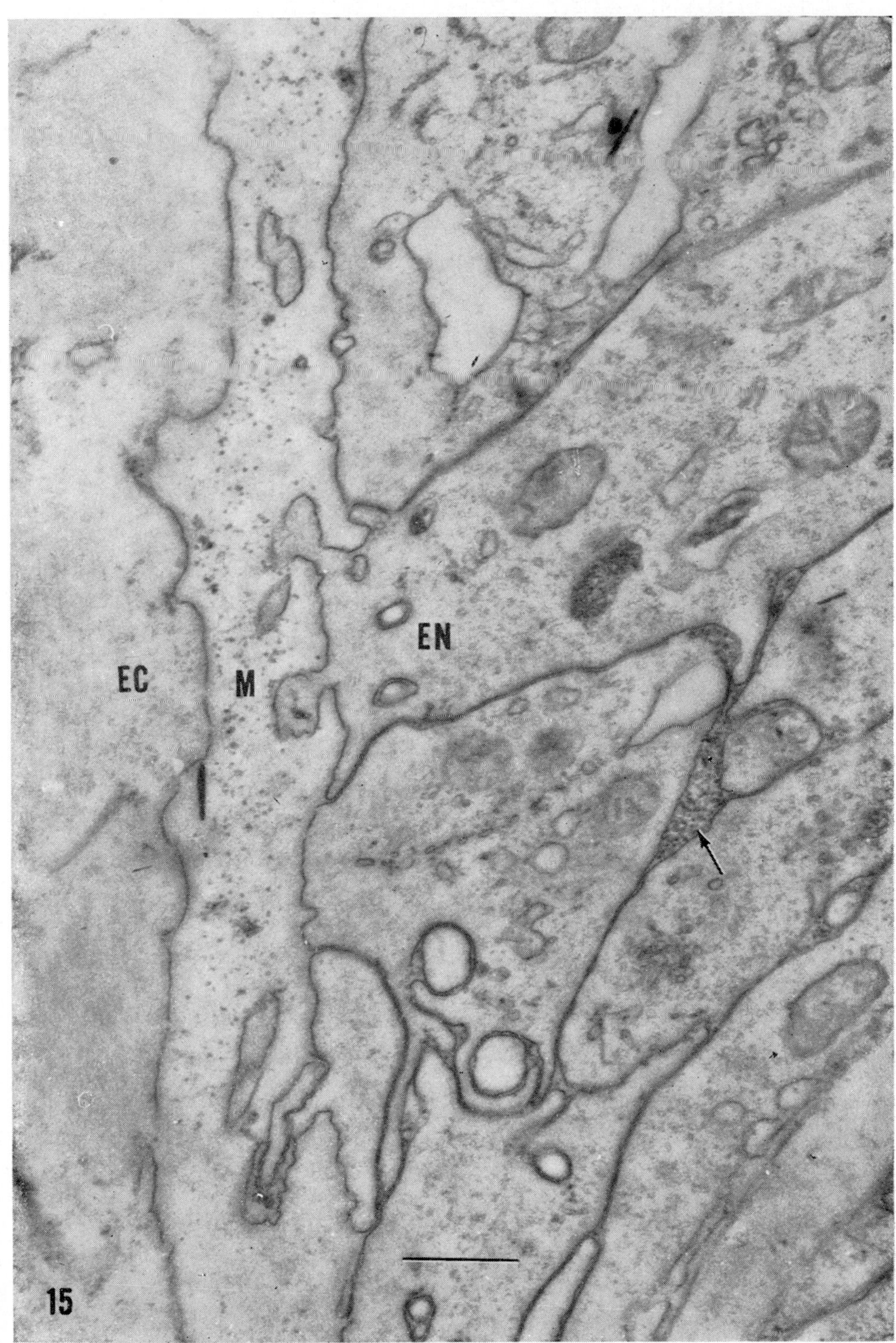
15
EC
M
EN

PLATE IX. Fig. 16. The ectoderm is at the top, the endoderm at the bottom and separated from each other by mesoglea. A rather robust process passes from an endodermal cell into the mesoglea.

Fig. 17. Longitudinal section of the junction of two muscle fibers in the ectoderm. The alternating light and dark densities on adjacent cell membranes yield a desmosome-like effect. Muscle filaments do not pass from one cell to the other.

Fig. 18. Flagella in the lumen of the hypostome surrounded by a membrane and exhibiting the characteristic pattern of filaments.

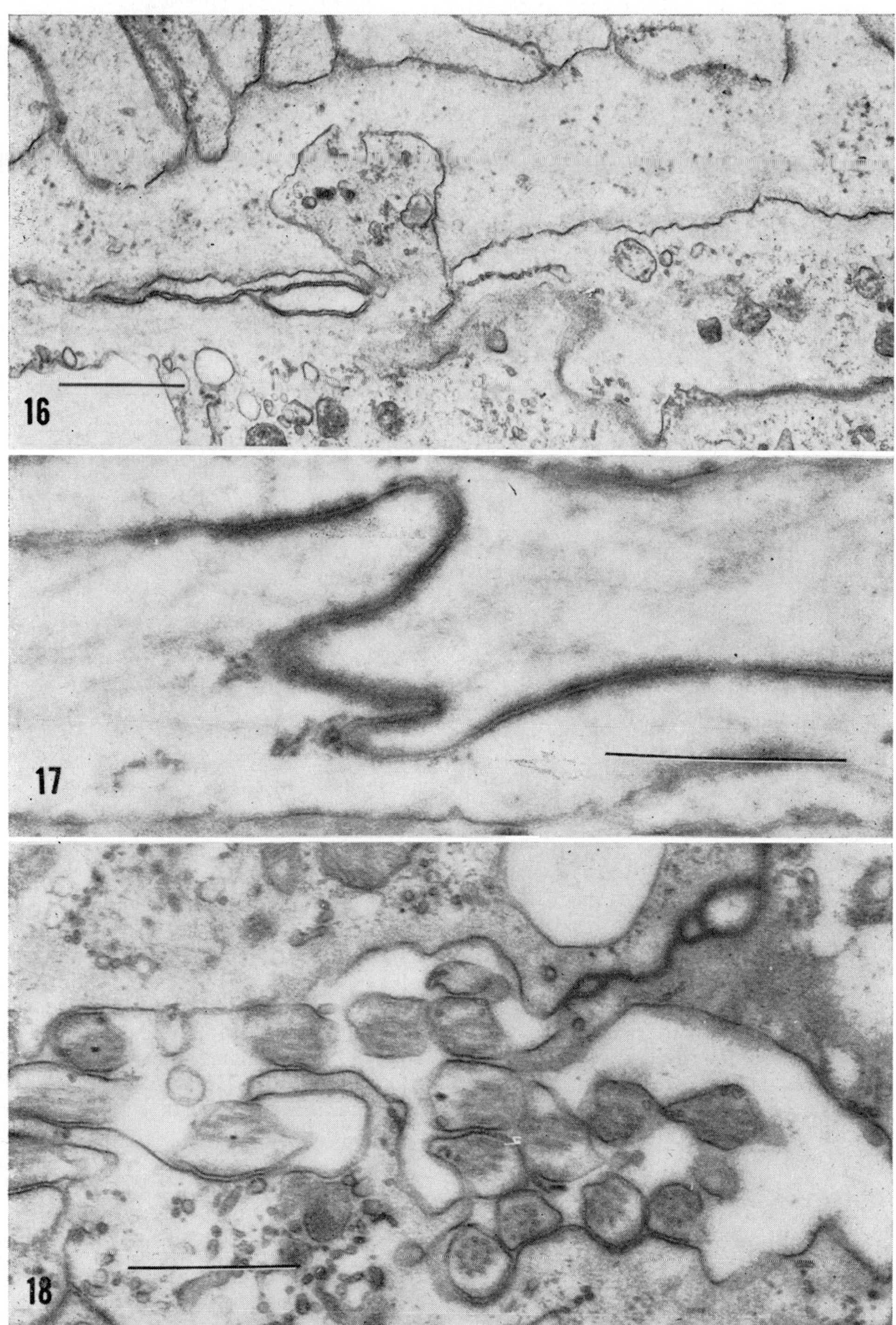
16
17
18

PLATE X. Fig. 19. The mesoglea (M) has granules and some very thin filaments. On the ectodermal (EC) side, it can be clearly seen that the mesoglea is not surrounded by a membrane, but rather extends between the membranes of adjacent ectodermal cells (arrows on the ectodermal side). The membranes of adjacent endodermal (EN) cells can be followed for a considerable distance. The membranes are very dense as they proceed from the mesoglea yielding a terminal bar effect. As the membranes are followed, accumulations of granules, similar to those seen in the mesoglea, can be found in the extracellular spaces (arrows on the endodermal side).

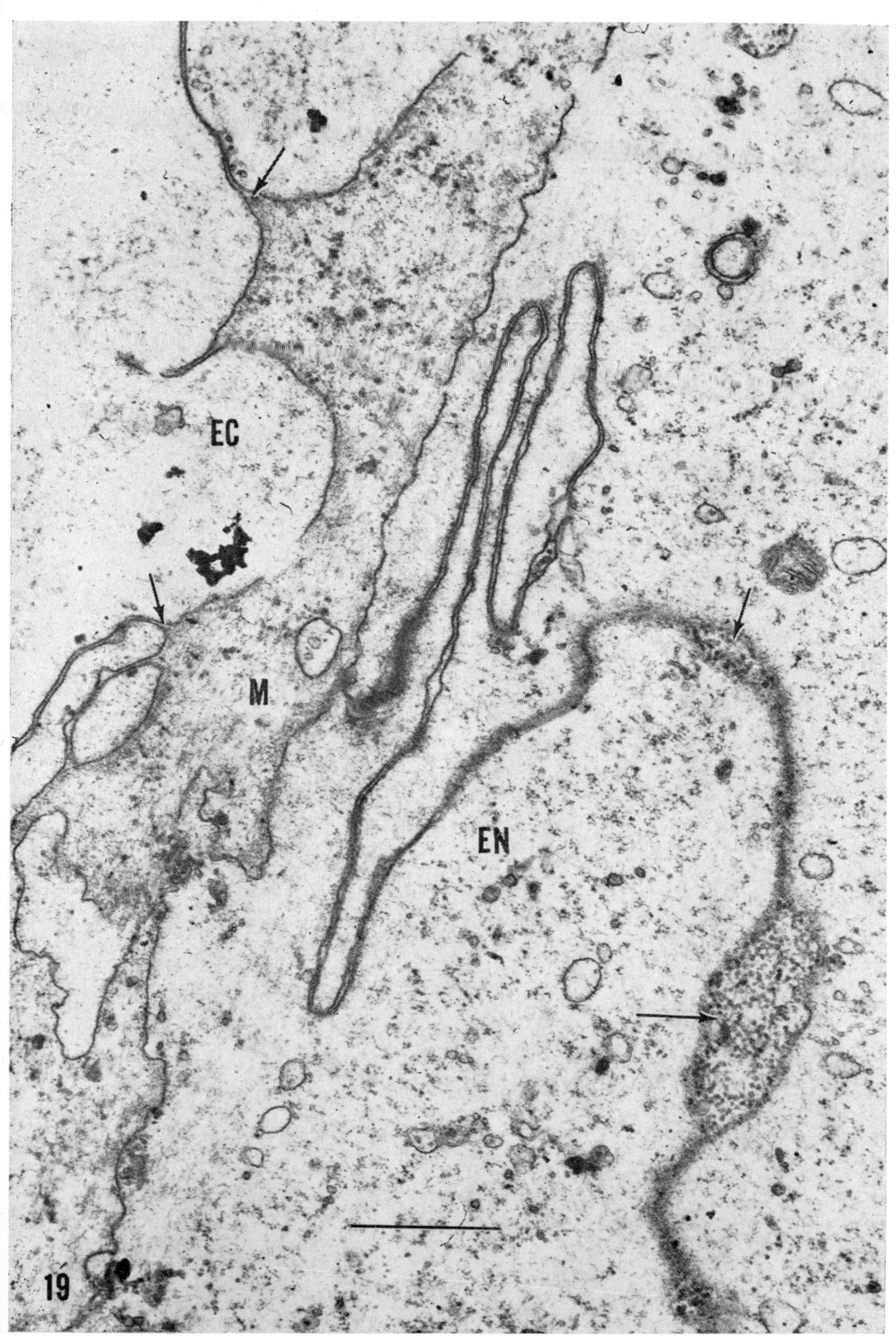
EC
M
EN
19

PLATE XI. Figs. 20 and 21. Points of contact between ectodermal (EC) and endodermal (EN) muscle where the mesoglea (M) is severely deficient or essentially lacking. Figure 21 is in the region of the hypostome.

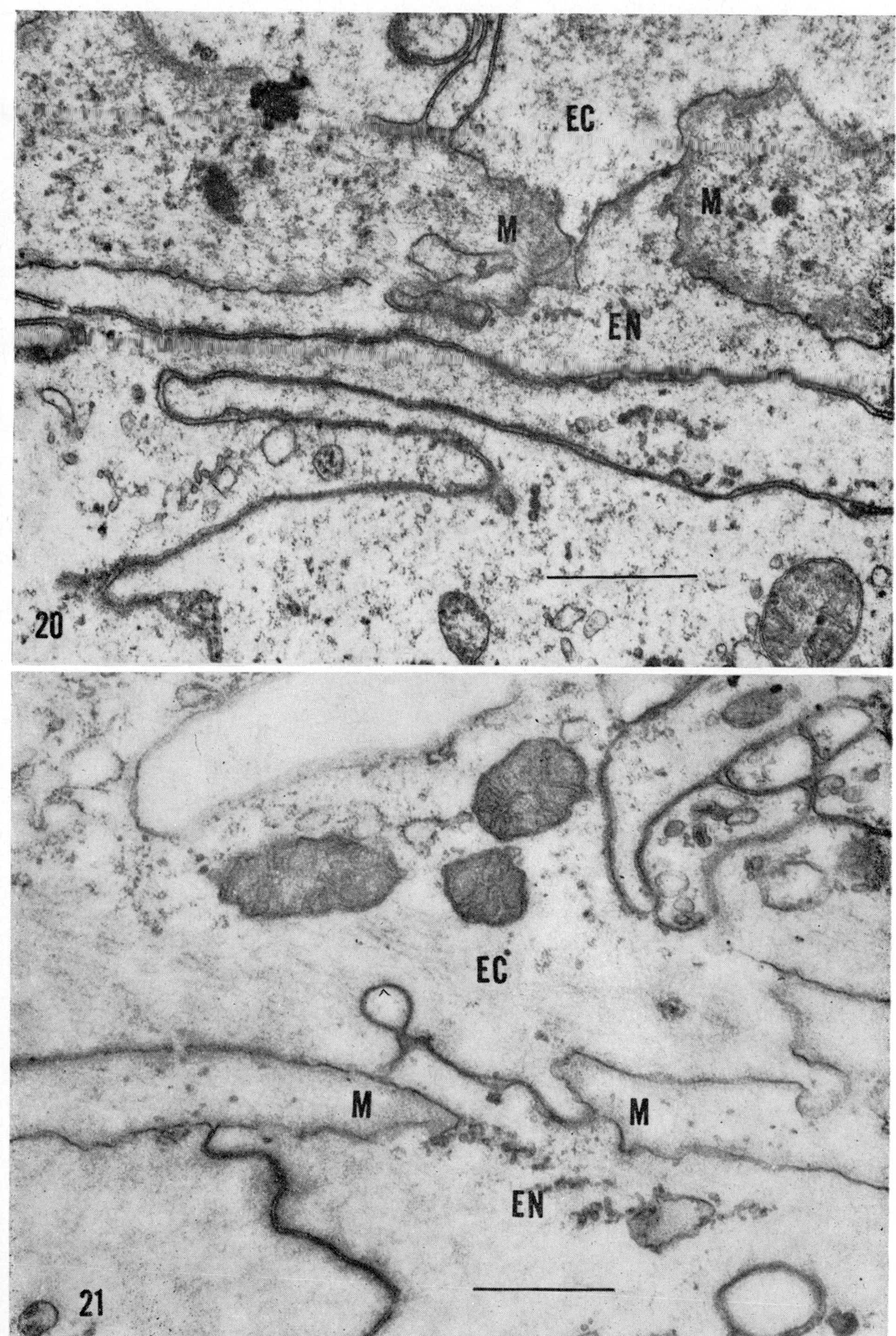
EC
M
M
EN
20
EC
M
M
EN
21

PLATE XII. Fig. 22. A ridge or low elevation in the ectoderm of the tentacle containing cnidocytes (C) apparently embedded in the cytoplasm of an epithelio-muscular cell (EP). A thin mesogleal layer (arrow) separates the ectodermal cells from the attenuated, highly vacuolated endoderm (EN).

Fig. 23. An extracellular space containing granules and enclosed by the cell membranes of four endoderm cells, yielding a star-shaped effect.

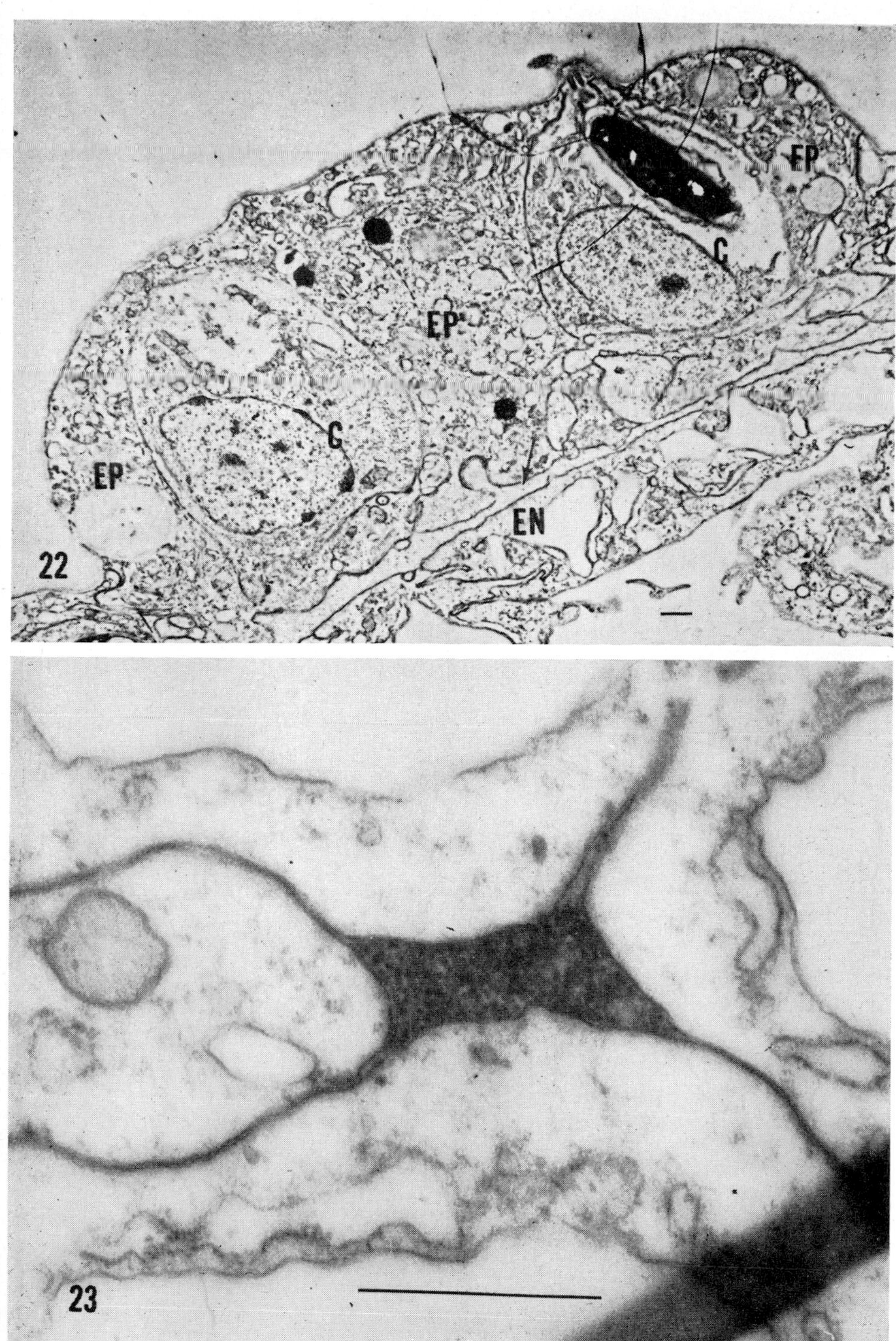
EP
C
EP
C
EP
EN
22
23

PLATE XIII. Fig. 24. Cnidocytes in the tentacle embedded in the cytoplasm of epithelio-muscular cells (EP). The cnidocytes are not syncytial, but are enclosed individually in their limiting membranes. One of the cnidocytes has muscle filaments (M). S is the surface of the animal. Near S, a cnidocil is seen.

Fig. 25. An extracellular space containing granules and enclosed by the membranes of endoderm cells and yielding a star-shaped effect.

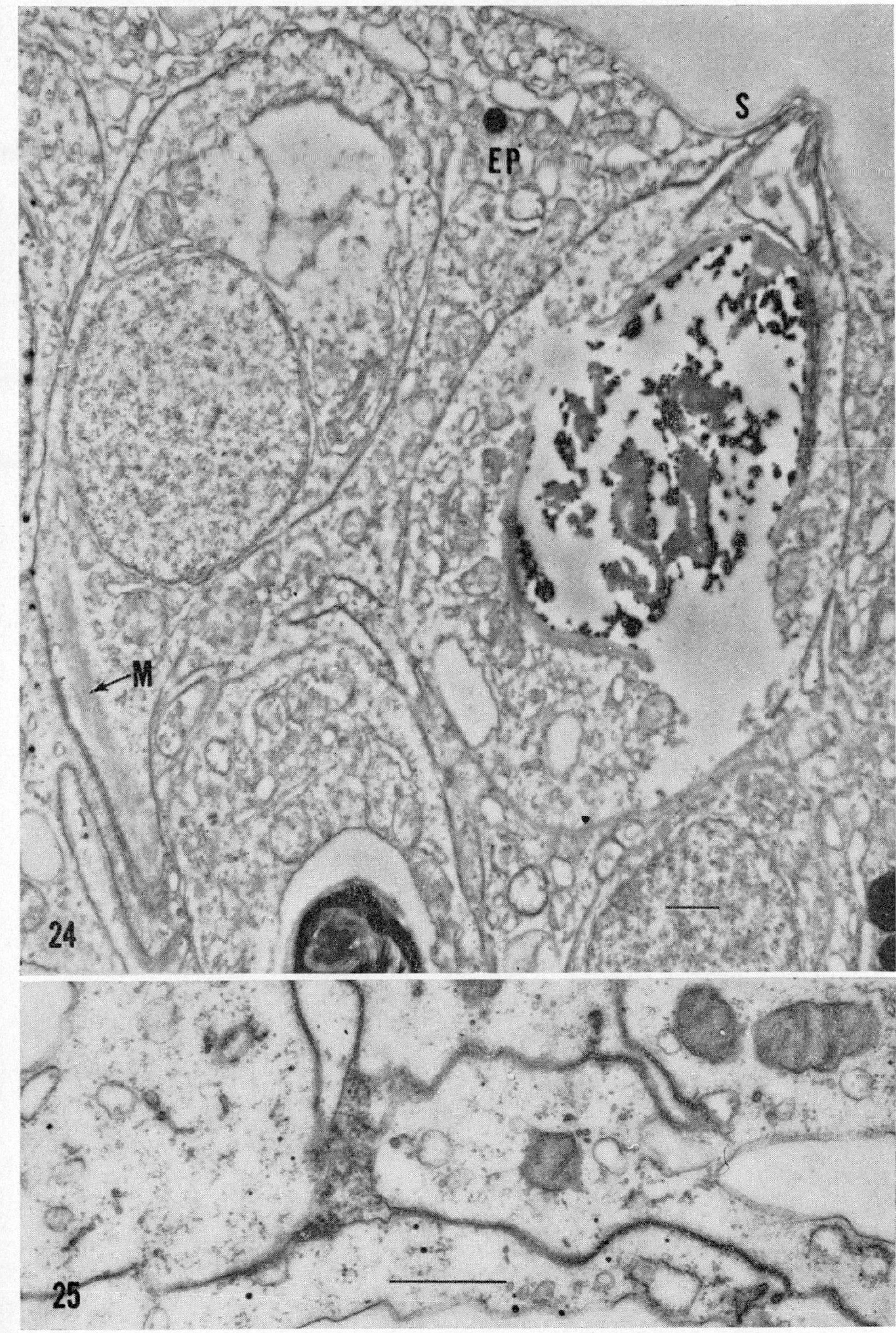
S
EP
M
24
25

PLATE XIV. Fig. 26. Section through the hypostome showing relations of ectoderm, endoderm and mesoglea (M). The epithelio-muscular cell (EP) contains vacuoles, organelles and inclusions as described previously and muscle filaments in its base. The digestive cells of the endoderm (EN) contain vacuoles, organelles and inclusion bodies and have muscle filaments in their base. S is the surface of the animal.

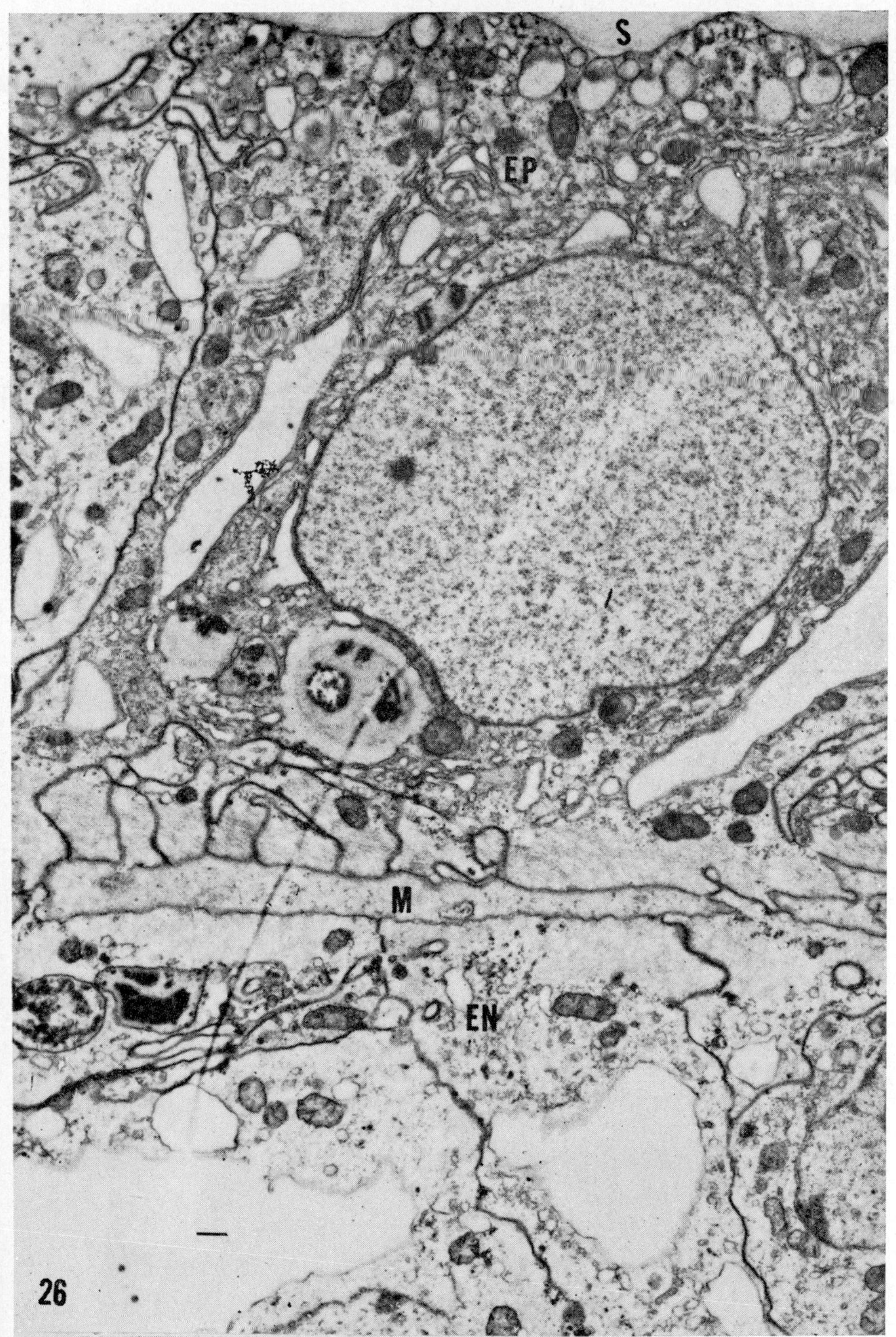
S
EP
M
EN
26

PLATE XV. Fig. 27. Section through the endoderm of the hypostome. Gland cells (G), with their vacuoles and digestive cells (D) containing inclusion bodies, probably absorbed food, line the lumen (L). The flagella and cytoplasmic processes extending from these cells are seen in the lumen.

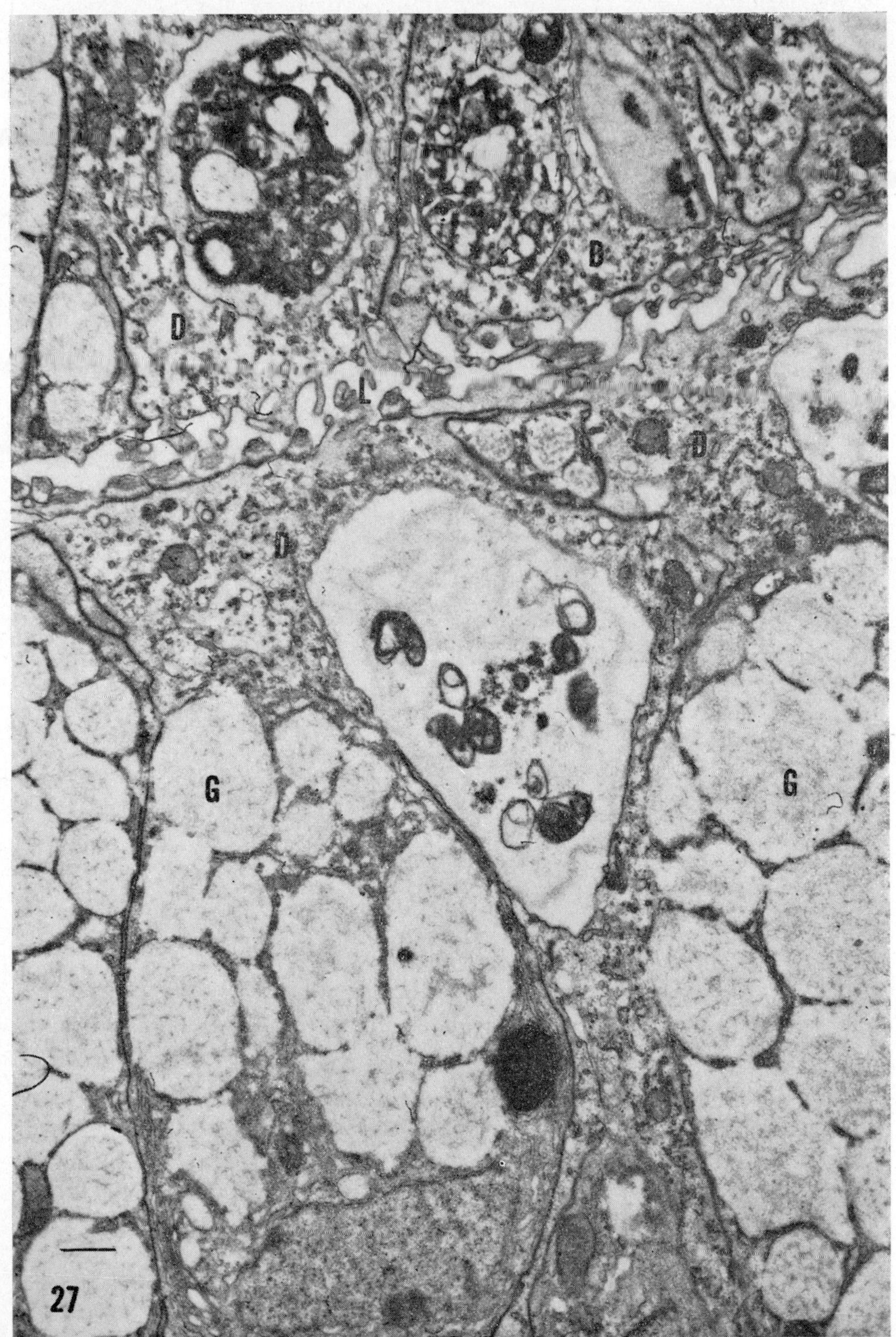
D
D
L
D
D
G
G
27

PLATE XVI. Fig. 28. Section through the junction of the hypostome and the tentacle. The arrows indicate the approximate plane of attachment of the tentacle (on the right of the arrows) to the hypostome. The interface of the endodermal cells (EN) and the mesoglea (M) has a characteristic scalloped appearance. Muscle filaments on the epithlio-muscular cells are perhaps better developd in the tentacle than in the hypostome.

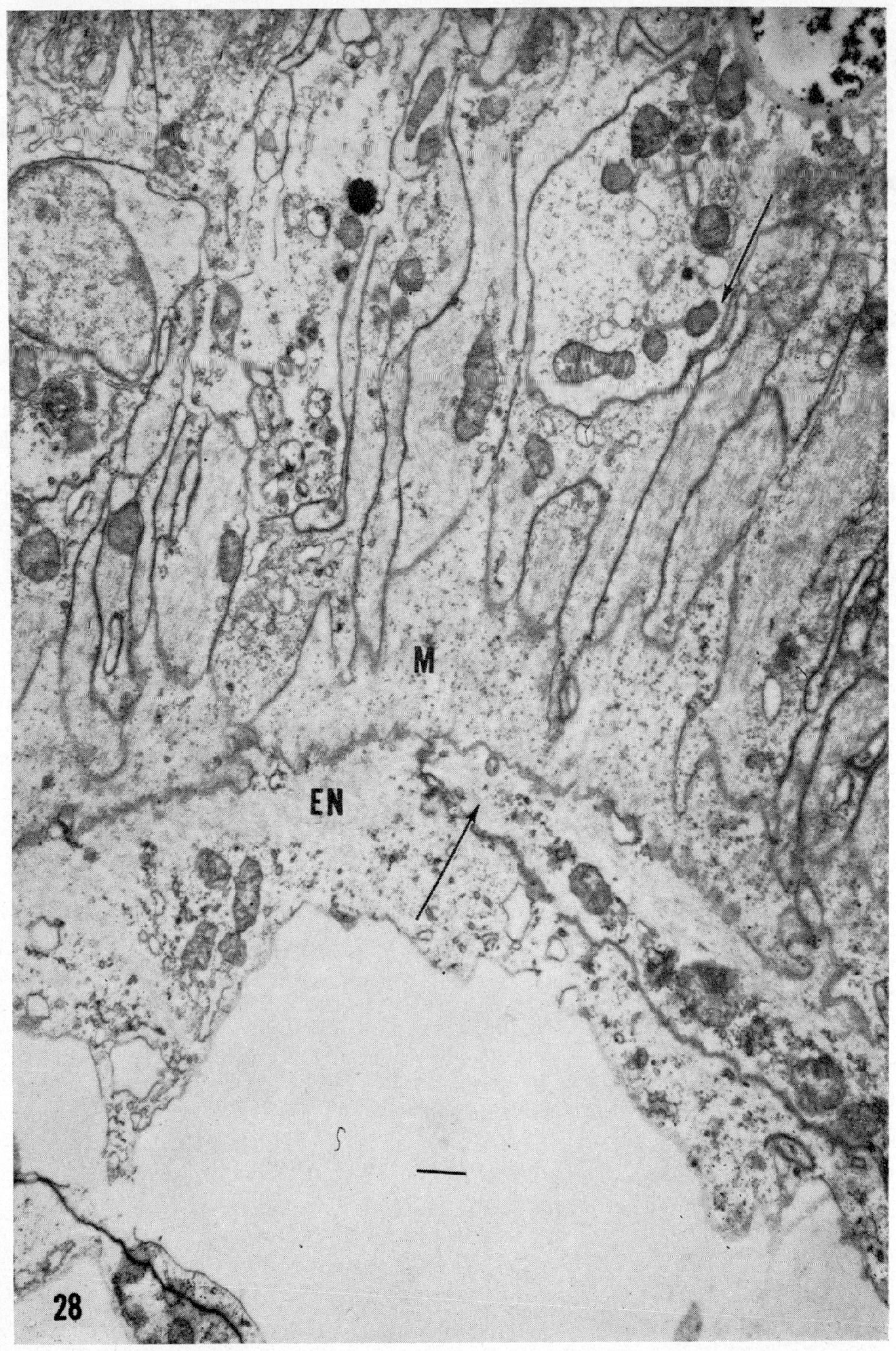
M
EN
28

PLATE XVII. Fig. 29. The gland cells of the ectoderm of the pedal disk. There is no cuticular substance on the surface (S). Small cytoplasmic processes extend from the surface of the cells. The granules (G) are probably the secretion manufactured by these cells, especially those with more double membranes and fewer and smaller granules farther from the surface, to cement *Hydra* to the substratum.

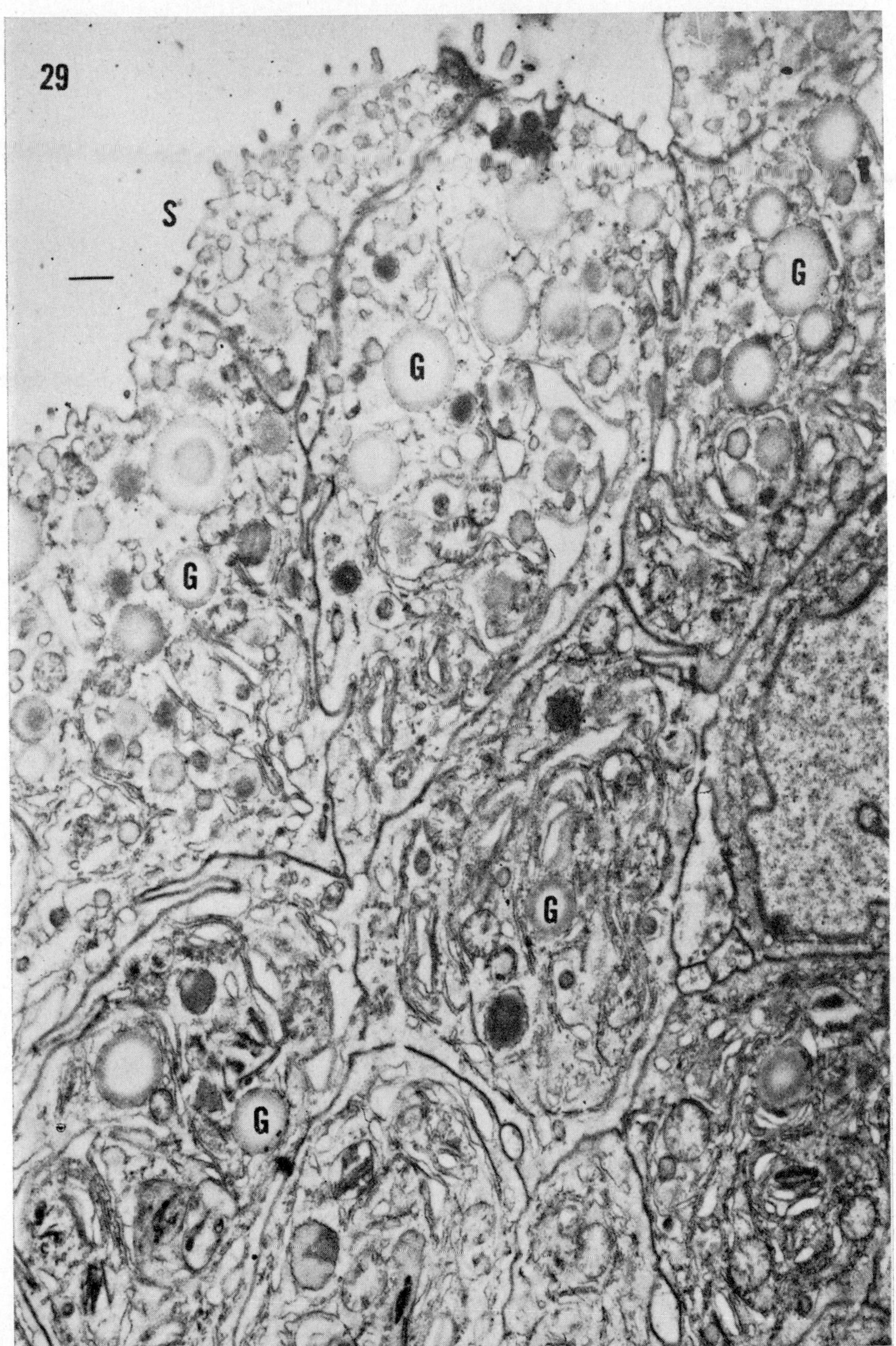
29
S
G
G
G
G
G
G

PLATE XVIII. Fig. 30. Place of origin of bud from mother. The arrow indicates approximately the point of attachment of the bud to the mother. Epithelio-muscular cells of the mother are on the bottom of the photograph. The more highly vacuolated epithelio-muscular cells of the bud are similar to the epithelio-muscular cells seen at the level of the peduncle. Similarly, the granules seen near the surface of the epithelio-muscular cells of both mother and bud are characteristic of epithelio-muscular cells of the peduncle. The cuticular layer is continuous over the surfaces of bud and mother.

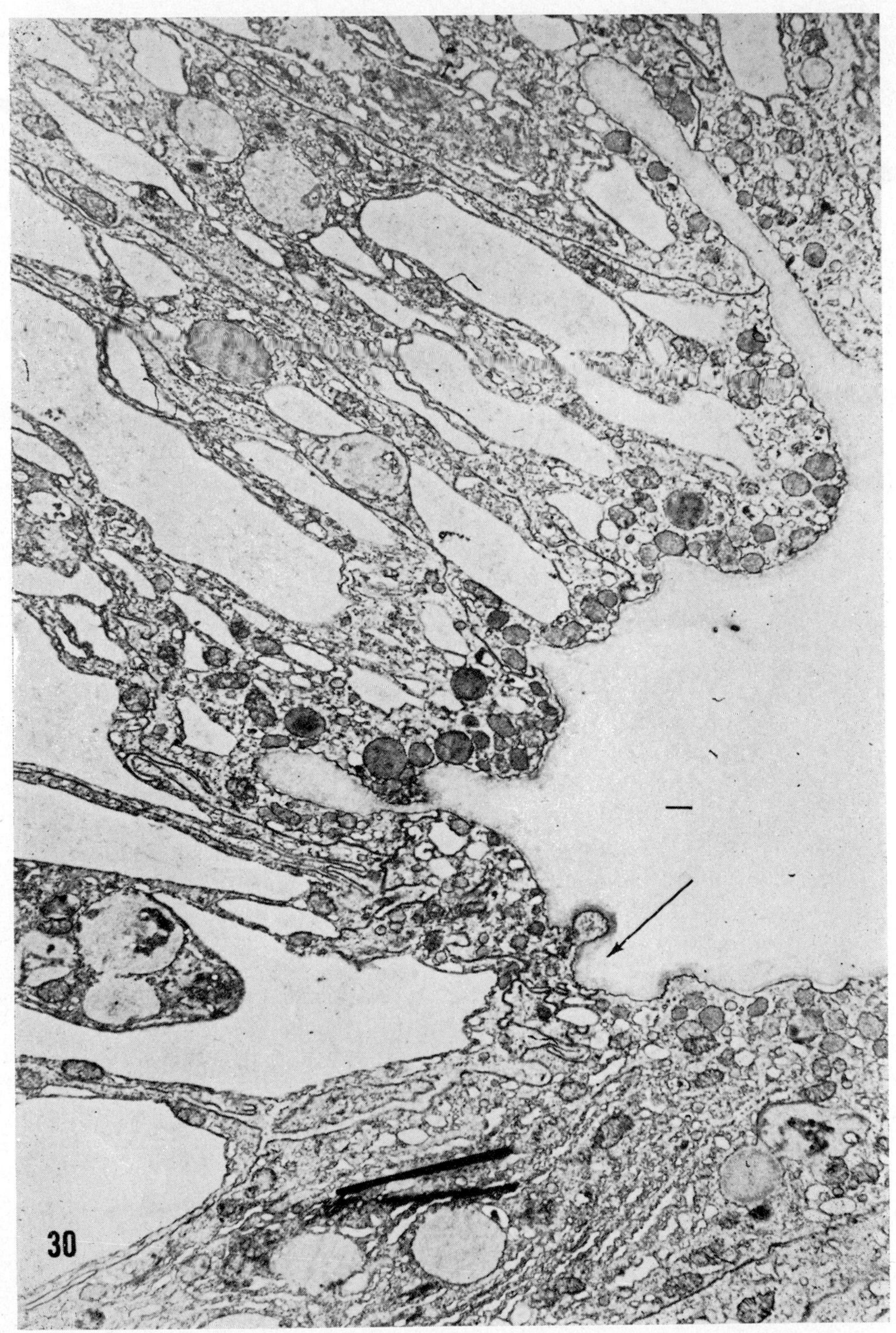
30

DISCUSSION

LOOMIS: At what point do interstitial cells start differentiating the four types of nematocysts?

HESS: I'm sure someone else later in the program could answer that. I have not actually worked on the structure of the nematocyst *per se,* just the cnidoblast.

SLAUTTERBACK: Dr. Hess, I'm afraid your fine micrographs have stolen the thunder from the rest of the electron microscopists here.

I did not want to raise the issue of what you have called the gland cell. I believe that on the basis of location, staining properties and appearance of the secretory granules in electron micrographs, your term includes two distinct cell types as has been suggested in the classical literature. We have been calling the cell which is more prominent in the hypostome region and resembles the goblet cell of the vertebrate digestive system, a mucous cell. The other type, which is more prominent below the hypostome and resembles the pancreatic acinar cell, we have called the zymogenic cell.

HESS: It seemed to me that these different appearances might be cyclical changes. Most of the cells have light vacuoles and only rarely do some of them stain darker in the electron microscope. I haven't done histochemical staining, and you might be right that two different cell types occur because many people speak of these two kinds of cells.

BURNETT: I would like to mention some histochemical results we have obtained on regenerating hydra. If the hypostome of the hydra is excised, we find that mucous cells begin to appear in abundance in the gastrodermis at the point of excision about 12-18 hours after cutting. The secretory material in these cells is PAS positive, stains with alcian blue, is metachromatic after toluidine blue or methylene blue staining, and is removable by hyaluronidase digestion. This material is most certainly an acid mucopolysaccharide. Gland cells appear six hours after excision. The secretory droplets in these cells are several times larger than those found in the mucous cells. Moreover, gland cells do not stain with alcian blue and are not metachromatic, but positive to Millon's reaction for proteins. These two types of cells are, therefore, quite different from one another both histochemically and morphologically.

I have a question. Were the cnidoblasts in the same cluster forming the same type of nematocysts?

HESS: I didn't notice the type of nematocyst, but all those within a cluster seem to be in the same stage of development.

FAWCETT: I would like to comment on that point. It has been our experience that within any single cluster of cnidoblasts, they are all forming nematocysts of the same kind. They are also precisely synchronized in their development. I would comment further, if I may, on the syncytial relationship that was mentioned. I noticed in Dr. Hess' pictures two distinct kinds of syncytial relationships. In a number of instances, the connections between cells appeared simply as small discontinuities of varying lengths in the pairs of membranes constituting the boundaries between cells. We have seen such apparent communications, but although our technique was seemingly good enough to make it unlikely that these were artifactitious breaks in the continuity of the cell membranes, this has nevertheless always been a disturbing possibility. There is another kind of syncytial relationship between cnidoblasts which is clearly not artifactual, and is of considerable interest in relation to the mechanism of cell division and the control of differentiation.

It is this kind of intercellular bridge, found in both interstitial cells (Fig. 1) and cnidoblasts (Fig. 2), that I would like to illustrate in order to emphasize the special nature and probable significance of the syncytial relationship between cnidoblasts. Groups of eight or sixteen cells arising by proliferation from a single interstitial cell remain connected by bridges a micron or so in diameter, enclosed by a specialized, thickened area of membrane that has a characteristic contour. There is no possibility that this localized thickening of the plasmalemma and special configuration of the surface could arise as an artifact of specimen preparation. Notice the heartshaped outline of the intercellular space and the definite ridge that encircles the waist of the intercellular connection. Dr. Slautterback and I believe that such bridges arise during division of the interstitial cells when the constricting cleavage furrow en-

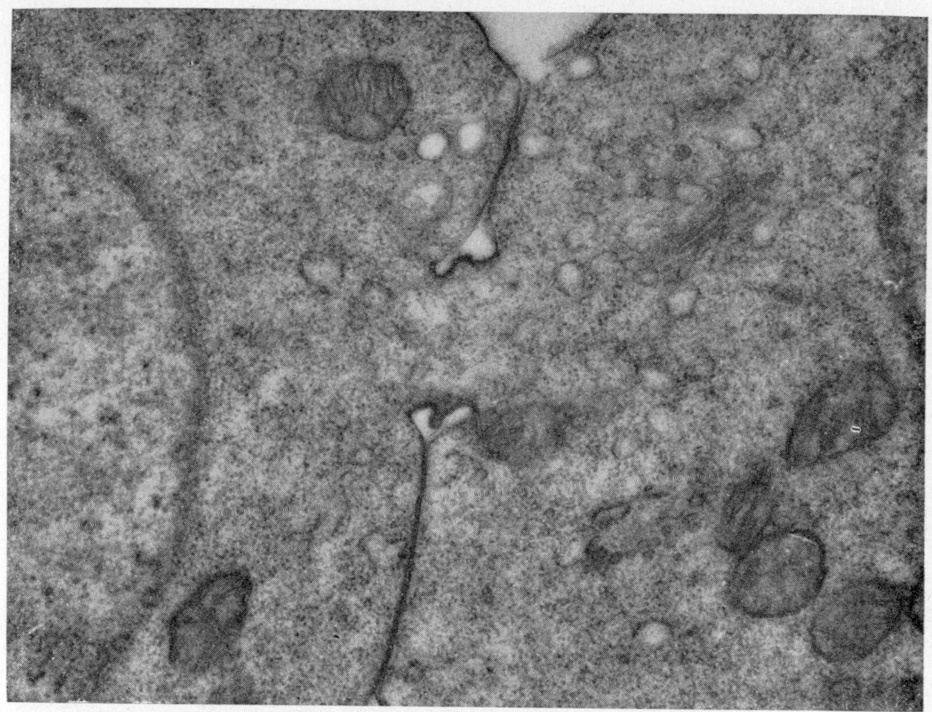

Fig. 1. Intercellular bridge of interstitial cells.

counters the spindle remnant, and is arrested by it for a time. This occurs very commonly in mitotic divisions in many kinds of germinal and somatic cells and gives rise to a transient structure called a *spindle bridge*. Usually, however, such connections between the daughter cells endure only for several minutes and then when the spindle remnants have resorbed the cleavage is completed. Evidently in the case being described here, cleavage does not resume and absorption of the spindle filaments leaves the daughter cells in open communication through short cylindrical bridges large enough to permit mitochondria and other formed elements of the cytoplasm to pass from one cell body to another. As a consequence of the matter in which they are formed, there is never more than one

---

Fig. 2. Intercellular bridge of cnidoblasts.

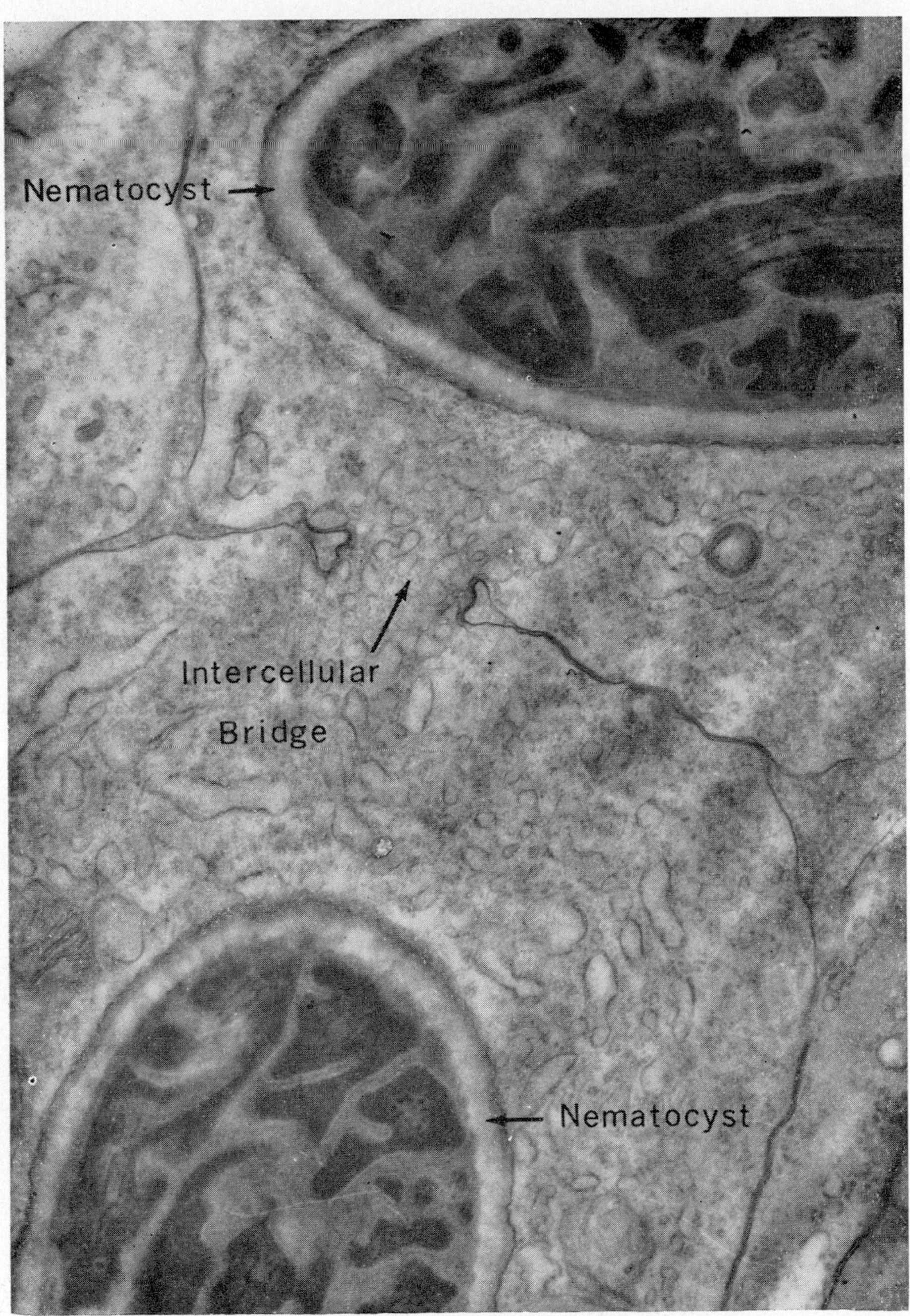
Nematocyst
Intercellular
Bridge
Nematocyst

such bridge between any two cells in the cnidoblast cluster. The bridges persist throughout the period of differentiation of the nematocysts. If the nematocysts are eventually to migrate as individual cells, the bridges connecting them must be severed at some time late in their differentiation, but this process has not yet been observed. We believe that the syncytial relationship of the cnidoblasts is probably the morphological basis for the synchrony of their differentiation. It is interesting that the same kind of synchrony is seen in the groups of developing germ cells in the testes and these are also connected by intercellular bridges that form in the same way.

CLAYBROOK: Do either of you find cytoplasmic bridges between different cell types, or are they only between two of the same kind?

HESS: I've only seen them between the same cell type. How about you?

FAWCETT: Bridges of the kind I have been describing occur only between cells of the same type.

HESS: I've seen a break in the cell membranes of the spermatids, like the first type of interconnection of which you spoke. We thought that it was an artifact until we saw cytoplasm and mitochondria in the intercellular bridge running between the two syncytial cells.

GAUTHIER: May we return to the subject of gland cells? If the two cell types represent only a cyclical change in one cell type, would you expect that starvation might produce a levelling off so that only one type would be present?

HESS: Well, I thought that the different appearances of gland cells indicated cyclical changes of one cell type, but others here apparently disagree.

GAUTHIER: In preliminary experiments with starved hydra, I have found that two distinct types of gland cells persist for as long as twelve days.

GOREAU: I am interested in the so-called microvilli you have shown. We have seen microvilli in gorgonian and scleractinian material which have a much more regular and permanent appearance than anything you have shown. The processes in your sections of *Hydra* epidermis look to me like temporary cytoplasmic pseudopodia. They certainly don't have the same well organized distribution that is seen, for example, in the epidermal cells of corals where the microvilli are arranged in a regular ring around the base of the flagella (Goreau and Philpott, 1956. *Exptl. Cell Research 10*:552). I'm also interested to see that the epidermal cells of *Hydra* are not flagellated.

HESS: All the flagella of *Hydra* arise from endodermal cells and extend into the lumen.

GOREAU: We've never found more than one flagellum per cell, whereas you seem to think there are more than one.

HESS: Yes, in the gastrodermis, each cell apparently has from two to four flagella.

The Fine Structure of Intercellular and Mesogleal Attachments of Epithelial Cells in Hydra[1]

RICHARD L. WOOD
Department of Anatomy, University of Washington School of Medicine, Seattle.

Cellular interactions in multicellular organisms have been examined both from the physiological and the morphological points of view. As a result of these studies it has become clear that there are certain general features of epithelia which are related to special kinds of adhesive properties. It is further realized that these special adhesive properties are not distributed uniformly over the cell surface. The epithelial layers of hydra share these general properties of epithelia, although the details of intercellular attachment sites seem not to have been studied extensively in the past.

Hydra consists essentially of a bicellular leaflet of epithelia and, therefore, is well suited for studies of epithelial cell interactions. The epithelia of hydra are perfectly good epithelia, but at the same time the individual cells serve several functions, many of which are not usually associated with functions of epithelium in a single layer in higher organisms. The presence of well developed terminal bar type attachment areas between these epithelial cells of hydra is certainly to be expected from our knowledge of higher organisms. Such areas do occur and the detailed structure differs from previously described intercellular attachments.

Basal processes of many epithelial cells in hydra contain muscle fibers. Special relationships between adjacent muscle fibers and

[1]This research was aided in part by Grant No. H-2698 from the National Institutes of Health, Public Health Service.

between muscle elements and connective tissue, or mesoglea, would also be expected, and indeed they also occur. The purpose of this presentation is to review some of these relationships as I have observed them using light and electron microscopy. These observations pose a great number of additional questions which will require some new approaches for further elucidation.

In this presentation I will refer to the intercellular attachments as desmosomes. I prefer desmosome as a general descriptive term for intercellular attachments because the term was originally proposed with a recognition of the functional relationship and basic similarity of the various forms of intercellular attachment (9). The concept of desmosome (literally "bonding body") seems to be well substantiated by micromanipulation experiments with various kinds of epithelium from different organisms.

The present observations were made on specimens of *Chlorohydra viridissima* and *Pelmatohydra oligactis.* Material was fixed in osmium tetroxide buffered in acetate-veronal (6) or s-collidine (1) at pH 7.4. The tissue was dehydrated in ethyl alcohol and embedded in a mixture of n-butyl and methyl methacrylates or in either Araldite or Epon epoxy resin (see Luft, ref. 5). Light micrographs were made from one micron sections cut from epoxy embedded blocks and stained according to the method of Richardson, *et al.* (7). The electron microscopy was done on an RCA-2C with an improved power supply and with a Siemens Elmiskop I.

The epithelial layers of hydra mostly consist of single layers of cuboidal to columnar epithelial cells. In the epidermis interstitial cells occur between the epithelial cells near their bases and nematocytes occur between epithelial cells at the outer surface of the animal. The gastroderm contains two easily identifiable cell types, nutrient cells and glandular cells. A thin lamella of mesoglea separates the two epithelial layers. This general configuration is demonstrated in the first illustration. Figure 1*a* is a light micrograph of a transverse section through the region of the hypostome in *Chlorohydra.* Glandular cells and basally located intracellular symbiotic *Zoochlorella* may be identified in the gastrodermis. Light areas near the mesoglea at the base of the epidermal cells represent cross sections of muscle fibers. Figure 1*b* shows a transverse section through the column of *Pelmatohydra.* The larger

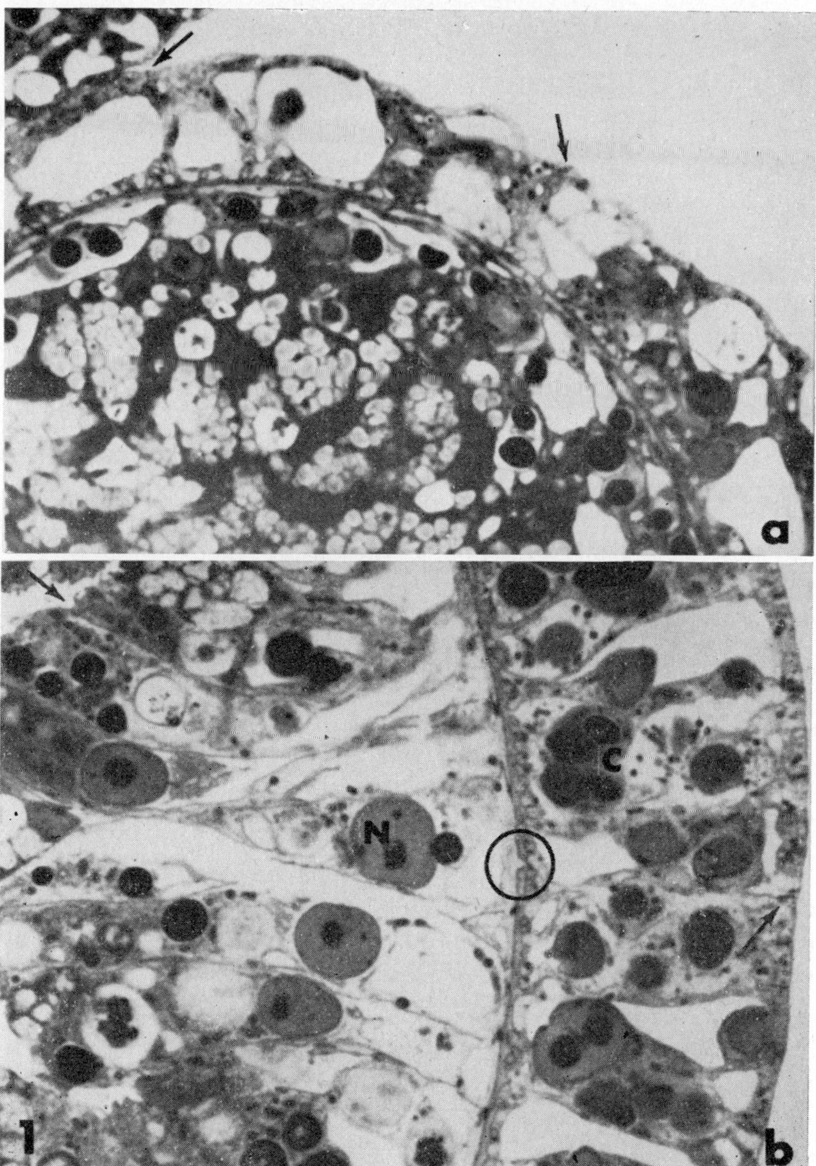

Fig. 1. Light microscope pictures of *a*, *Chlorohydra* and *b*, *Pelmatohydra*. In *a* the epidermis is at the top and the gastrodermis at the bottom. The two layers are separated by the mesolamella along which muscle fibers may be seen. In *b* the epidermis is at the right and the gastrodermis at the left with the mesolamella between. Note the obvious muscle fibers at the base of the epidermis and the connection between epithelia at the circle. Desmosomes appear at the arrows. The black circular objects in the gastrodermis of *a* are *Zoochlorella;* in *b* similar structures are food particles. C, cnidoblasts; N, nucleus. *a*—2200X. *b*—2200X.

size and lack of *Zoochlorella* make *Pelmatohydra* easier to examine. At the free outer surface, adjacent epidermal cells are bound together by terminal bar type desmosomes (arrows). These desmosomes were not described in earlier light microscope studies of hydra or in more recent electron microscope studies by other workers (2, 4, 11). Interstitial cells, nematoblasts and gastrodermal nutrient cells are seen clearly in Figure 1*b*.

These general features of hydra epithelia are shown to even better advantage in low magnification electron micrographs. Figure 2 is an electron micrograph of a section through the gastric region of *Chlorohydra*. The prominent dense bodies in the gastrodermal cells are *Zoochlorella*. Other identifiable features include nuclei, microvilli, other cellular inclusions and muscle processes. The two epithelial layers are separated by the thin mesolamella which appears dense in this picture. Desmosomes appear as areas of increased density between adjacent cell surfaces, especially near the outer surface of epidermal cells and the lumenal surface of gastrodermal cells (arrows). Similar densities occur between adjacent membranes of interdigitated muscle processes (Fig. 2, circle).

In both species of hydra examined the desmosomes which are present near the free surfaces of epidermal and gastrodermal cells display a very complex morphology when viewed at higher magnification. The two apposed plasma membranes each exhibit the dual profile of the "unit membrane" of Robertson (8), the two peaks of density being about 70 Ångstrom units apart. The increase in density noted by light microscopy and in lower magnification electron micrographs is seen to be due to a condensation of intracellular material and to the presence of a specially oriented intercellular matrix. These features are shown in Figure 3, *a* and *b*, an example of an epidermal desmosome in a specimen prepared in the usual way and then stained with phosphotungstic acid prior to embedding. In this preparation the junction of at least three different epidermal cells is represented. The condensation of intracellular material appears somewhat vague at this magnification but the organization of intercellular material is well demonstrated. The two apposed cell surfaces are connected directly by a series of parallel densities oriented perpendicular to the plane of the plasma membranes. The intercellular space is thereby divided into a series of compartments.

From examination of oblique or longitudinal sections of these desmosomes it is clear that the intercellular connections are not

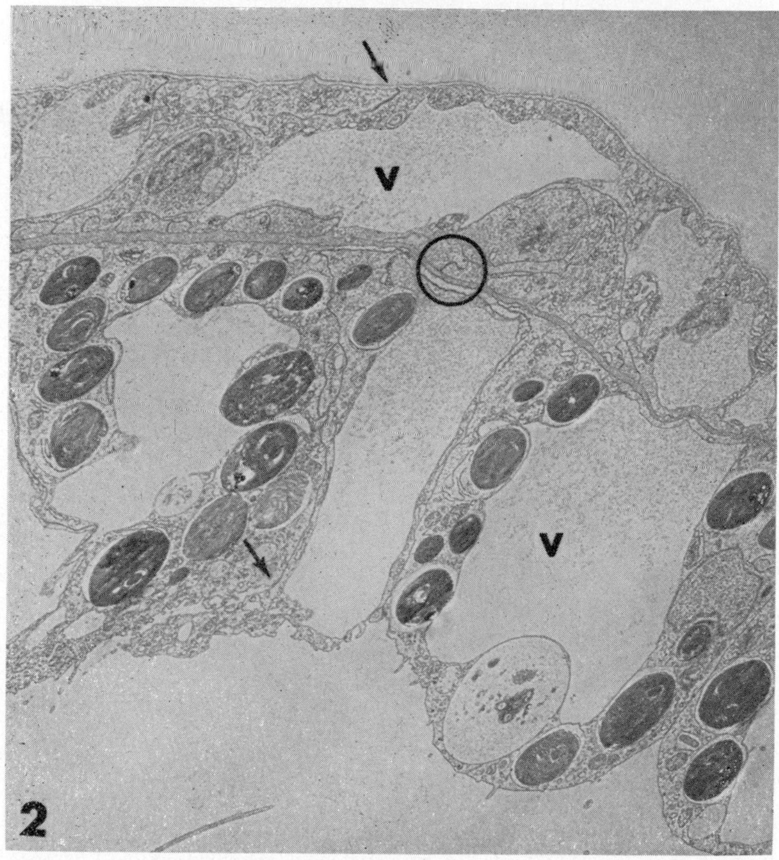

Fig. 2. Low magnification electron micrograph of *Chlorohydra*. The epidermis is at the top and the gastrodermis at the bottom. *Zoochlorella* appear in the gastrodermal cells. Cross sections of muscle fibers lie adjacent to the mesolamella in the epidermis. Desmosomes are apparent in both the epidermis and the gastrodermis (arrows). Specialized muscle-to-muscle attachment is indicated by increased densities such as at the small circle. Note the large intracellular vacuoles in both epithelial layers. V, intracellular vacuole. 2700X. (Originally published in *J. Biophysic. and Biochem. Cytol.*, 6: 343-352, 1959).

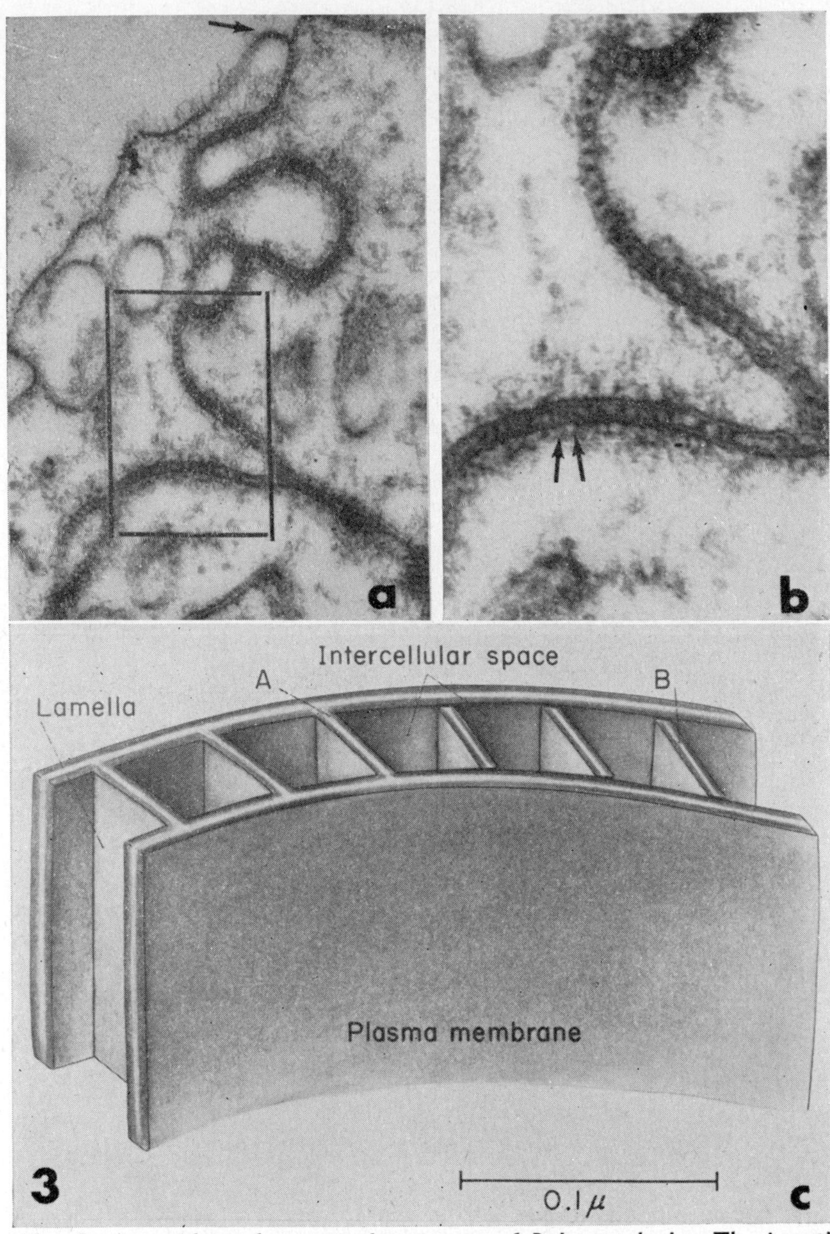

Fig. 3. An epidermal septate desmosome of *Pelamatohydra*. The junction of three cells in *a* shows the reflection of cell surfaces into the attachment region (arrow) and the prominent cross connections. At *b* the lower central portion of *a* (framed) is shown at higher magnification. At the double arrow the outer dense component of the lower plasma membrane appears to be continuous with the dense lines of the intercellular septa. The diagram at *c* illustrates the arrangement of septate desmosomes as visualized from these observations. See text. *a*—53,000X. *b*—130,000X. (These illustrations originally appeared in *J. Biophysic. and Biochem. Cytol., 6:* 343-352, 1959).

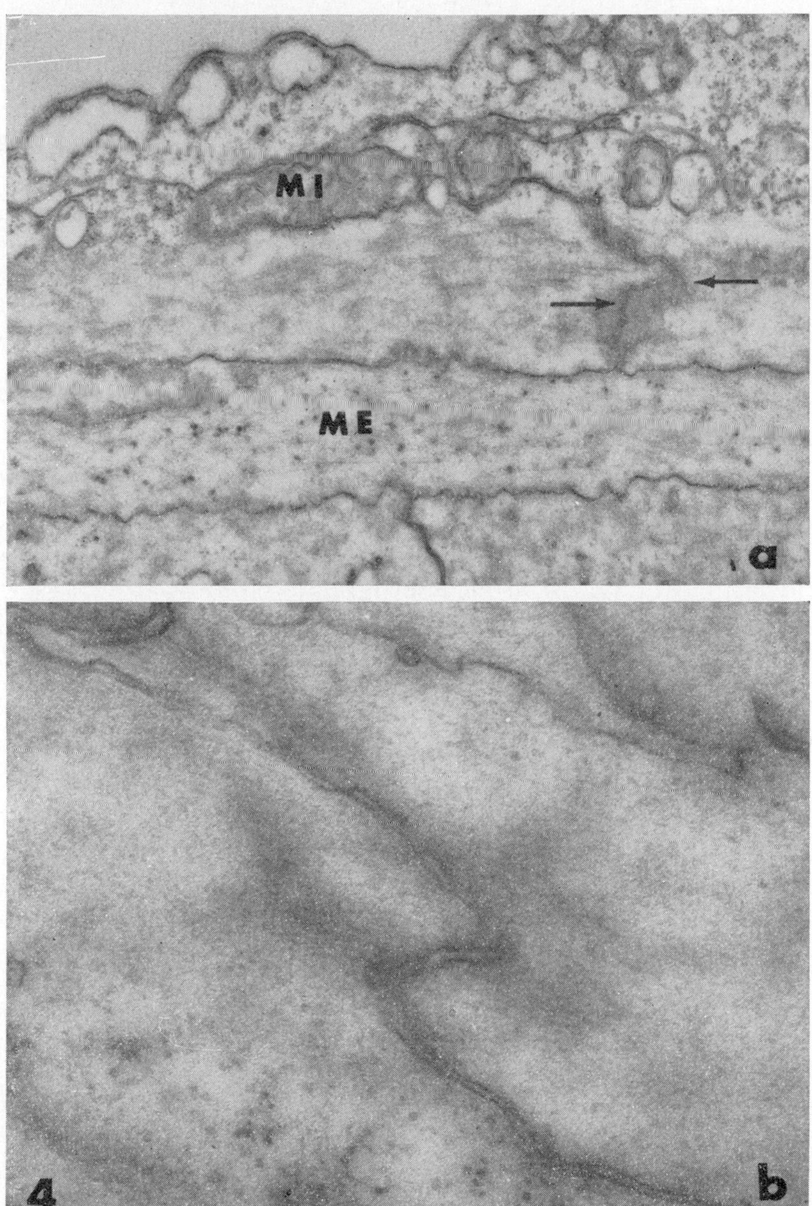

Fig. 4. *a*. End-to-end apposition of muscle fibers in the epidermis of *Pelmatohydra*. Note the irregular line of contact and the increased density associated with the two cell surfaces (arrows). The myofilaments appear as small streaks oriented towards the attachment zone. The subjacent mesoglea exhibits very fine filaments more or less randomly arranged. *b*. End-to-end apposition of gastrodermal muscle fibers at high magnification. The filaments in gastrodermal muscle appear less conspicuous than those in the epidermis. M, mitochondrion; ME, mesoglea. *a*—17,000X. *b*—80,000X.

simple bars but actually form lamellar partitions, or septa. The exact nature of the septa is not yet clear but there is some indication that they may be continuous with the outer dense components of the two apposed "unit" membranes (Fig. 3*b*, arrow). A diagrammatic representation of this type of desmosome is shown in Figure 3*c*. The two plasma membranes are joined by septa which may possibly have direct connections to the outer components of the apposed plasma membranes. Lack of continuity, as illustrated at B, is more commonly seen than continuity shown at A, so it is uncertain which configuration is more accurate. Perhaps both conditions occur along the course of the same septum.

Another type of intercellular attachment occurs in hydra where muscle processes are apposed end to end. Myofilaments appear to insert into regions of increased density and the two cell surfaces are maintained always in close approximation. This relationship, shown in Figure 4 (*a, b*) resembles the intercalated disc of vertebrate cardiac muscle. The intercalated disc is now recognized as a kind of desmosome (see Sjöstrand and Andersson, ref. 10). This type of attachment is particularly clear in longitudinal sections of the epidermis (Fig. 4*a*). In cross section they appear at the base of the gastrodermis and may be distinguished as irregular, dark streaks in light micrographs (Fig. 1*b*).

In the basal region of the tentacles, and in the upper part of the column, there is a special type of relationship of the muscle processes to the mesoglea. This type of attachment may also be identified by light microscopy in favorable preparations. Figure 5*a* is a light micrograph of a longitudinal section of a tentacle near its junction with the hypostome. Near the mesoglea an area of increased density is quite apparent, but the details of its structure are not obvious. A similar region viewed in the electron microscope (Fig. 5*b*) shows that the density is caused by a specialized muscle insertion on mesoglea. The attachment is accomplished by means of a narrow finger of epitheliomuscular cell cytoplasm which becomes intimately associated with an area of increased density in the adjacent mesoglea. The cytoplasmic finger contains a condensation of material which appears to be organized into a series of small tubular elements arranged at right angles to the plane of the plasma membrane (Fig. 6). The disposition of these tubules sug-

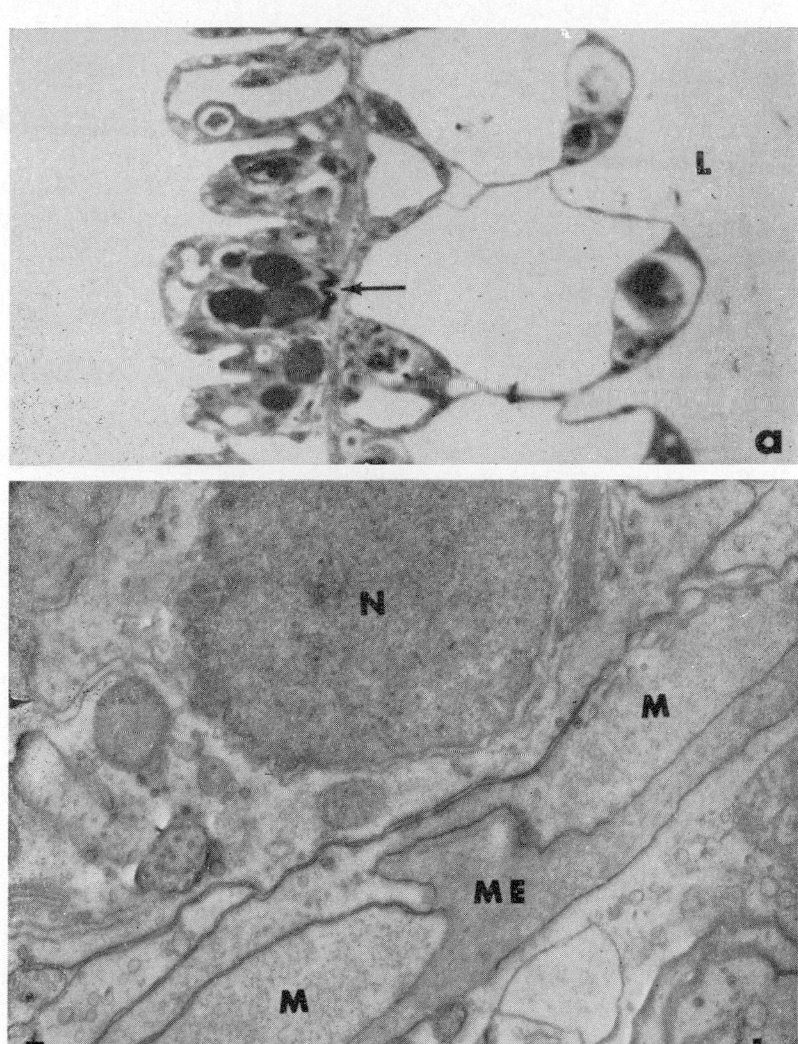

Fig. 5. Attachment of muscle to mesoglea in *Pelmatohydra; a* is a light micrograph of a longitudinal section of a tentacle. The epidermis is at the left and its scalloped surface indicates partial contraction of the tentacle. The dense line at the base of the epidermis (arrow) indicates a specialized form of attachment of muscle to mesoglea. A similar region viewed in cross section with the electron microscope is shown at *b*. Epidermal muscle fibers lie adjacent to the mesoglea. An extension of one muscle fiber becomes associated with a projection of mesoglea. See text. L, lumen; N, nucleus; M, muscle; ME, mesoglea. *a*—2,000X. *b*—20,500X.

gests a supporting function such as might be required in areas where there is increased mechanical stress.

The final example of a possible attachment mechanism in hydra which I will present is another arrangement of epithelial cell surfaces at the level of the mesoglea. In my preparations, both

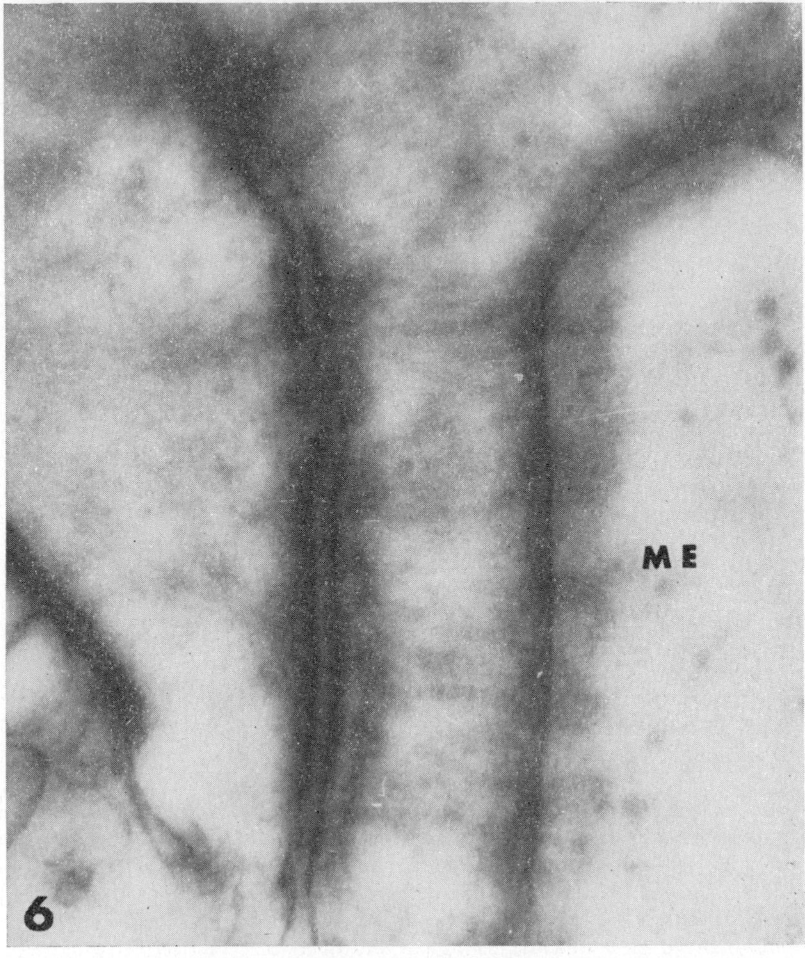

Fig. 6. High magnification of muscle attachment to mesoglea at a tentacle base in *Pelmatohydra*. The mesoglea is to the right. The cytoplasmic finger of the muscle fiber extends vertically through the center of the picture. Note the transversely oriented tubular structures (arrow) and the patterns of increased density. See text. ME, mesoglea. 120,000X.

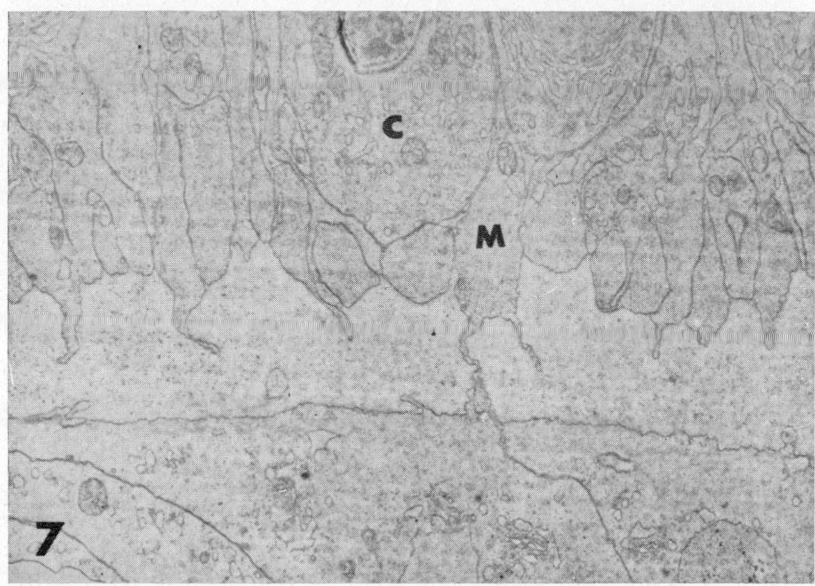

Fig. 7. Mesogleal relationship of epidermal muscle processes (top). The muscle fibers extend irregular processes into the mesoglea, some of which traverse the mesoglea completely (center). Those which traverse the mesoglea may abut against similar processes from the gastrodermal cells (bottom). C, cnidoblast; M, muscle. 7,000X.

for light microscopy and for electron microscopy, the mesogleal surface of epitheliomuscular cells is plicated and irregular. Frequently the mesoglea is completely traversed by narrow cytoplasmic processes (Fig. 1*b*, circle; Fig. 7). These connections were seen and illustrated by Hadzi in 1909 (3) but have not captured the attention of morphologists again until rather recently. They extend from epithelial cells situated in both layers. Within the mesoglea, or at one epithelial surface, the processes may abut against the opposite epithelium either along a fairly broad surface or in a very limited area (Figs. 7,8). So far as has been observed, the processes extending across mesoglea represent regions of contact between the two epithelial layers but not cytoplasmic continuity. Two distinct plasma membranes have always been seen although a reduction of the spacing between the apposed membranes is often evident. In fact, the typical 150-200 Å separation may essentially disappear, as is illustrated in Figure 8.

The irregular profile of epithelial cell surfaces being presented to the mesoglea could possibly reflect a mode of insertion into the extracellular matrix, as suggested by Hess, Cohen and Robson (4). Cell contacts across the mesoglea could be related to an attachment function but could also be related to the transfer of nutrients from gastrodermis to epidermis or to some mechanism of direct integration between the two muscle layers.

In this paper I have attempted to present a brief account of some of the various types of attachment that occur between epithelial cells and between the epithelial cells and mesoglea in hydra. The conclusion that all of these specializations represent kinds of cellular attachment is based on comparison with other organisms and on attempts to correlate structure with function. These attempts take into consideration special physiological problems related to the fresh water environment and the mode of feeding of these organisms. A permeability barrier for the organism seems essential and attempts to find a structural basis for this barrier have been unsuccessful in the past. I have postulated that the septate form of desmosome could be important in preventing the influx of excessive fluid to the intercellular spaces (12). There is no direct evidence, however, that septate desmosomes are any more effective in this respect than are ordinary terminal bars found in ductile epithelium or gut of higher forms. In fact, I am not sure that one can say positively that terminal bars function to preserve the intercellular milieu in any situation but evidence seems to favor such an interpretation.

At end-to-end and lateral contacts of interdigitating muscle fibers a strong adhesion is something which would appear essential for the efficient transmission of force during contraction of the muscle fibers. By the same token, the special kinds of attachments of muscle to mesoglea might be expected in areas of particular stress, such as presumably occurs at the bases of the tentacles. All these forms of attachment must also be interpreted as having importance for preserving relative cell positions during active movements of the animal. The chemical or molecular organization of the cell surfaces is certainly not yet known in sufficient detail to permit conclusions about the actual mechanism of attachment either between adjacent cells or between cells and mesoglea. I believe, however, that additional information will be obtained through further studies using techniques for dissociating cells and by using specific enzyme digestion. Analysis of appropriately treated material with high resolution electron microscopy may provide further information not only on the mechanism of intercellular attachment but also on the molecular structure of cell membranes themselves.

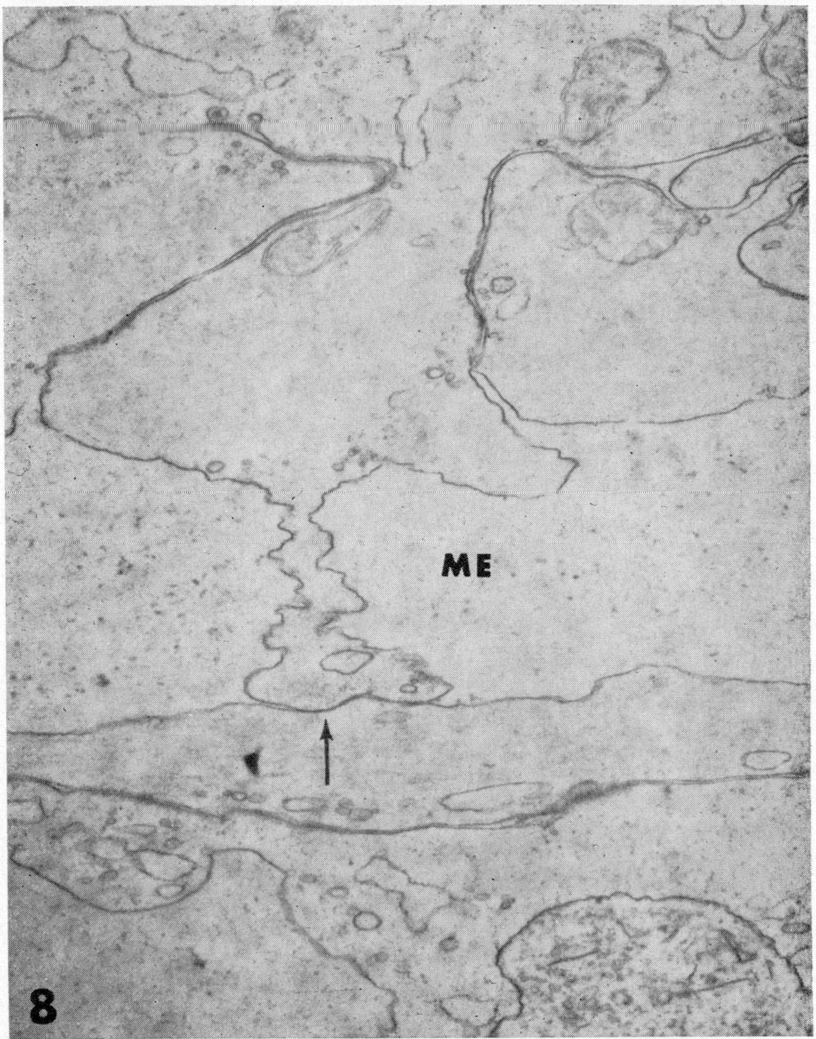

Fig. 8. Interepithelial connection across mesoglea of *Pelmatohydra*. The epidermal process (top) abuts against a gastrodermal muscle fiber. Note the collapse of the normal intercellular separation at the region of contact (arrow). ME, mesoglea. 13,000X.

REFERENCES

1. BENNETT, H. S., and J. H. LUFT. 1959. s-Collidine as a basis for buffering fixatives. *J. Biophysic. and Biochem. Cytol. 6:* 113-114.

2. CHAPMAN, G., and L. TILNEY. 1959. Cytological studies of the nematocysts of Hydra. I. Desmonemes, isorhizas, cnidocils and supporting structures. II. The stenoteles. *J. Biophysic. and Biochem. Cytol. 5:* 69-84.

3. HADZI, J. 1909. Ueber das Nervensystem von Hydra. *Arb. zool. Inst. Wien. 17:* 225-268.

4. HESS, A., A. COHEN and E. ROBSON. 1957. Observations on the structure of hydra as seen with the electron and light microscopes. *Quart. J. Micr. Sc. 98:* 315-326.

5. LUFT, J. 1961. Improvements in epoxy resin embedding methods. *J. Biophysic. and Biochem. Cytol. 9:* 409-414.

6. PALADE, G. 1952. A study of fixation for electron microscopy. *J. Exp. Med. 95:* 285-297.

7. RICHARDSON, K. C., L. JARETT and E. H. FINKE. 1960. Embedding in epoxy resins for ultrathin sectioning in electron microscopy. *Stain Technology 35:* 313-323.

8. ROBERTSON, J. D. 1959. New observations on the ultrastructure of the membranes of frog peripheral nerve fibers. *J. Biophysic. and Biochem. Cytol. 3:* 1043-1047.

9. SCHAFFER, J. 1920. *Vorlesungen über Histologie und Histogenese.* W. Englemann, Leipzig, pp. 69-100.

10. SJÖSTRAND, F., and E. ANDERSSON. 1954. Electron microscopy of the intercalated discs of cardiac muscle tissue. *Experientia 10:* 369-370.

11. SLAUTTERBACK, D., and D. W. FAWCETT. 1959. The development of cnidoblasts of Hydra. An electron microscope study of differentiation. *J. Biophysic. and Biochem. Cytol. 5:* 441-452.

12. WOOD, R. 1959. Intercellular attachment in the epithelium of *Hydra* as revealed by electron microscopy. *J. Biophysic. and Biochem. Cytol. 6:* 343-352.

DISCUSSION

WAINWRIGHT: Do you have any ideas concerning the site of synthesis of the mesoglea?

WOOD: In Hyman and other textbooks it is claimed that the mesoglea comes from both epithelial layers. I really have little more to add. It is always strictly extracellular and has no limiting membrane, as Dr. Hess has already pointed out. It corresponds to the connective tissue of higher forms. I don't know exactly how it arises.

HESS: I've seen mesoglea in very young buds almost immediately after their formation.

FAWCETT: I have no reason to regard the mesoglea as different from any other epithelial basement membrane except for its greater thickness. Where one has two epithelial or endothelial layers arranged base-to-base in higher forms, one finds a layer of amorphous, PAS positive material which looks very much like a thin mesoglea. I've always found this a very attractive prospect in hydra research. Perhaps here is the best place to study the structure and properties of basement membranes, and we might gain information from the mesoglea that could be carried over to the basement membranes which are such physiologically important structures in higher forms.

I would ask you a question on terminology. I wonder why you choose not to call these specialized zones of attachment "terminal bars"? I certainly agree with you that "desmosomes" is preferable from every point of view to the term "attachment plaques," but isn't there an adequate functional reason for making a distinction between desmosomes and those devices that occur next to the free surface extending for the full length of the cell boundary and which may very well have the function of preventing access of material to the intercellular space. Isn't it desirable to distinguish these elongated structures from the desmosomes which are circular plaques that occur at many points along the confronted surfaces of the epithelial cells and seem to be solely for attachment?

WOOD: I agree, Dr. Fawcett, but in my own terminology I regard the term desmosomes as a more general term. I then say this is a "terminal bar" type of desmosome. I'm sorry I didn't make it clearer in my presentation. This concept of the generality of the term desmosome comes from Schaffer's original description. I think "Schussleisten," which, of course, was the terminal bar, is an earlier term. Schaffer regarded the terminal bar as possibly arising from fusion of a series of small plaques. I've used the term desmosome in this general sense. I don't feel rigid about it, however.

HESS: We all try to get hydra fixed in an extended state. Some of the things we see in the mesoglea might be very different, I think, depending on the state of contraction of the hydra.

LUNGER: I have electron micrographs of *Campanularia* endoderm showing "terminal bar" desmosomes similar to those demonstrated for hydra by Dr. Wood.

WOOD: This has been observed in several other forms. They appear in planaria, and one is described briefly in Grimstone, Horne, Pantin and Robson's publication on *Metridium*.

SLAUTTERBACK: I'm willing to call these things "terminal bars," but we must not put a functional significance upon this name because we don't have any way of knowing that these structures are excluding something from the epithelium and preventing it from reaching the mesoglea. As far as I know the only obvious function is attachment, is that right? To put it another way, we should not apply the name terminal bars to the desmosomes of hydra because the function of terminal bars, namely the impeding or preventing the flow of water, electrolytes or other substances between cells, has not yet been proved to exist in any organism or tissue other than mammalian kidney.

WOOD: I think that the concept of terminal bar involves more than just this concept of separating the lumen from the intercellular space. It is a type of attachment which surrounds the entire surface of the cell. In longitudinal sections it has a bar-like structure which appears dense with certain types of stain. I agree that there is no direct evidence that these specialized desmosomes of hydra function to prevent passage of water or other material intercellularly, but I think that the idea is certainly reasonable because hydra is a fresh water invertebrate and must osmoregulate somehow. There is no kidney to do this and a reduction of exposed cell surface would be one way to improve the situation.

FAWCETT: There is a piece of evidence not found in hydra which indicates that terminal bars do have the function that has long been attributed to them. In recent work on the proximal convoluted tubule of the mammalian nephron, Miller found that when he administered hemoglobin solution to mice, the hemoglobin that filtered through the glomerulus and accumulated in the lumen of the tubule is electron dense and served as a good contrast medium. In electron micrographs one can follow the electron density of the hemoglobin between the cells of the proximal tubule as far as the terminal bar but no farther. Thus, at least for higher forms, large molecules do not penetrate between cells and the traditional interpretation of the terminal bar as a device for sealing the intercellular spaces now has some experimental substantiation.

HESS: Some substances might even use those cross striations as the steps of a ladder to climb into the hydra.

WOOD: I've thought of these cross connections as a system of baffle plates that might slow down penetration between the cells.

Discussion on: Is there a Nervous System in Hydra?

HESS: Electron microscopists say that they can't see a nervous system in hydra. And some of them say that a nervous system is not needed to account for the movements of hydra because the muscle cells in both ectoderm and endoderm contact each other allowing muscle to muscle transmission to take place.

Dr. George Mackie from the Department of Zoology, University of Alberta, has a few slides showing some silver stains of the nervous system. He might have something more convincing to convey about the presence of nerve tissue in hydra.

MACKIE: This is a brief report on the results of a recent attempt to stain nerves in the body wall of hydra and *Cordylophora* using the classical Holmes silver technique. This work is still in its initial stages. I will begin with *Cordylophora*.

General topography of the nerve net. There is only one neuron-system in *Cordylophora*, unlike *Velella* which has two histologically distinct plexuses. Neurons are abundant in the ectoderm of tentacles (Fig. 2) and hydranth (Fig. 1). We have the following figures for relative abundance of three tissue elements in a hydranth preparation where all showed well:

Epithelio-muscular cells	Neurons	Cnidoblasts
231	94	64

Neurons also run in the ectoderm of the stem. In the hydranth the neurons lie external to the muscle fiber sheet, running in the spaces between the stems of the epithelio-muscular cells. They do not follow the cell outlines, seen in surface view.

Neuron types. Structurally there seems to be little difference between neuro-sensory elements and purely nervous elements. Approximately one in eight neurons has a process running up to the surface with a hair projecting externally (Fig. 3, 4, 8, 9), but of those which are entirely sub-epithelial the majority have what seems to be a reduced or rudimentary sense hair projecting into the surrounding tissue space (Figs. 4, 7). It is possible that such cells are modified sensory elements that have become or are becoming transformed into neurons in the strict sense. However, this does not exclude the possibility that they retain a sensory function, serving for instance to record deep touch or to give position sense. The fibrous processes or neurites are similar in all these elements, whether the cell has a hair or not.

Interconnections. The neurites associate freely, running side by side for long or short stretches, but there is nothing to suggest that they regularly form continuous connections. This nervous system is quite unlike the closed system of *Velella* which shows every sign of being a syncytium. It is much more like the non-syncytial open system of *Velella.* The only evidence for continuous connections is that here and there one finds binucleate neurons and in some places there are suspicious-looking pairs of neurons which could be the two halves of a binucleate pulled apart, but still in primary connection. This gives me the opportunity to insert a remark about the retention of primary connections between cells which was discussed earlier, following the paper by Hess. Such connections have long been known in a variety of coelenterate cell types including young cnidoblasts, interstitial cells and epithelio-muscular

---

Ectodermal nervous system of *Cordylophora* (Figs. 1-9) and hydra (Figs. 10-12) as seen in silver-stained whole mounts. Scale indicates 10 mμ. Fig. 1. area of hydranth wall showing parts of five neurons; Fig. 2. neurons in a tentacle; Fig. 3. neuro-sensory cell; Fig. 4. the three types of neurons; Fig. 5. nerve fibers in contact with young cnidoblast; Fig. 6. bipolar ganglion cell; Fig. 7. well-extended neurons in expanded epithelium; Fig. 8. neuro-sensory cell showing root of hair in cytoplasm; Fig. 9. neuro-sensory cell; Fig. 10. neuro-sensory cell in contact with cnidoblast; Fig. 11. nerve fiber tract: only two out of four fibers are in focus; Fig. 12. bipolar ganglion cell.

Abbreviations: cn. cnidoblast; g. ganglion cell; hs. subepithelial hair; n. nerve fiber; p. process of neuro-sensory cell running to surface carrying external hair.

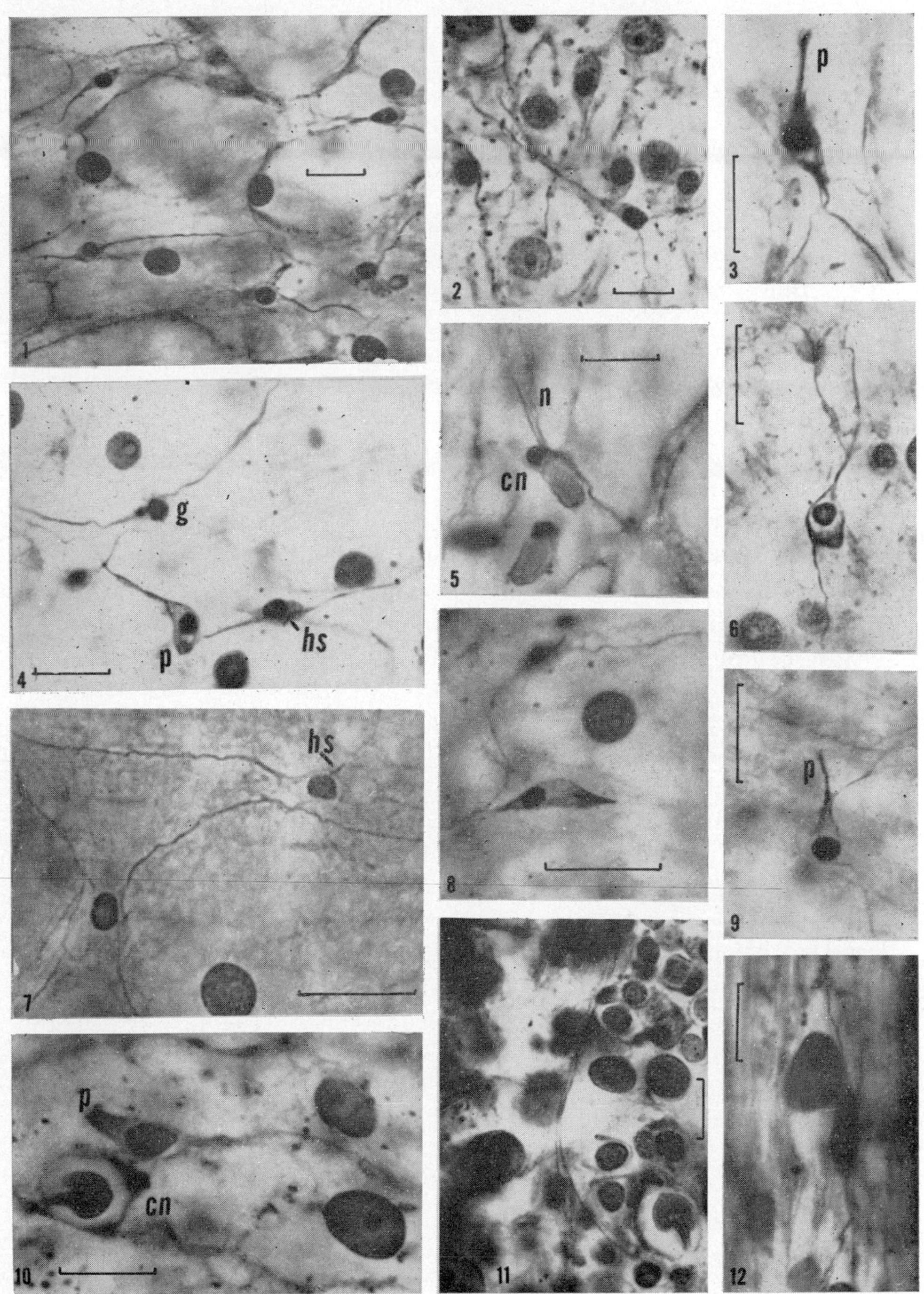
1
2
3
p
4
g
p
hs
5
n
cn
6
7
hs
8
9
p
10
p
cn
11
12

cells. In cases where the intercellular bridge is long and slender and still contains the relic of the mitotic spindle apparatus (Hirschler's fusome) the structure may bear a strong resemblance to a nerve fiber, especially in silver preparations where the fibers take the stain like nerve fibers. I suspect that such fibers may have been mistaken for nerves by certain workers.

"Innervation" of cnidoblasts. Given the abundance of neurites and cnidoblasts it is not surprising to find frequent instances where the two are in contact (Fig. 5). A rough estimate suggests that about one in five cnidoblasts are in contact with part of a neuron or neurosensory cell. No cases have been found where a neurite terminates directly upon a cnidoblast such as Spangenberg and Ham describe in *H. littoralis*. The contacts are apparently quite casual and undifferentiated. Perhaps we should not speak of innervation until we can show that these associations have functional significance.

Comparison of Cordylophora and Hydra. Hydra has proved harder to examine than *Cordylophora* because the tissue is histologically denser and more elaborate. However, the silver preparations do quite clearly show nerve elements. All that can be said at this stage in the work is that the system appears generally similar to that of *Cordylophora*. Conventional neuro-sensory cells (Fig. 10) such as Hadzi describes have been seen as well as subepithelial ganglion cells (Fig. 12), some of which have a rudimentary hair such as occurs in *Cordylophora*. If there is a noteworthy difference between the two forms it would seem to be the greater tendency in hydra for neurites to run in bundles. This has been seen near the hypostome, where bundles of up to four or five neurites (Fig. 11) have been followed for short distances, running around the animal in a circular direction. As to the connections, which many claim to be continuous, I have nothing to say at the moment, except that I have not seen any junctions which I would confidently interpret as being continuous.

HESS: Does anyone else have any comments?

CLAYBROOK: I am very sorry that Dr. Spangenberg of the Texas group was not able to attend this meeting to present her studies of the nervous system in *H. littoralis*. I am afraid I cannot do a very good job of describing her methods and conclusions.

Dr. Spangenberg used a methylene blue vital staining procedure, with a neutral red counterstain, to demonstrate the nerve cells in intact *Hydra*. I refer you to her recent publication (Spangenberg and Ham, 1960, *J. Exp. Zool. 143*, 195-202) for detailed descriptions.

I observed many of Dr. Spangenberg's methylene blue preparations under phase contrast, and can report that they compare very closely to Dr. Mackie's silver preparations. Nerve cells with from one to seven fibrous processes were observed with interconnecting fibers between many cells. While a complete nerve net could not be stained all at once in any one animal, nerve networks in all regions of the body were seen in various specimens.

As Dr. Mackie reported, cnidoblasts are often found in close contact with nerve cells. This doesn't indicate necessarily that there is innervation of the cnidoblast, but the frequency of coincidence is suggestive of that.

Dr. Spangenberg also identified multi-polar cells with the distinct morphology of neurons in *Hydra* preparations dissociated into single cells with Hertwig-Schneider fluid. I think there is little doubt that nerve cells and a nerve net do exist in *Hydra*.

HESS: If one wanted to be skeptical, it might be said that the "nerves" that the Texas group shows associated with the cnidoblasts are the discharged tubes of nematocysts.

BURNETT: I have recently received some photographs from Semal Van-Gansen at the University of Brussels. She has dissected out nerve elements from hydra with a fine needle. In the epidermis she finds the typical nerve net described by Hadzi (Fig. 1). In the gastrodermis she does not find a net. Instead she finds a more sparse distribution of nerve cells which do not resemble the small

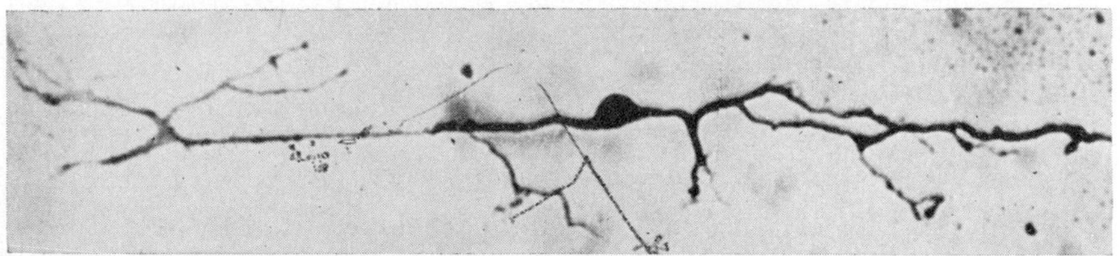

Fig. 1. Isolated epidermal nerve cell (Semal Van-Gansen).

bi-polar and tri-polar neurons of the epidermis. Those in the gastrodermis possess extremely long processes which branch profusely (Fig. 2). She has suggested to me that perhaps the epidermal net serves to coordinate the fast contraction of the longitudinal fibers, and the neurons in the gastrodermis control the slower contracting circular muscle fibers. She has been able to find sensory cells both in the epidermis and gastrodermis. I have been able to consistently demonstrate an epidermal nerve net by simply fixing a whole hydra for ½ hour in 100% alcohol and then staining for a few minutes in 0.1% methylene blue. The nerve set is especially clear in the transparent areas of the tentacles and peduncle. If this interlacing network of bi-polar and tri-polar cells is not a nervous system then morphologically it is a unique system in the animal kingdom and one that must be reckoned with. Personally, I feel certain it is a nerve net.

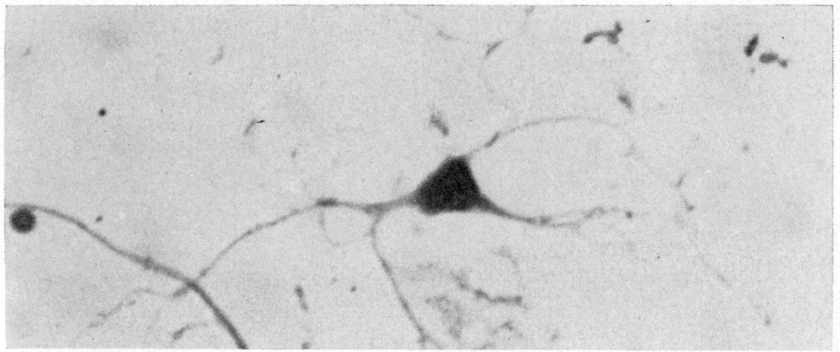

Fig. 2. Isolated gastrodermal nerve cell (Semal Van-Gansen).

HESS: Couldn't these "nerve cells and fibers" be cell membranes radiating out from the intercellular spaces? Do the intercellular spaces stain? This is a dissection, is it not?

BURNETT: Yes, this is a dissection.

HESS: Well, the cell membranes could be left intact radiating from intercellular spaces filled with extensions of mesogleal substance. Impregnation of these elements could yield a picture appearing like nerve cells and fibers.

SLAUTTERBACK: Before the argument is lost by default I'd like to inject a little bit of skepticism. I have no way of proving that the nervous system does not exist, in fact, I am not sure that I really doubt it. (I was expecting Dr. Fawcett to stand up ahead of me and say this.) But I would like to say that most of us who have hunted for nerve cells with the electron microscope have been unable to find any. It is at least possible that this is because the morphology of invertebrate nerves or hydra nerves is not readily recognizable. But this is disturbing in view of the fact that there are clear morphological criteria for the identification of nerves in vertebrate tissues; they are readily recognizable with the electron microscope. In fact, I'd say more easily identified than in the light microscope. Then too, it seems to me that the musculo-epithelial cells are so beautifully organized for conduction in hydra, that we don't really have to postulate the existence of a nervous system which we can't see in order to account for the behavior pattern. I recognize that it will probably take arguments more cogent than these to refute a concept which has delighted biologists for at least 70 years. I have only to say that we can't see a nervous system. We'd like things a little more sure.

HESS: Muscle to muscle connections, of course, are present even in mammalian smooth muscle. It wouldn't be an impossible situation for hydra to use muscle to muscle transmission to execute its movements.

PASSANO: I doubt that this answers our discussion, but it might be of interest to tell this group of our success in recording action potentials from hydra. A few years ago C. B. McCullough and I tried to find out whether or not hydra showed non-decremental through conduction by looking for nerve action potentials. We attempted to pick up activity of individual neurons, but what we got, probably, were near-simultaneous action potentials from several contiguous cells.

We had results with two types of preparations. The tentacle-hypostome preparation (we cut off and discarded the column just below the tentacular base) was threaded on a silver rod through the mouth. In addition to serving to immobilize the animal the rod served as a neutral electrode. While observing with a water immersion objective we brought the tip of a conventional capillary microelectrode close to the cell body of one of the bipolar cells underlying the epidermis between the tentaclular bases. Occasionally we picked up fairly strong, slow spikes, lasting 20 to 50 milliseconds and somewhat various in shape. They were always associated with strong tentaclular contractions and always clearly came before any movement was discernable in the area under observation. The tentacular reaction to glutathione did not elicit action potentials, however.

The other successful preparation also gave action potentials associated with strong muscle contractions. Here we used an intact hydra suspended from the surface film and surrounded by a wire ring to immobilize the animal and to be the indifferent electrode. The microelectrode picked up action potentials after penetrating the basal disk, when the gastrodermal longitudinal muscles contracted.

We believe that these electrical changes associated with either tentacular or column "quick withdrawal" responses were nerve action potentials, not muscle action potentials, since they came well prior to muscle contraction, only with the quick, coordinated contractions of all the muscle fibers, and since we only picked them up sporadically.

HESS: From a nerve cell? Can you get your electrode inside a nerve cell of hydra?

PASSANO: We think that they are from nerve cells, since we attempted to place our recording electrode in the small bipolar cells that underlie the epidermis. Since we did not have direct coupled amplifiers available, we are not able to say whether or not we ever penetrated nerve cells. Frankly, I doubt it.

Nematocyst Development[1]

DAVID B. SLAUTTERBACK
Department of Anatomy, The University of Wisconsin, Madison, Wisconsin.

To a cytologist one of the most intriguing aspects of the nematocyst is that it is a secretory product like many another, but unlike those commonly studied, it possesses a very high order of structural detail. To my knowledge, there are few rivals in this respect, among them being the protozoan trichocyst which serves to remind us that the coelenterates are not the only group with such highly organized secretory products. Though understanding it not at all, we are accustomed to the extremely intricate structures which cells, in an enviable demonstration of community effort, can construct in the extracellular space, such as hair and teeth. Still more commonplace, and seemingly more intelligible, are intracellular deposits of crystalline material. It does not stretch our imagination seriously to conceive of the mechanism which brings about this level of organization, impressive though it may be; for we can produce this same or similar structure in the laboratory without the intervention of cells. But comprehension of the mechanisms involved in the intracellular elaboration of such a highly organized body as the nematocyst challenges the best of our imaginative capacities. Speaking for the cytologist, the rewards are well worth whatever effort is required for we can reasonably anticipate even more than elucidation of this one mechanism common to a single group of animals. Certainly new and better understanding of the organelles with which all cells must work will ensue. This afternoon we will hear several approaches to the understanding of nematocysts, their production, structure and functions. For my part I shall make a rather free interpretation of my assigned

[1]The work reported here was done during the tenure of U.S. Public Health Research Grants RG5651 and RG6934.

topic, devoting most of my time to one of the lines of differentiation available to interstitial cells—the cnidoblast. Since Dr. Hess has shown you excellent low power electron micrographs for orientation I shall not include them in my presentation.

The small, relatively undifferentiated interstitial cell is found in the gastroderm where it gives rise (at least) to the zymogenic and mucous cells, and in the ectoderm where it may differentiate into cells of the gonads, cnidoblasts and possibly some others. Figure 1 is an electron micrograph of a pair of interstitial cells in the ectoderm of hydra. The nucleus is large and the nucleolus very dense, but undoubtedly the most impressive feature of these cells is the large number of cytoplasmic granules which are molecules of ribonucleoprotein (RNP). In the cytoplasm of these cells, aside from the ribonucleoprotein granules, or ribosomes, as they are known to biochemists, there are no elements of the endoplasmic reticulum, or at least they are very sparse. The Golgi complex is represented, but only by a very few vesicles, showing a low degree of organization. Another pair of interstitial cells is seen in Figures 2 and 3. They illustrate the fact that the nuclear membrane of these cells has a specialization common to many other cell types, as at "Po" in the figure. These small circles which appear in a tangential view of the nuclear membrane, and in longitudinal sections as indicated by the arrows, represent what have been called nuclear pores. Whether or not they are physiologically "pores" or "holes" in the membrane, I think remains unproved. But in any case, it is likely that they represent specialized areas for transmission of materials from nucleus to cytoplasm. This is exactly the kind of thing one would like to see in a cell which is about to differentiate, or for that matter, in a cell which is undergoing rapid mitotic division. However, the great desire to believe in such things, does not really substantiate their functional significance. So, while they may represent the lines of communication along which the nucleus tells the cytoplasm "now it's time to divide," or "now it's time to differentiate," this is largely speculative.

These pores may be seen to better advantage in Figure 4, where a rather large piece of nuclear membrane has been cut in tangential section. The abundance of these structures in the nuclear envelope can be seen clearly.

Another pair of interstitial cells is illustrated in Figure 5. These show the same complex; the absence of endoplasmic reticulum membranes and *now* an intercellular bridge (mentioned earlier today) which shows a distinct confluence of cytoplasm between the conjoined cells. And as usual, there is an accumulation in the extracellular space of small dense particles. They measure about 250 to 300 Angstroms and in all respects resemble the particulate glycogen described by Fawcett and Selby in the atrial muscle of turtle heart and by now in numerous other cell types. I should point out, however, that it is not very common to find glycogen particles extracellularly except here in the ectoderm of hydra. And in these cells, glycogen, in my experience, as particulate glycogen, has never been demonstrated intracellularly. Never within the interstitial cells nor developing cnidoblast; only extracellularly. This would fit well with the suggestion that glycogen is broken down at the cell membrane.

Returning to the intercellular bridges, your attention is directed to its thickened membrane which seems to impart enough rigidity to the structure to resist deformation by the frequent shape changes of the animal as a whole. The plasmalemma is continuous from one cell to the other through the tubular bridge, although it is sharply reflected upon itself twice, and bears a peculiar annular expansion midway along the length of the bridge. Figure 6 is a striking demonstration of this form and the continuity of cytoplasm between the two cells. The vesicles in the center of the bridge could hardly be said to belong to either one cell or the other. Probably the most important function of the intracellular bridge is to synchronize differentiation and thus provide large numbers of cnidoblasts in the same stage—reaching maturity at the same time. But, also in the early stages of cnidoblast development, when the cell is primarily concerned with proliferation, these intercellular bridges undoubtedly serve to synchronize the mitoses. It is possible, with some speculative stretch of the mind to suppose that the substance which synchronizes these mitoses must therefore be a soluble substance, readily and rapidly transmitted from one cell to the other. And, so we have here some evidence for the fact that the nucleus when telling cytoplasm to begin a mitotic division, transmits this information by some relatively small molecule, or at least a rapidly diffusible one which quickly can reach an equilibrium level within the group of developing cnidoblasts. In my experience these are usually 14 to 18 cells joined in a cluster, from which it is evident that a rapid diffusion rate is necessary to keep them all very closely synchronized.

This synchrony is illustrated by the pair of interstitial cells in Figure 7. The dense clumps of granules are the chromatin material, and only remnants of the ruptured nuclear membrane persist. These are not two daughter cells in anaphase, they are in late prophase, so the mitoses are quite closely synchronized. When these cells divide for the last time, the diplosome remains near the plasmalemma (Fig. 8). The remnants of the achromatic figure, the spindle fibers can be seen clearly (S). They appear to be thin tubular structures on the order of 200 Angstrom units in diameter. Whether or not these spindle fibers have any progeny, or any remnant left in the fully differentiated cnidoblast, cannot yet be said. The possibility exists, and I shall point out at a later time what I believe to be their fate.

You will see at "G" in the figure, a large number of vesicles belonging to the Golgi complex. Most of them do not have ribonucleo-protein granules upon their surfaces; but some do and still others have granules on one side and none on the other which may be interpreted as supporting the arguments for the continuity between the endoplasm reticulum and the Golgi complex.

Dr. Fawcett pointed out earlier today that some groups of cells are not joined together by intercellular bridges of the very intricate structure that you have just seen, but rather by simple discontinuities of the membranes, an example of which appears in Figure 9. It is difficult indeed to argue that these are not artifacts of preparation techniques. But one can only say that they are frequently seen, and they appear in cells which otherwise seem very well preserved. However, two of the cells in the micrograph are bound together by an intercellular bridge of the specific type, and, it is not at all uncommon to see both types of continuity within the same cluster. In fact, joining the same two cells together.

Now when the endoplasmic reticulum begins to appear, we see coincidentally the first appearance of the nematocyst. The reticulum first appears as scattered vesicles in the cytoplasm, rather spherical in appearance (Fig. 10); they have a very low density content. You can see at the arrows, for instance, a small amount of material within those vesicles. The nematocysts are indicated by "Ne"; one in the upper left hand corner and one in the lower right hand corner. It is quite difficult to determine exactly which name belongs with which nematocyst. But I would like to say by way of record here, that within one cluster all of the nematocysts we have seen are definitely of the same type and they continue to be the same type throughout the stages of differentiation. The relatively homogeneous area is the capsule of the nematocyst, and the granular area will become the tube. Around the open end, where the operculum will finally appear, there is a very dense aggregation of smooth vesicles which clearly belong to the Golgi Complex "GC." Notice again, the presence of glycogen granules between cells.

In Figure 11 there is a cluster of cnidoblasts, early in their differentiation, and you see several sections of nematocysts and the nuclei of these cells. The intercellular bridges are quite conspicuous and now the endoplasmic reticulum has become considerably more prominent. The latter is seen mostly as sections of tubular structures, but there is some tendency to form flattened cysternae, typical of such secretory cells as the pancreatic acinar cell, for example. This section, however, has missed the Golgi zones. This particular illustration serves primarily to point out the remaining cytoplasmic bridges, and the progressive increase in vesicles of the endoplasmic reticulum. Figure 12 is a higher magnification view of cells at a slightly more advanced stage to emphasize the persistence of the intercellular bridges and the continuity of organelles, not simply continuity of cytoplasmic matrix, but organelles seem to be shared between the cells.

As the nematocyst develops, it acquires the appearance in Figure 13. The Golgi complex is becoming very much more abundant. The centrioles, which are really a diplosome, remain at the open end of the forming capsule. The capsule is the lighter amorphous or faintly fibrous part, and the darker granular material is the forming tube protruding from the open opercular end of the capsule. Notice that the Golgi complex forms a close-fitting cap over the growing end of the tube. There is a continuous membrane surrounding this forming nematocyst which is agranular, and in all respects resembles that of the Golgi complex. You will see that the Golgi complex is formed as usual in vertebrates of flattened vesicles, expanded vesicles, and small spherical ones. It has been said that such appearances are not common in invertebrates and represent more of a vertebrate type of Golgi complex, so then hydra cnidoblasts have a vertebrate type of Golgi complex, if that's the case. The large body here at the top of the figure is lipid droplet, and in our experience lipid droplets are a ubiquitous finding in all secretory cells. Of course, lipid droplets are found in virtually all cell types, but a relatively sudden accumulation of lipid seems to go hand in hand with the differentiation of these secretory cells.

In another section of the opercular end of a developing nematocyst (Fig. 14) the Golgi membranes surrounding the growing tubule can be seen more clearly. In the Golgi zone, the three types of vesicles are evident and especially prominent in this micrograph, is this large expanded one (indicated by an arrow) whose contents appear every similar to those of the nematocyst capsule. The only appreciable difference seems to be a slightly greater density of the material in the nematocyst than in the Golgi vesicle. One can often see areas where these Golgi vesicles seem to increase gradually in size getting larger and larger, and finally one of the vesicles seems to join by fusion of its membrane with that of the membrane surrounding the nematocyst tube or rod. This process is illustrated in Figure 15. It bears a remarkable resemblance to the mode of release of secretory granules in other cells in which the Golgi membrane surrounding the granule fuses with the plasmalemma and the membrane is broken at the point of fusion releasing the secretory product and adding the Golgi membrane to the plasmalemma. As you can see the endoplasmic reticulum is continuing to develop. We are not yet past the peak of protein synthesis in this cell. That similar configurations are present in the isorhizas is evident from Figure 16. Here a large Golgi vesicle is being added to the nematocyst tube. Though some degree of uncertainty remains as to the identity of these developing nematocysts, those which you have seen before were probably desmosomes, but this one is an isorhiza, though whether it should be regarded as holotrichous or atrichous, I cannot say. But again, you see the centrioles at the opercular end, and the Golgi complex aggregated around the open end of the nematocyst.

Figure 17 illustrates a very recent observation in our laboratory. The micrograph shows a cross section of the neck region of a developing nematocyst. The accumulation of vesicles of the Golgi complex indicates the forming tube has not yet extended very far out of the capsule. Immediately surrounding the Golgi membrane, which encases the nematocyst, is a row of very small tubules. They are about 180 Å in diameter with a lumen about 75-80 Å in diameter and a wall thickness of about 50 Å. In the upper right quadrant of the figure they are seen in perfect cross section. The function of these elements is not yet clear, but some of their structural relationships may be significant. In the interstitial cells they are found in groups scattered through the cytoplasm. Within the groups tubules are arranged at right angles to each other. They are evidently continuous with the tubules which have been interpreted as spindle fibers in Figure 8. In intermediate stages they are as figured here and in later stages (as Fig. 27) they continue to surround the nematocyst, oriented parallel to its long axis and are continuous at one end with the rootlets of the stiff rods (described later in this paper) and at the other with dense coils of tubules in the nuclear zone and seen as fibrous bodies in Figure 27. The only suggestion of function is seen in the relationship at the arrow in Figure 17. Here one tubule appears to be in direct communication with one of the small spherical vesicles of the Golgi complex. Whether this indicates a separate mechanism for the production of nematocyt capsule is not yet clear.

Now to return very briefly to the endoplasmic reticulum, Figure 18 shows a fairly early group of cells with small tubular elements of the reticulum. In Figure 19 you will see a fairly late stage in the development of the cnidoblast. The cell has about reached the peak of its synthetic activity, and the endoplasmic reticulum now assumes a more packed formation and you see many flattened sacs which are disposed in a concentric array around the nucleus. The wider spaces (also marked with a star in Fig. 20) are areas where the reticulum has been cut obliquely and are not in reality such wide diameter structures. And finally the condition illustrated in Figure 20 is reached when the reticulum fills most of the cell. During the formation of the nematocyst, the Golgi complex is at all times in close proximity to the tip of the forming tube and that tube is formed out in the cytoplasm. It may become very very long and coiled around through the cytoplasm, but the Golgi complex caps the growing tip.

In Figure 21 is a cnidoblast which has passed its peak of synthetic activity. We considered for sometime that the expansion of these endoplasmic reticulum vesicles was a fixation artifact due to osmotic differences in the fixative as compared to those within the cell. But by using a very wide variety of osmotic strengths and hydrogen ion concentrations, we have convinced ourselves that this is exactly what happens to the reticulum after it has passed the peak of synthetic activity. It begins to swell up, perhaps with an acute hydration of its contents. I wouldn't like to extend myself on that point, but in any case they do become vesicular again.

In Figure 22 you will see a nematocyst, which shows how this forming tubule continues around through the cytoplasm. The absence of Golgi vesicles from this section clearly indicates that there are still more coils of tubule elsewhere in this cell for if the tip were here we would see the Golgi membranes surrounding it.

The cell in Figure 23 shows a still more advanced condition and this one is an early stenotele. The Golgi membrane surrounding the nematocyst is clearly discernable, and now we begin to see a concentration or aggregation of dense granules which were once randomly distributed. It is in this zone that the spines and thorns of the nematocyst tube will be formed. In this micrograph there are four sections through the coiled tube which is still outside of the nematocyst capsule. The darker bodies are mitochondria, and the endoplasmic reticulum is clearly vesicular and considerably decreased in amount indicating the end of the synthetic phase. Though not present in this illustration, the Golgi complex is still active evidently collecting and concentrating material synthesized earlier in the now regressing reticulum.

A more advanced stenotele cut longitudinaly is seen in Figure 24. The tubule has been withdrawn and the open end of the capsule is closed by the operculum. The laminated structure of the operculum can be seen in Figure 31. The arrows point to the elements which were originally distributed at random throughout the substance of the forming tube, and have now just begun to form the tubular wall and the spines and thorns. So this, I am sorry to say, is the stage soon after the retraction of the tube, which was as you saw before, wound throughout the cytoplasm. And I presume that this retraction is a very rapid process because we have never seen (or recognized) it in progress. On the other hand it may be that some of the tubes which we see lying coiled out in the cytoplasm having a cross section somewhat thicker than usual, are these tubes undergoing withdrawal. In any case it is clear that there is no visible structure in the tube before it has been withdrawn into the capsule and that all of the intricate structures which appear later on are formed without immediate contact with cytoplasmic organelles and the mechanism of this astonishing feat remains an enigma.

Figure 25 illustrates some of the elaborate detail of the structure of a stenotele and points out that the endoplasmic reticulum, which has reached a vesicular stage, is now disappearing and that the phospholipids of that membrane have gone some place else. It might be interesting to follow the displacement of these phospholipids with histochemical procedures, but we have not as yet tried such things.

The isorhiza in Figure 26 illustrates a similar course of events in that type of nematocyst: the endoplasmic reticulum has become vesicular and vanished to a very large degree. The coiled tube is indicated at "T," and I presume that this is a holotrichous isorhiza because, in some areas (arrows), we see what appear to be developing thorns. At "Cn" in the upper right of the figure is the region where before we saw the diplosome and now we see what Hyman has referred to as the stiff rods which surround the operculum, a part of the cnidocil appartus.

A similar degree of differentiation is seen in Figure 27, but the section has passed through the operculum and the cnidocil. One of the centroiles of the basal granule is at the base of the cilium, which, I believe, is just in the process of forming, and is quite broad in diameter. And just outside it, you can see one of the stiff rods. Now this is not the dense part, which you saw in the section immediately preceding, but this is the part which corresponds to the body of the cilium itself. The endoplasmic reticulum is much diminished. The Golgi complex has retreated to the basal area of the cell and has often been described here, by silver stains, as a dense body in the basal part of the cnidoblast, but I believe it is simply an inactive Golgi complex. Immediately below it are very fine filaments which by newer techniques appear to be fine tubules (see Fig. 17).

Figure 28 is a fortuitous section through a stenotele which is fully developed. The parts of the nematocyst are readily recognizable including the operculum (O), two of the three spines, and the faintly striated tubule. The membrane surrounding this structure is quite obvious. The cilium with its basal granule and one of the "stiff rods" are also prominent. Now I think it's obvious that this so-called stiff rod is very similar to the cilium in structure, but you can see faint longitudinal striations in the cilium which are absent in the stiff rod. Another structure which appears often in this zone is the multivesicular (MV) body which most closely resembles the lysosomes of DeDuve. I should also like to point out that there are very fine filaments visible in this micrograph which are attached to the cilium and to the stiff rods; in more favorable sections they also appear to be attached to the circumference of the operculum, and may serve in the mechanism of firing the nematocyst.

In Figure 29 is a cross section of a stenotele. In the center of the micrograph the three heavy spines of the base of the tube can be seen; a dense material is gradually accumulating in them from the periphery inward. The peculiarly convoluted material around the spines is the base of the tubule itself and the conspicuous cross striation of it has a repeat period of about 150 Å; that is, each light line measures about 75 Å wide as does each dark line. The fact that this same periodicity is seen in longitudinal section (Fig. 30) suggests that the tubule is composed of a crystalline array of rod shaped molecules. (I am not able to explain the difference between my measurements and those of Dr. Chapman though it is not impossible that they vary with degree of development or dehydration.)

I am not going to deal extensively with the cnidocil structure at this time, but I would like to make a few additional observations. In Figure 31 you will see that the stiff rods of the cnidocil appear first as a straight row of dense bodies connected by a fine dense line. And at one end of that row of bodies, there is a basal granule of an unmodified cilium (not visible in this section). This cilium can be seen in figure 32 where the stiff rods, now quite well developed have begun to form a circle around the operculum. Notice that it is surrounded by fine filamentous structures which show a repeat period somewhat larger than 300 Å. This section is slightly oblique to the plane of the rods so that in the upper left it has passed through the modified ciliary part and in the center and to the right has passed through the cross-striated rootlet. There are 21 of these plus the true cilium.

In the next illustration you can see the relationship between the rootlet-like structure and the ciliary-like structure of the stiff rod. If you follow the membrane around the ciliary part you see that it passes below and peripheral to the upper end of the clearly cross-striated rootlet. It is remarkable that the rootlet which in the ordinary cilium is supposed to lend structural and functional stability, should be offset in this way. Though there is little evidence to support the notion at this time, such an arrangement might function as a hinge with the ciliary part bending outward and the rootlet remaining fixed.[3]

Figure 34 shows a slightly oblique section through the completed apparatus. Notice the 21 rods and the eccentrically placed cilium. Again the fine filamentous material which interconnects all parts of the apparatus and the operculum.

The last two micrographs (Figs. 35 and 36) are taken from a section of a very different animal, but I want to use them to illustrate an important consideration about the functioning of the endoplasmic reticulum in the cnidoblast. It is not evident from the developing cnidoblast that the ribonucleoprotein granules must be or even can be attached to a membrane of the endoplasmic reticulum in order to function in the synthesis of new protein. It has been argued for some time that only the free granules of ribonucleoprotein are active and that *after* synthesis is completed the free granules move with their product to the endoplasmic reticulum where the product is separated and added to the contents of the lumen of the vesicle. We have seen in the proliferating interstitial cells that free granules *are* active in the production of protein "for domestic consumption," i.e. new protoplasm. In the case at hand we have a secretory cell in the gut of a small earthworm,

[3]It should be pointed out that the tubules illustrated in Figures 8 and 17 appear to be continuous with the rootlets of the stiff rods.

Enchytraeus fragmentosus (Fig. 35). This cell is a very active protein secretor and this is the peak of its synthetic activity. It has become completely filled with endoplasmic reticulum plus a few secretory droplets and a very few mitochondria. In Figure 36 I think I can convince you that there are no free ribonucleoprotein granules in this cell; thus, attached RNP granules induce synthesis of protein for export from the cell; whether or not free ones do, I cannot say.

(I cannot distribute the responsibility for the interpretations presented here, but I would like to acknowledge the important contribution of Prof. Don W. Fawcett to this work.)

Figures 18, 23 and 15 are reprinted here by courtesy of the *Journal of Biophysical and Biochemical Cytology.* They appeared in volume 3, page 441 of that Journal.

The following abbreviations have been used in the accompanying illustrations:

Centriole—Ce
Cnidocil Apparatus—Cn
Endoplasmic Reticulum—ER
Golgi Complex—GC
Intercellular Bridge—B
Lipid Droplet—L
Mitochondrion—M
Multivesicular Body—MV
Nematocyst—Ne
Nematocyst Capsule—C
Nematocyst Tube—T
Nucleus—N
Nuclear Envelope—Np
Nuclear Pores—Po
Nucleolus—No
Operculum—O
Particulate Glycogen—Gy
Plasmalemma—P
Ribonucleoprotein Granules—RNP
Spindle Fibers—S
Zymogen Droplet—Z

Fig. 1. A pair of interstitial cells showing granular cytoplasm. 8,900X.

Fig. 2. Nuclear pores in an interstitial cell. 10,000X.

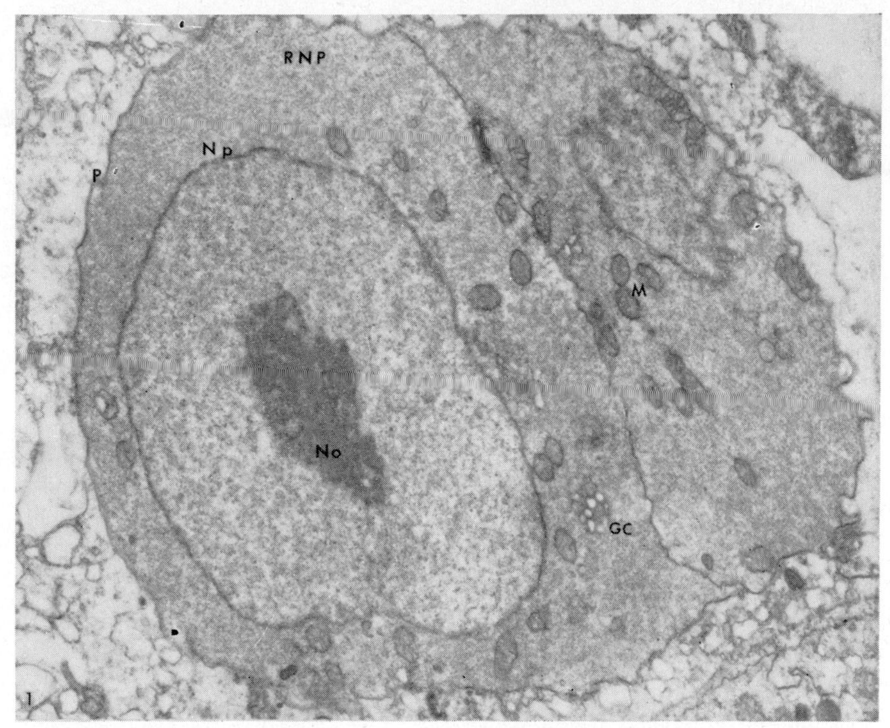
RNP
Np
P
M
No
GC
1

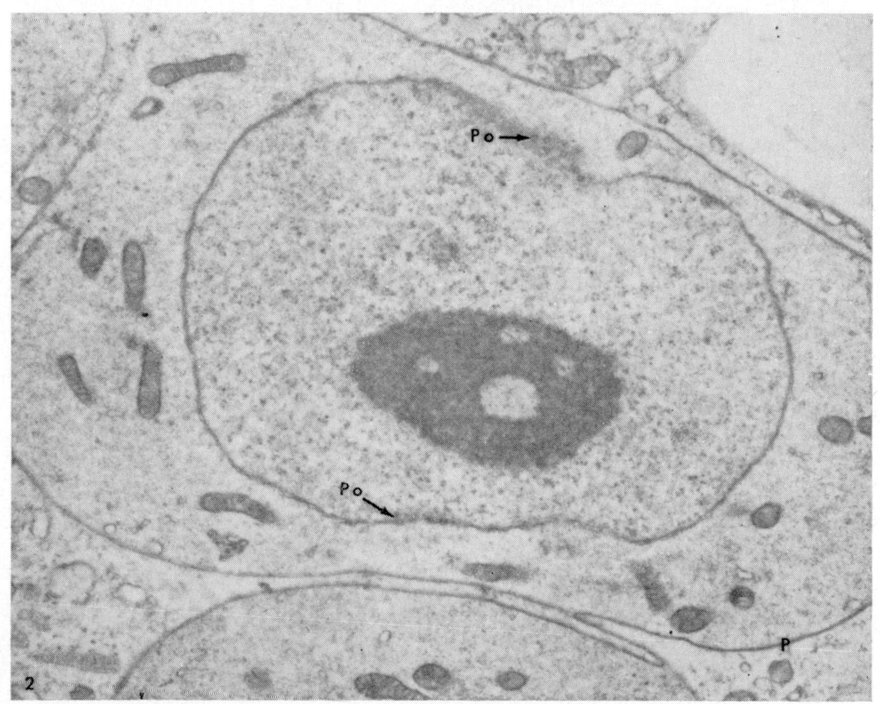
Po
Po
P
2

Fig. 3. Same cell as Figure 2 somewhat enlarged. 13,000X.

Fig. 4. Tangential section of the nuclear envelope in an interstitial cell showing the distribution of "nuclear pores." 32,000X.

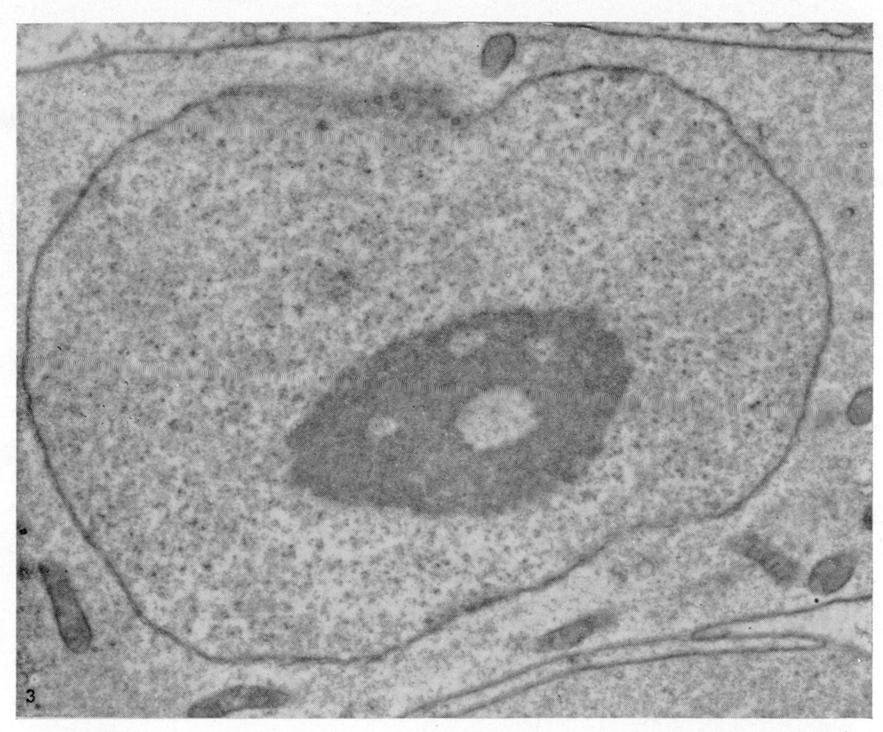
3

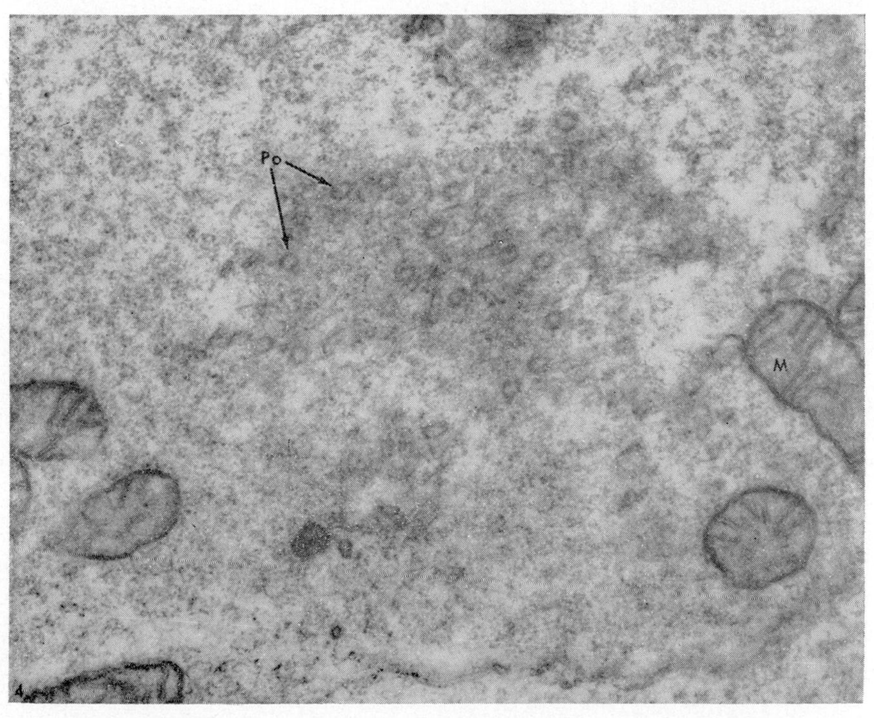
Po
M
4

Fig. 5. A pair of interstitial cells bound together by an intercellular bridge. 12,500X.

Fig. 6. Enlargement of intercellular bridge similar to Figure 5. 22,000X.

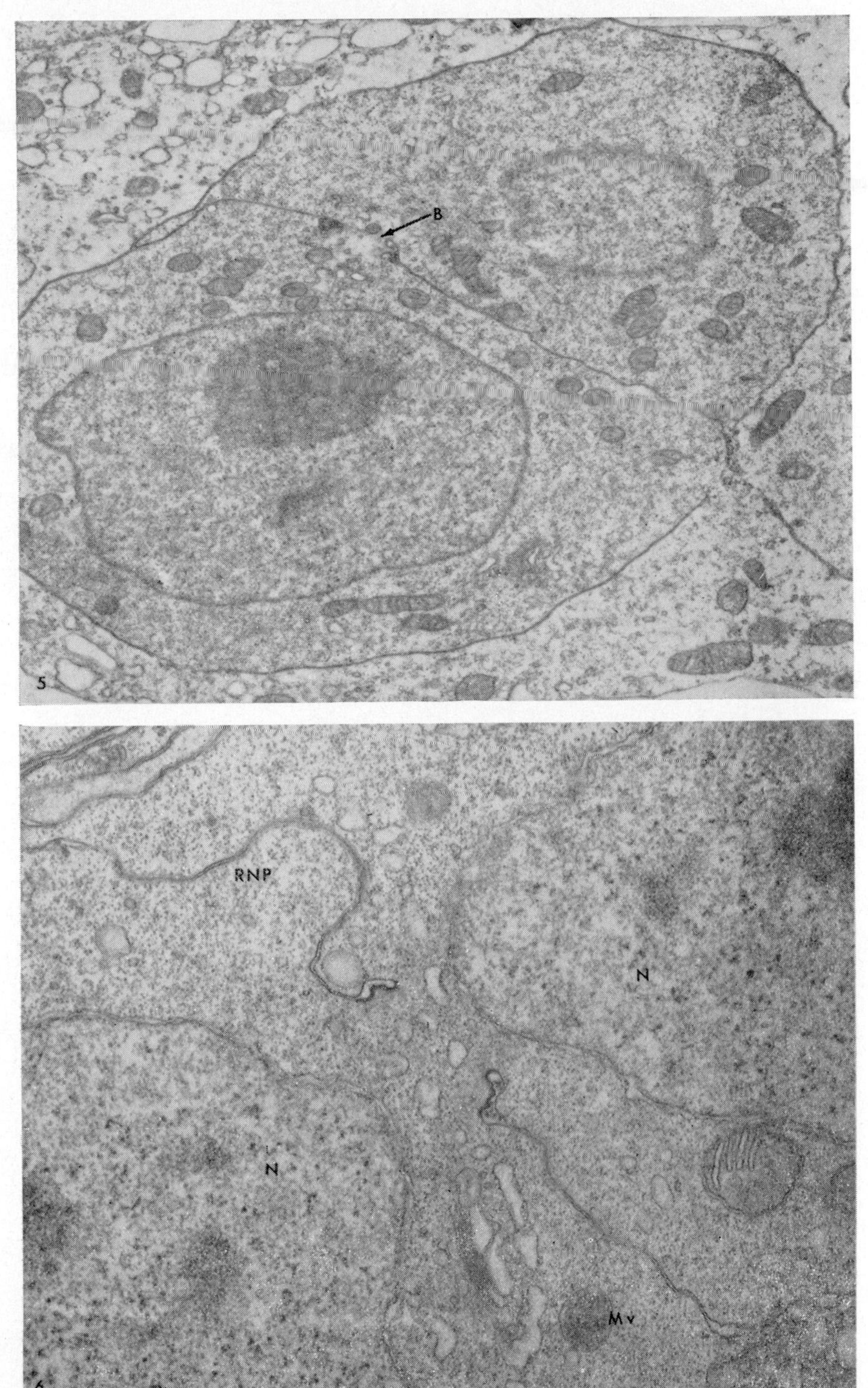
B
5
RNP
N
N
Mv
6

Fig. 7. Two interstitial cells from a single cluster, both in late prophase. 9,500X.

Fig. 8. Diplosome of an interstitial cell with attached spindle fibers which are in fact tubules. 29,000X.

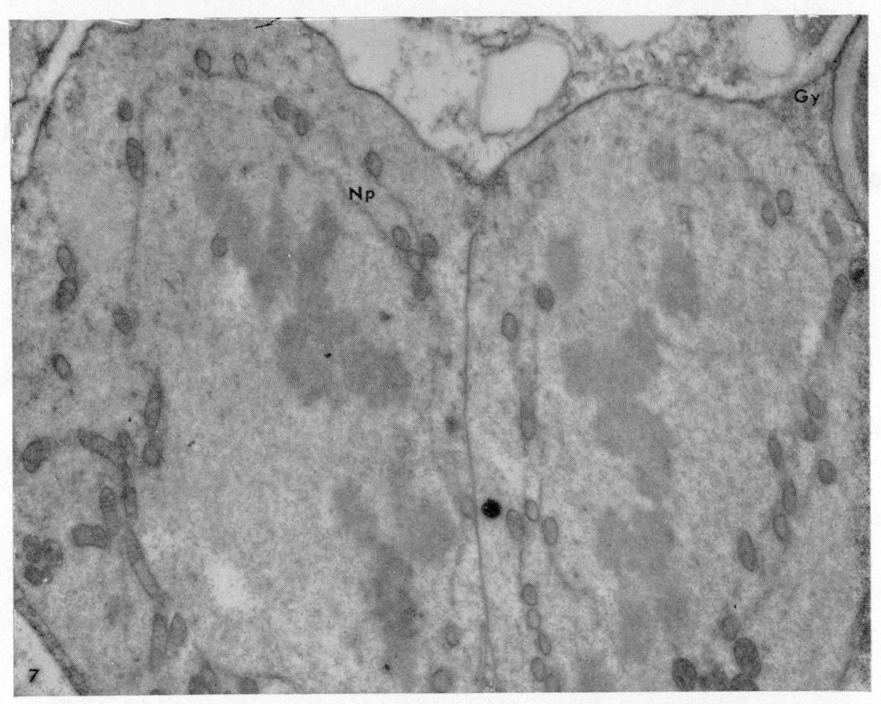
Gy
Np
7

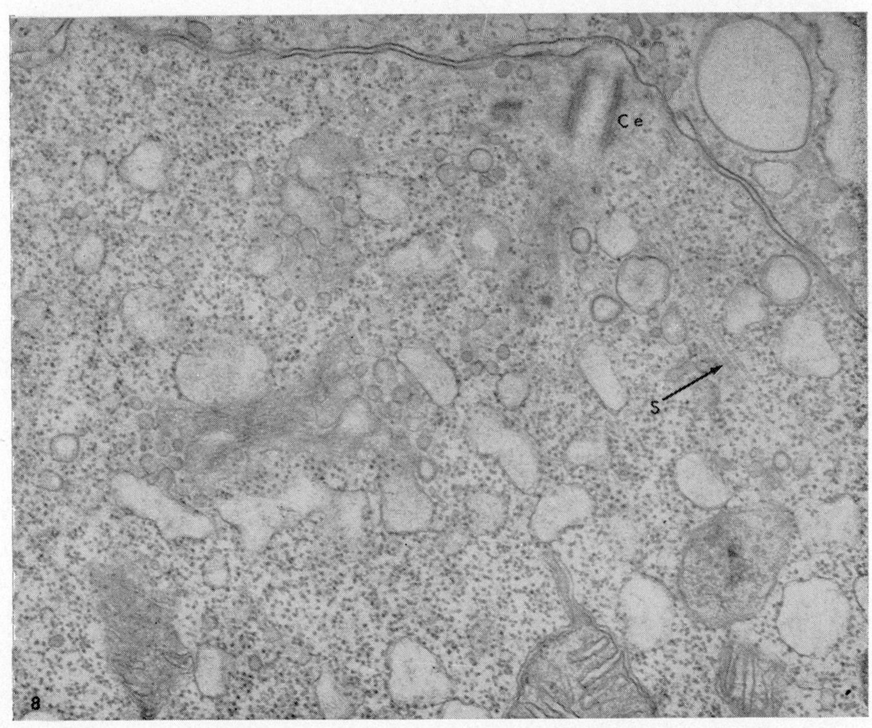
Ce
S
8

Fig. 9. Two types of protoplasmic continuity in a cluster of interstitial cells. 12,000X.

Fig. 10. Early cnidoblasts showing beginning development of endoplasmic reticulum, Golgi complex and nematocyst coincidentally. 17,000X.

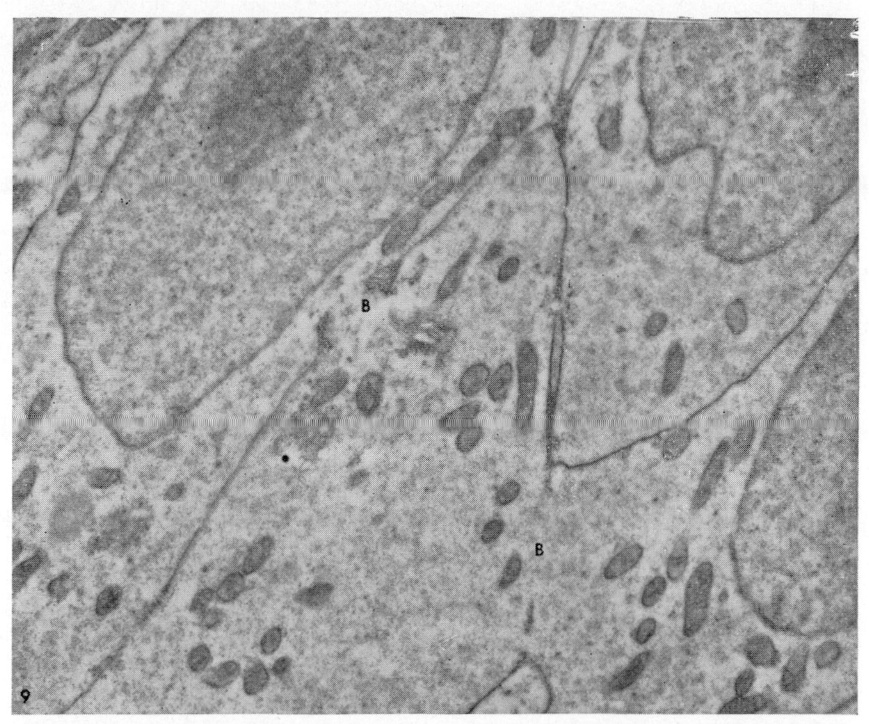
B
B
9

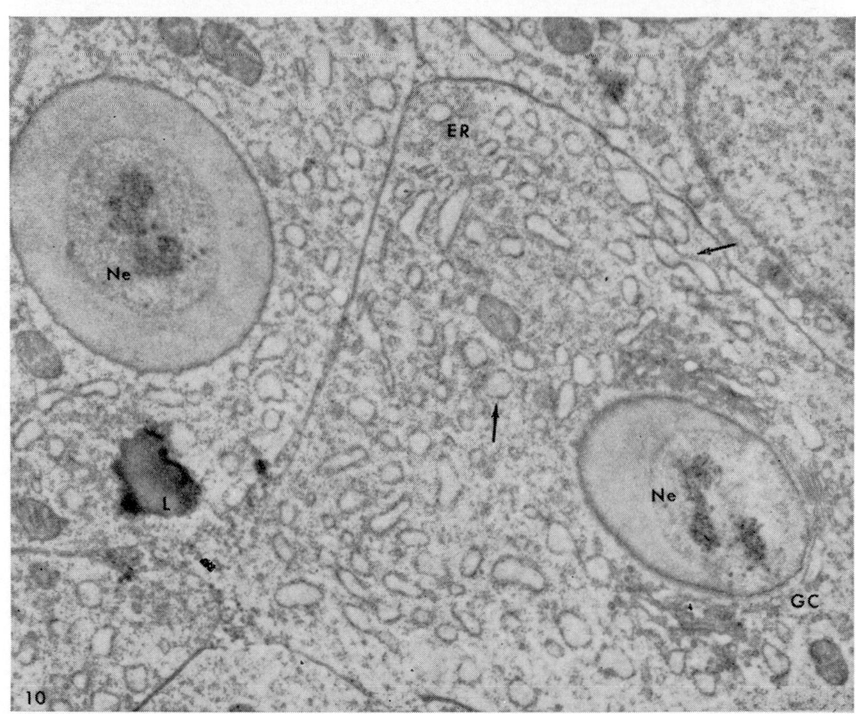
ER
Ne
L
Ne
GC
10

Fig. 11. A cluster of cnidoblasts slightly more advanced than those in Figure 10. 17,000X.

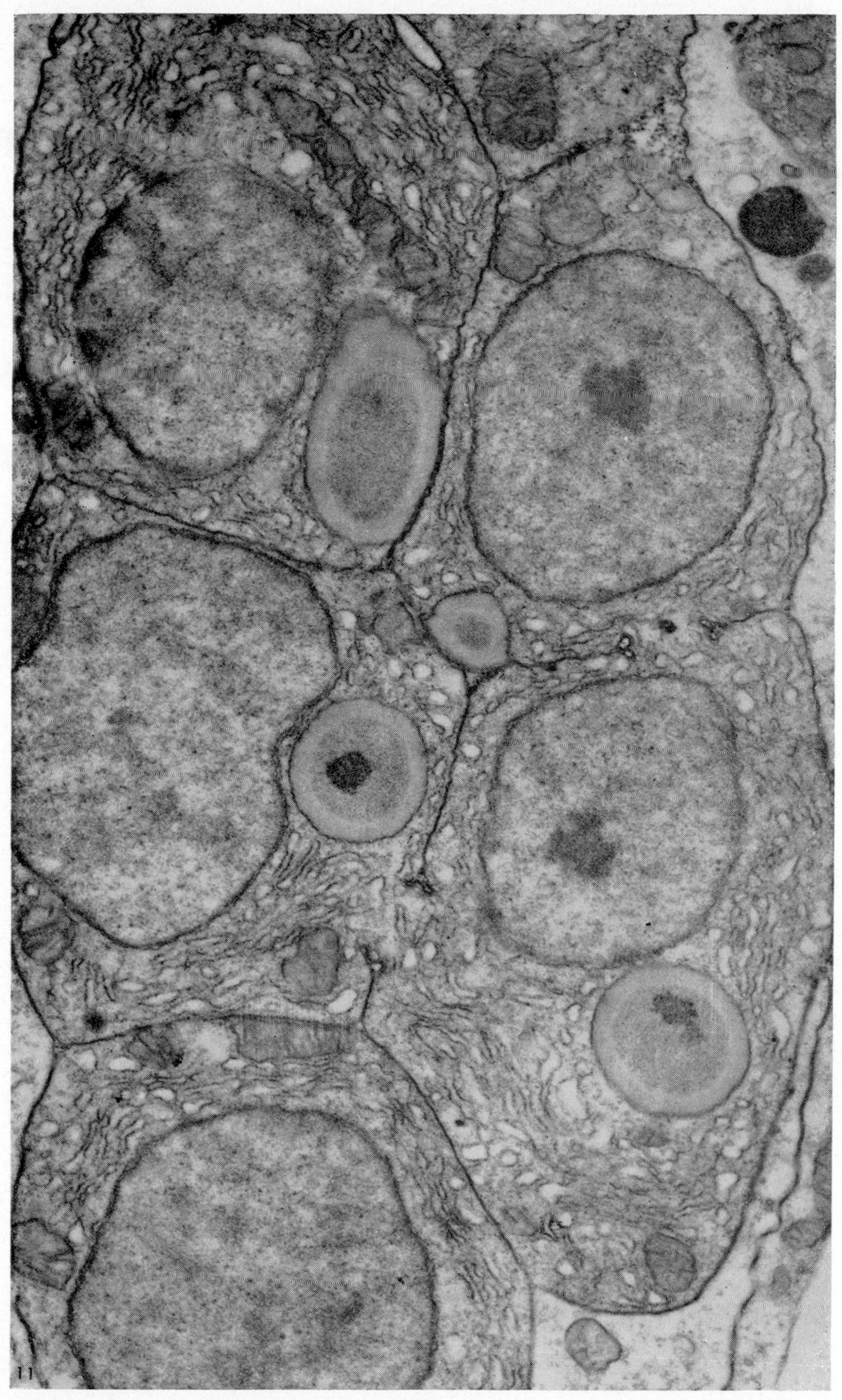
11

Fig. 12. An intercellular bridge in a pair of cnidoblasts slightly more advanced than those in Figure 11. 22,000X.

Fig. 13. This longitudinal section of a nematocyst shows the cap-like arrangement of the Golgi complex over the growing tip of the tubule. 15,000X.

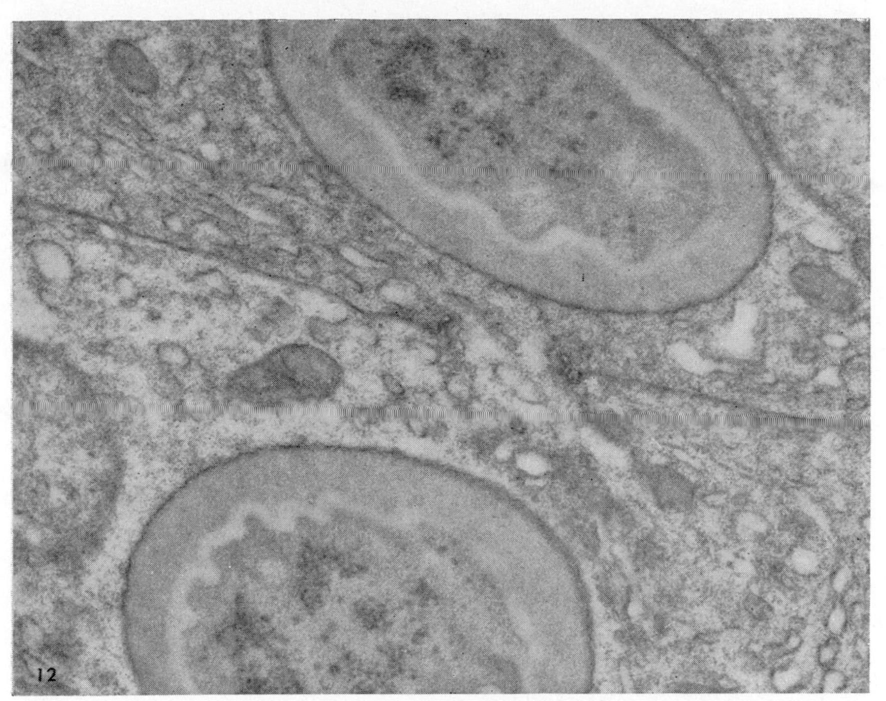
12

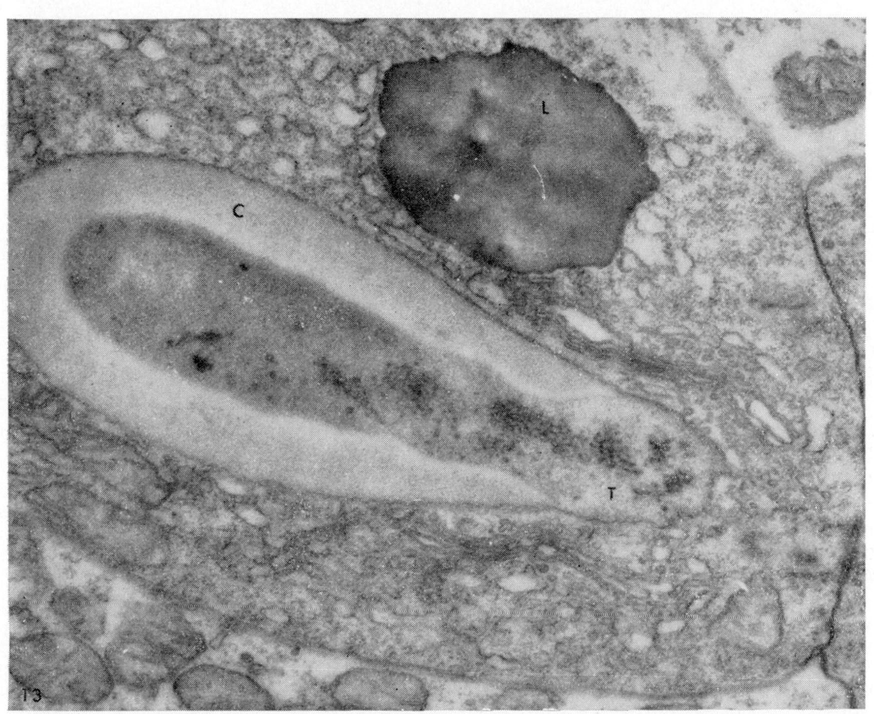
L
C
T
13

Fig. 14. Similar to Figure 13, but somewhat enlarged. 19,000X.

Fig. 15. The membrane of a large Golgi vesicle has just fused to the membrane surrounding the nematocyst and in this way added its content to the previously synthesized tube material. 32,000X.

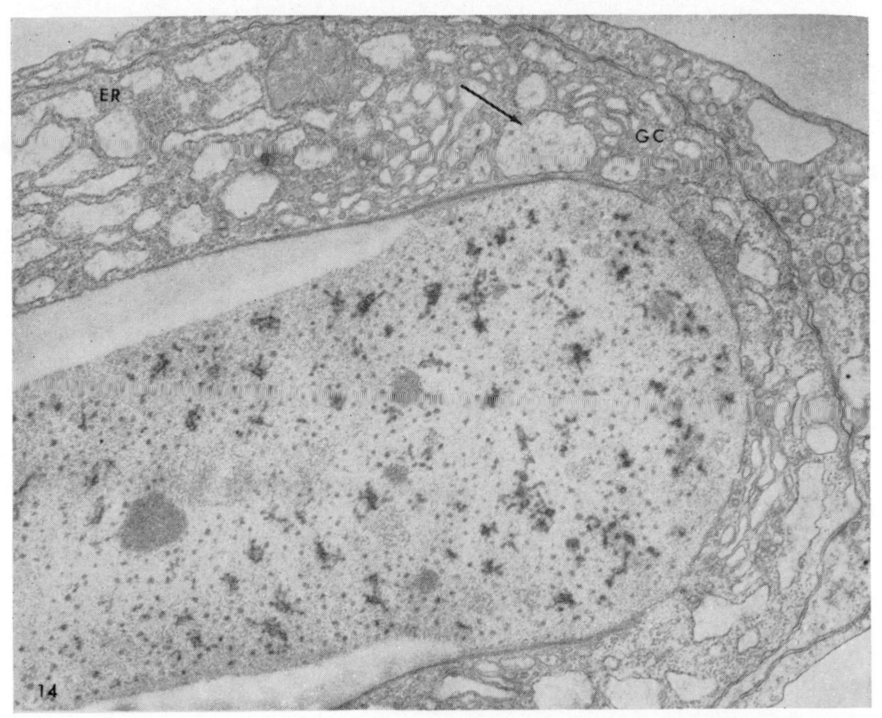
ER
GC
14

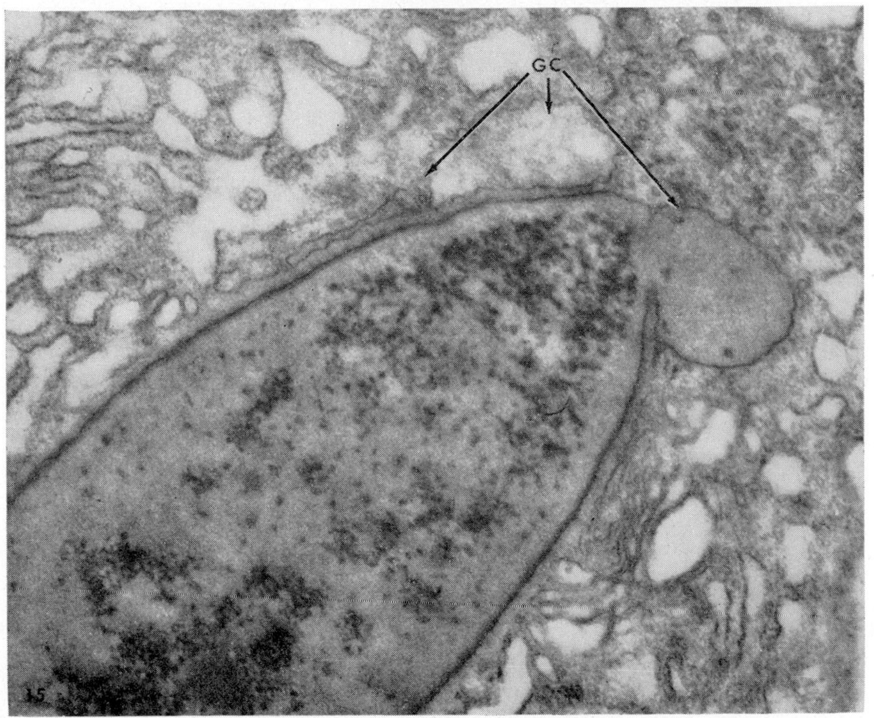
GC
15

Fig. 16. A cnidoblast containing a developing isorhiza. The same process illustrated in Figure 15 is seen here. 23,000X.

Fig. 17. Cross section of the neck of a developing nematocyst. 46,000X.

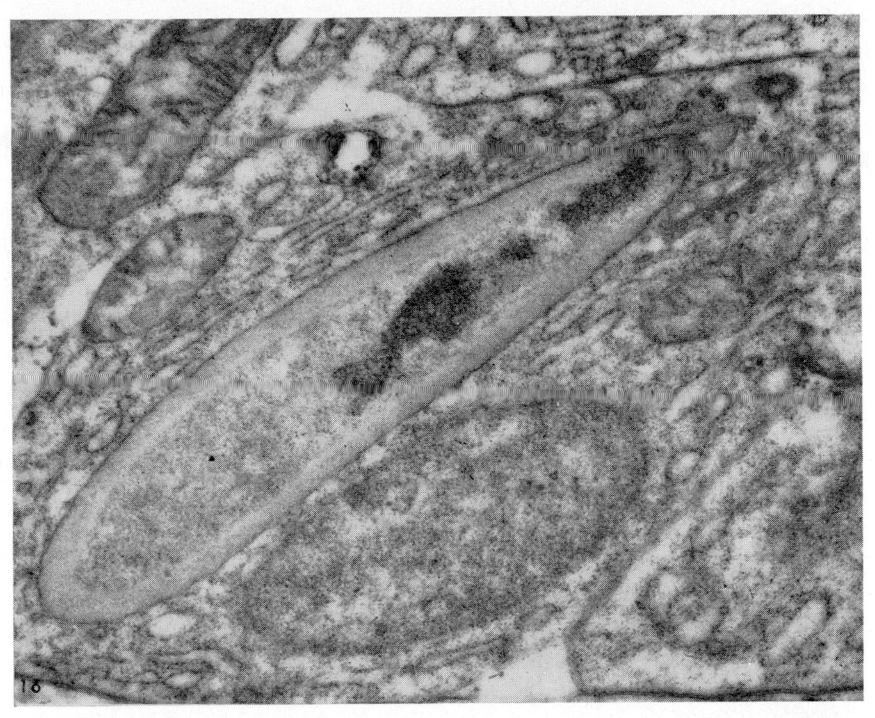
16

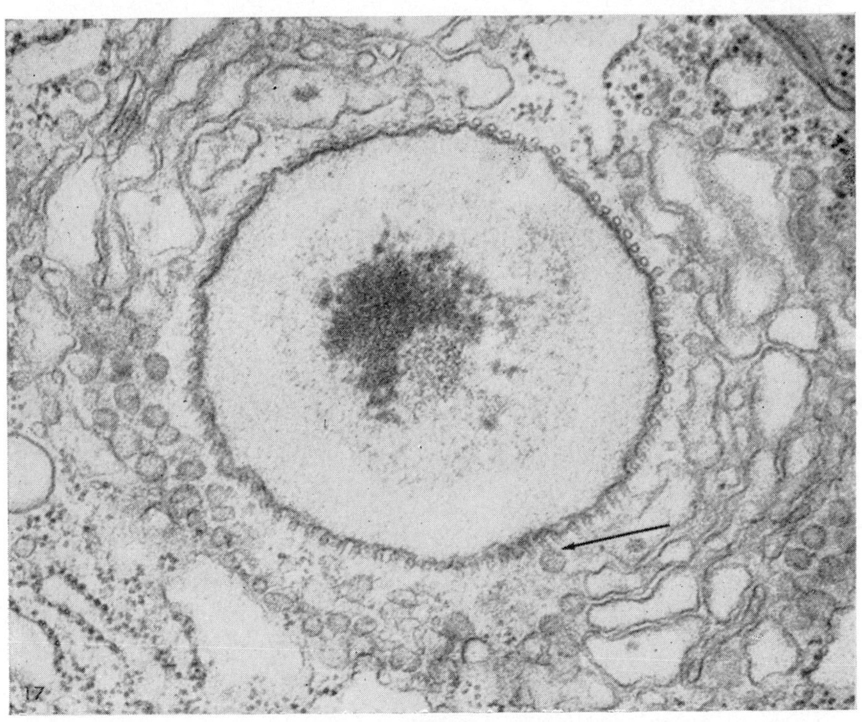
17

Fig. 18. A cluster of early cnidoblasts undergoing synchronous differentiation. 13,500X.

Fig. 19. A cnidoblast approaching the peak of synthetic activity. 20,000X.

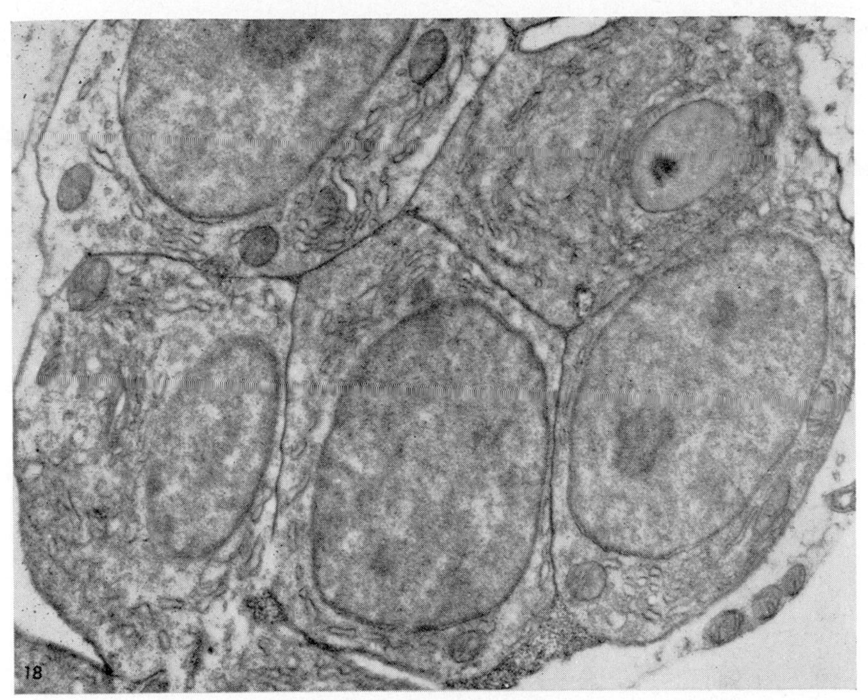
18

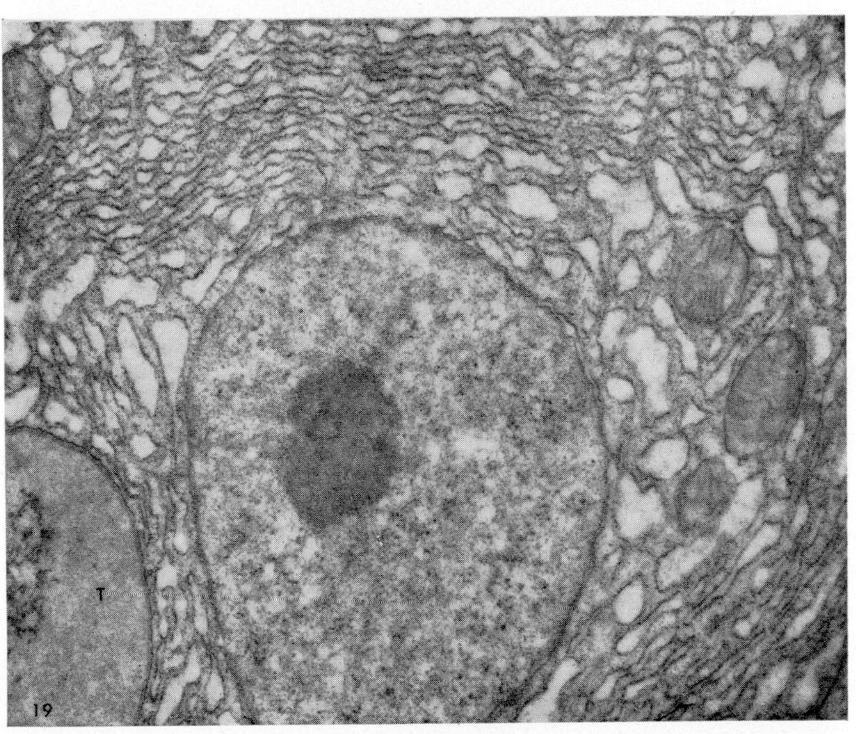
T
19

Fig. 20. In this cnidoblast protein synthesis is going on at the maximum rate. 22,000X.

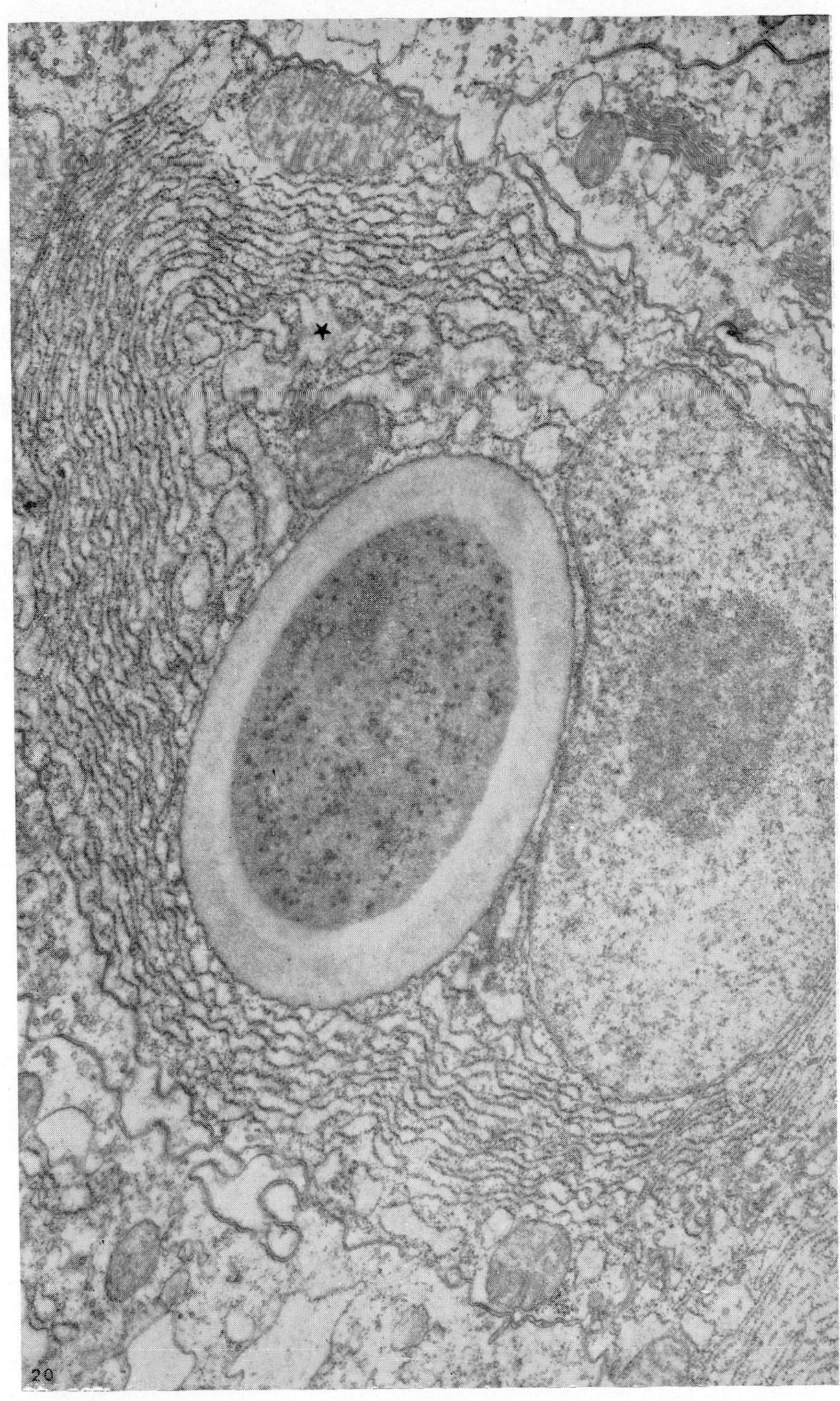
20

Fig. 21. This cell has passed the peak of synthetic activity and the reticulum has begun to vesiculate. 8,900X.

Fig. 22. A considerable part of the coiled external tube has been cut in longitudinal section. 15,000X.

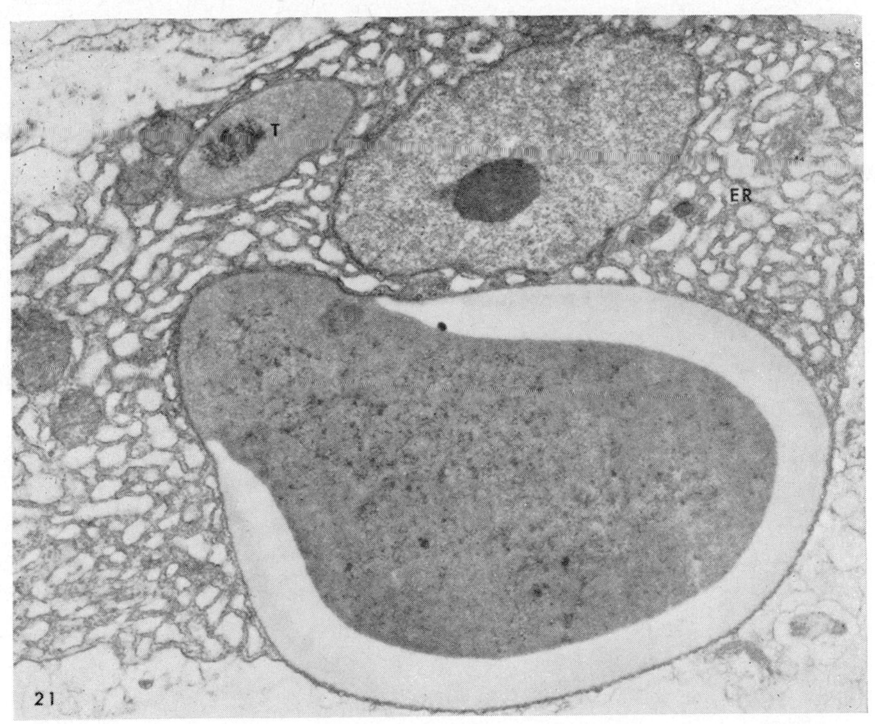
T
ER
21

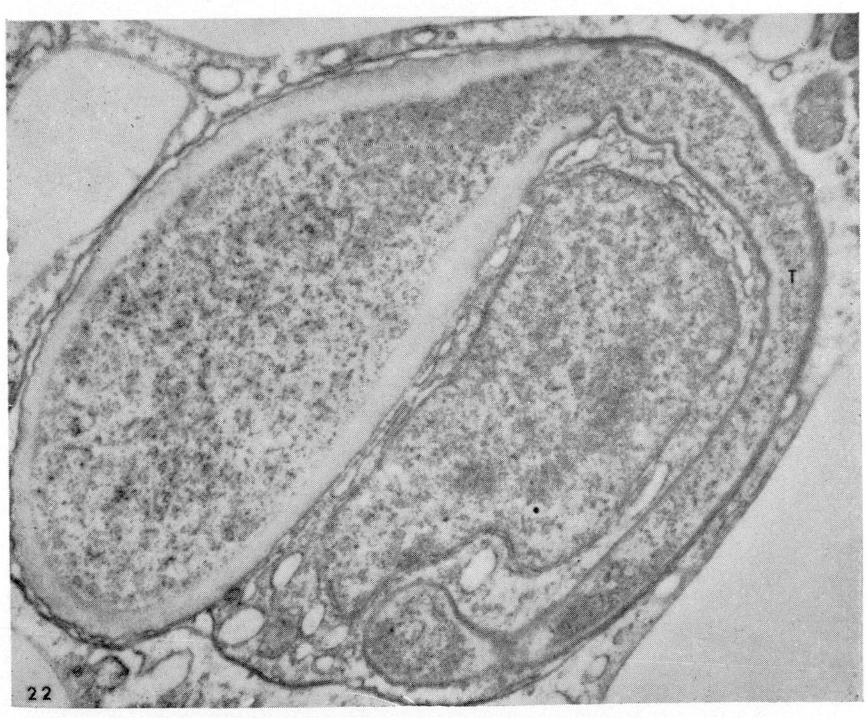
T
22

Fig. 23. Further regression of the endoplasmic reticulum is evident in this cnidoblast, as are several sections of the coiled tube. 8,900X.

Fig. 24. The tube has been withdrawn into the capsule and the open end closed by an operculum. Fine structure of the tube has begun to form. 21,000X.

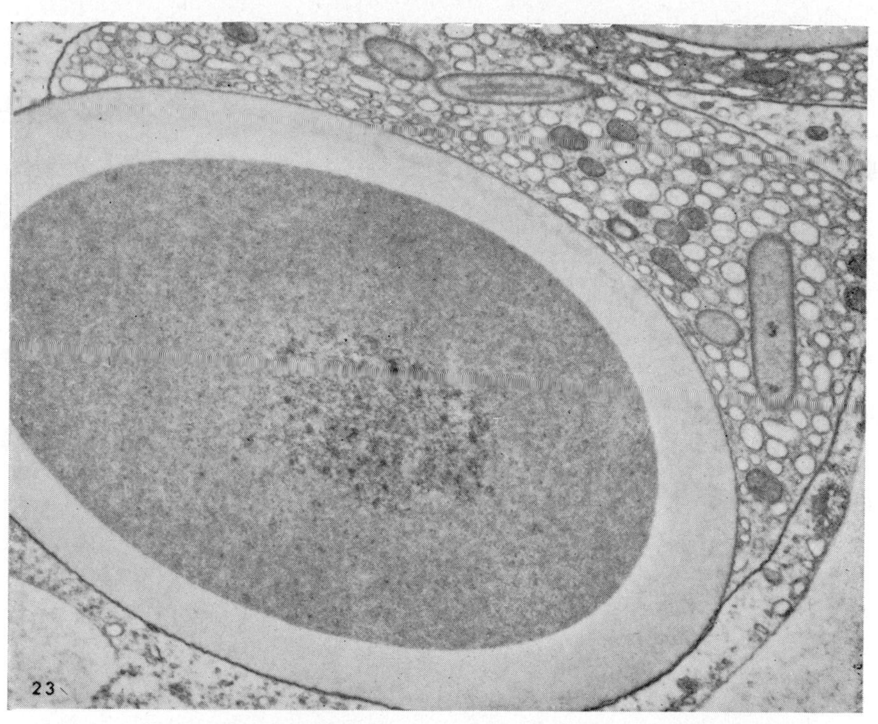
23

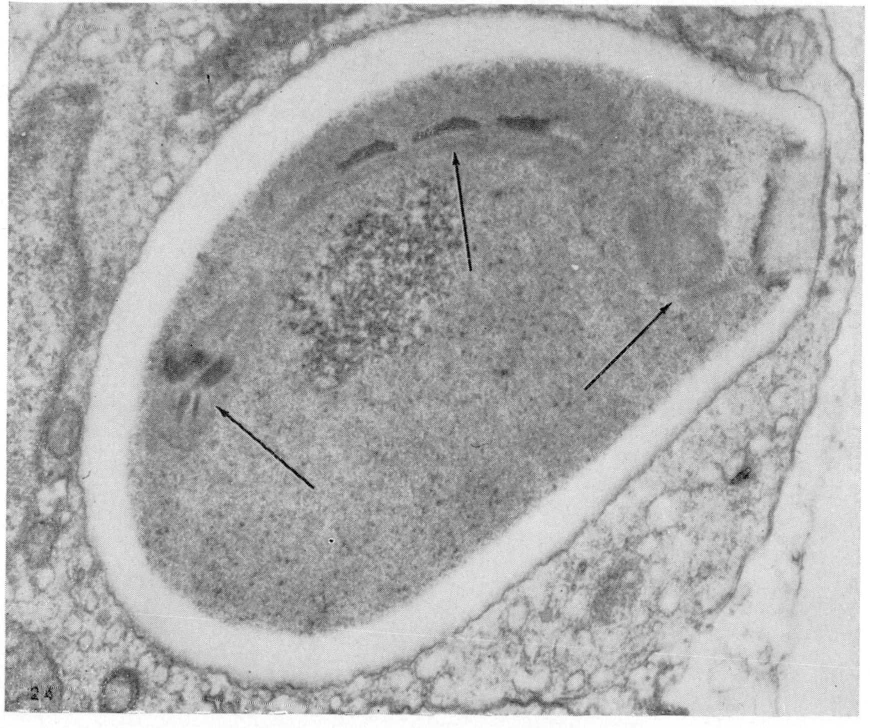
24

Fig. 25. A nearly mature stenotele. Rupture of the capsule is artifactual. 11,500X.

Fig. 26. A longitudinal section of an isorhiza showing regression of the endoplasmic reticulum and development of the cnidocil apparatus. 18,500X.

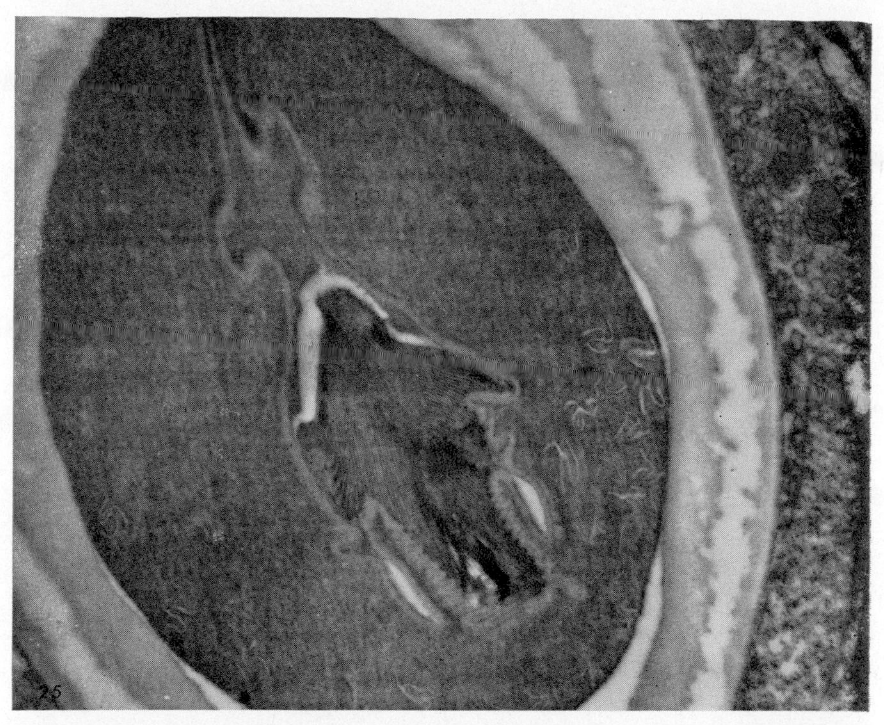
25

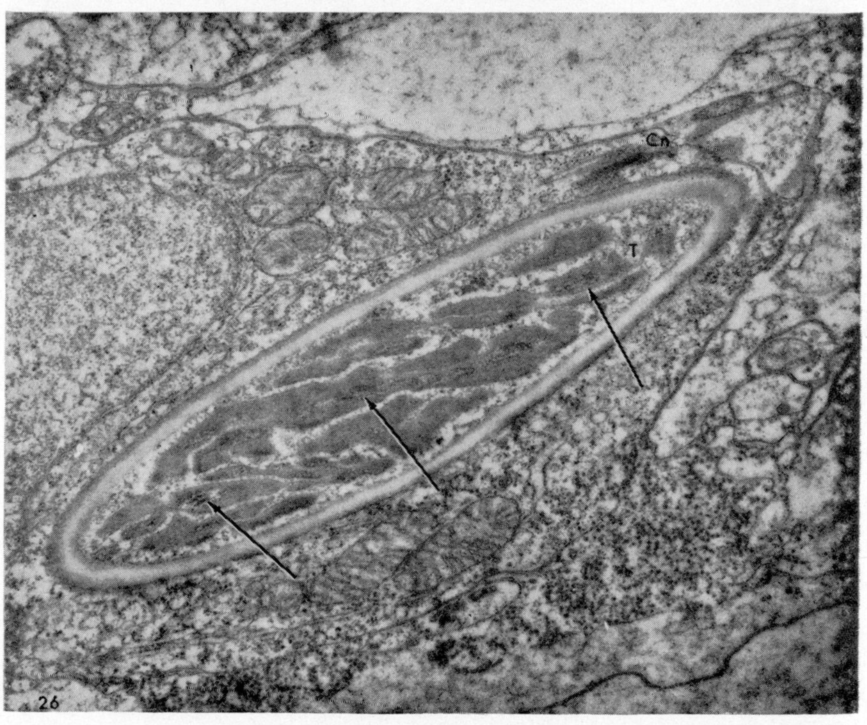
Cn
T
26

Fig. 27. This figure is similar to Figure 26 but the nematocyst is a stenotele. 10,500X.

Fig. 28. A stage similar to that in Figure 27 but somewhat enlarged. 16,500X.

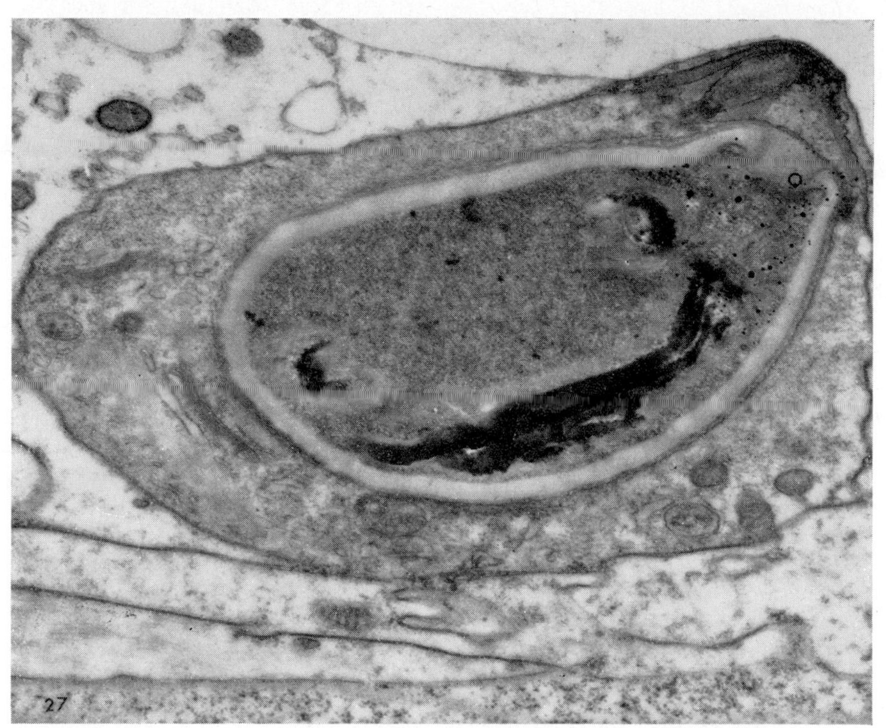
O
27

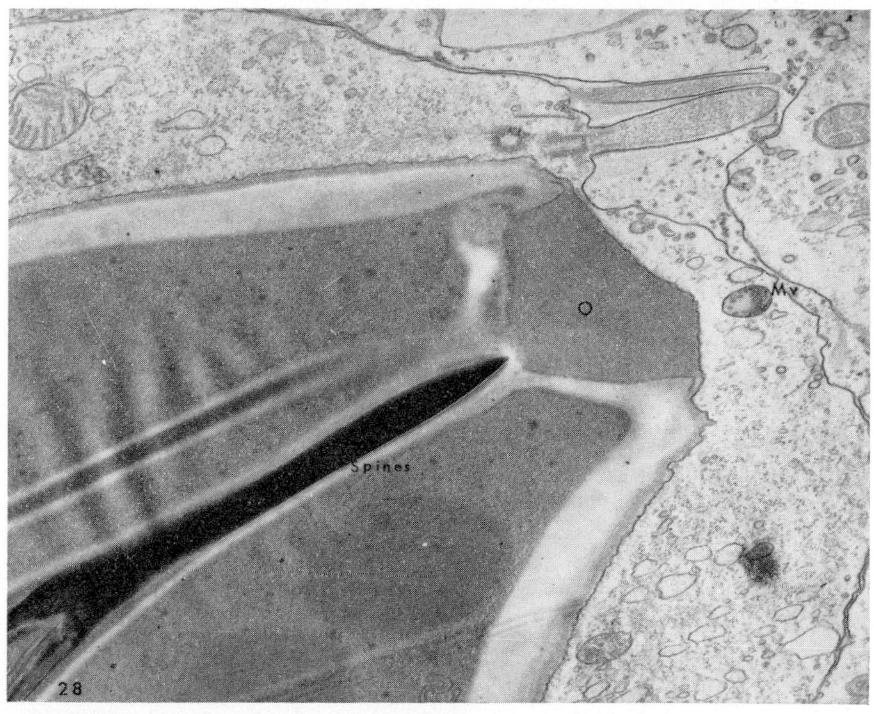
O
Mv
Spines
28

Fig. 29. Cross section of a stenotele tubule. 42,000X.

Fig. 30. Longitudinal section of a stenotele tubule. 30,000X.

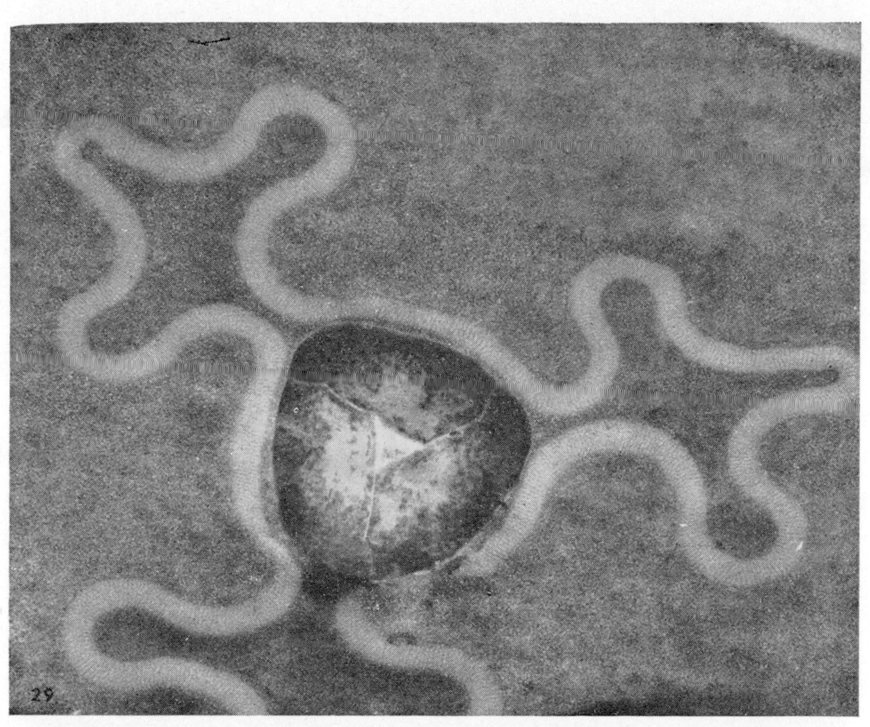
29

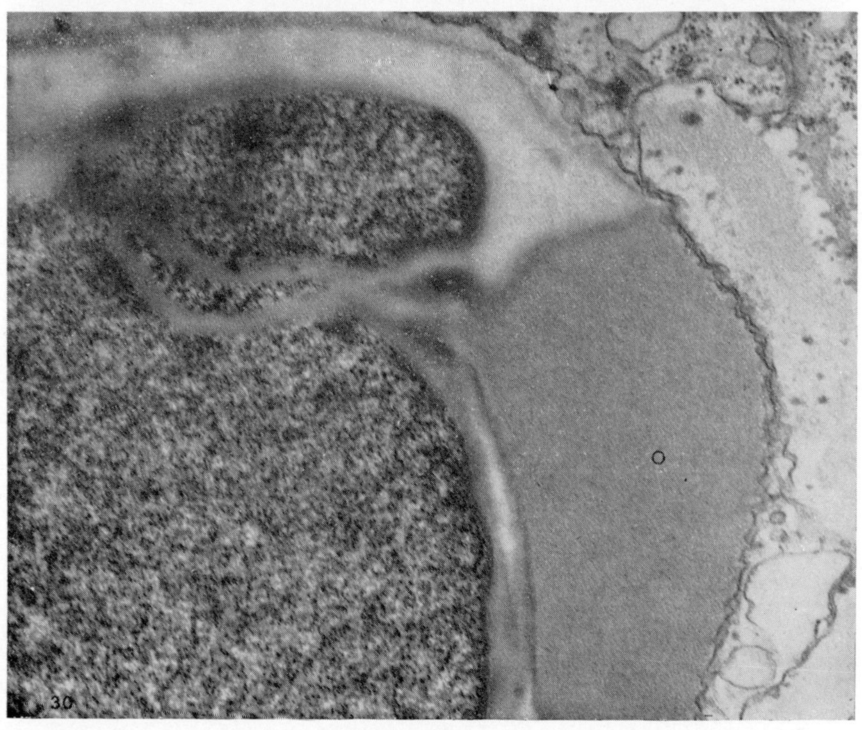
30
O

Fig. 31. This is the same cell as in Figure 24. Notice lamination of operculum and straight row of dense bodies of early cnidocil. 44,000X.

Fig. 32. An oblique section through the opercular end of a stenotele showing partial encirclement by the developing cnidocil. 29,000X.

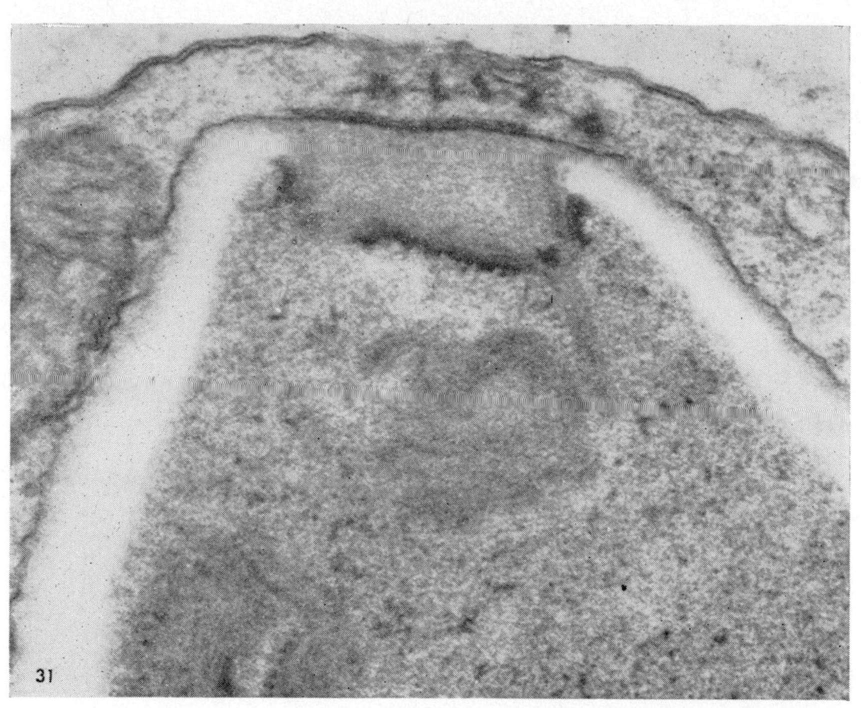
31

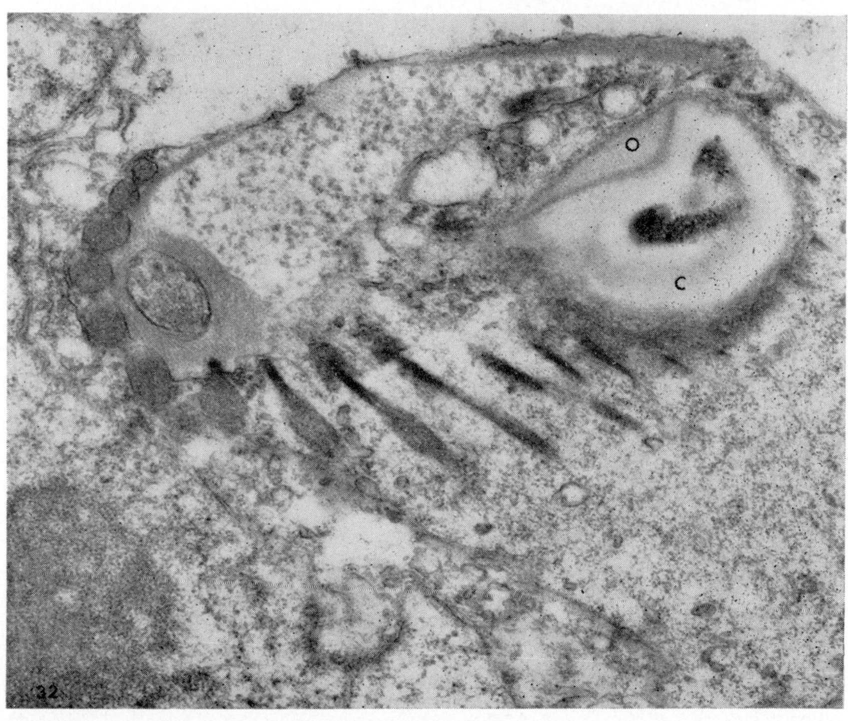
O
C
32

Fig. 33. Longitudinal section of a "stiff rod." 49,000X.

Fig. 34. Oblique section of a fully differentiated cnidocil apparatus. 32,000X.

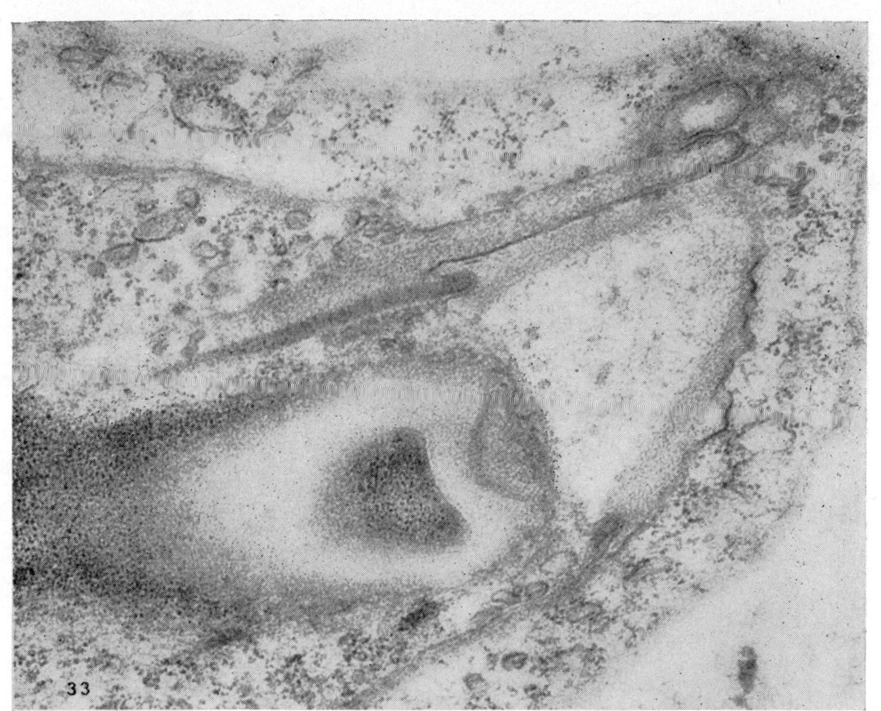
33

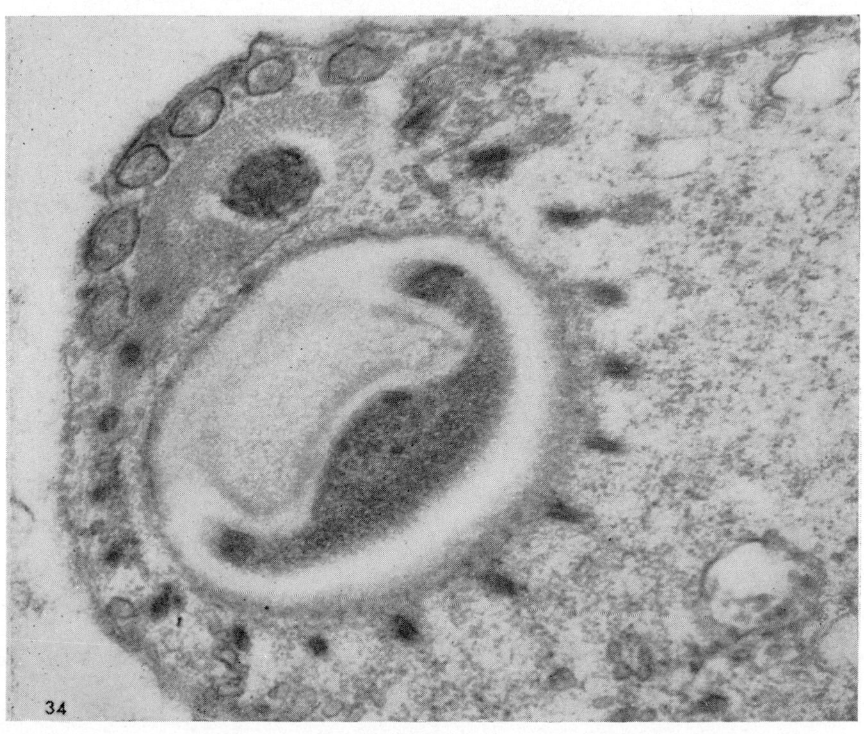
34

Fig. 35. This is a zymogenic cell from the gut of an earthworm, *Enchytraeus fragmentosus.* 24,000X.

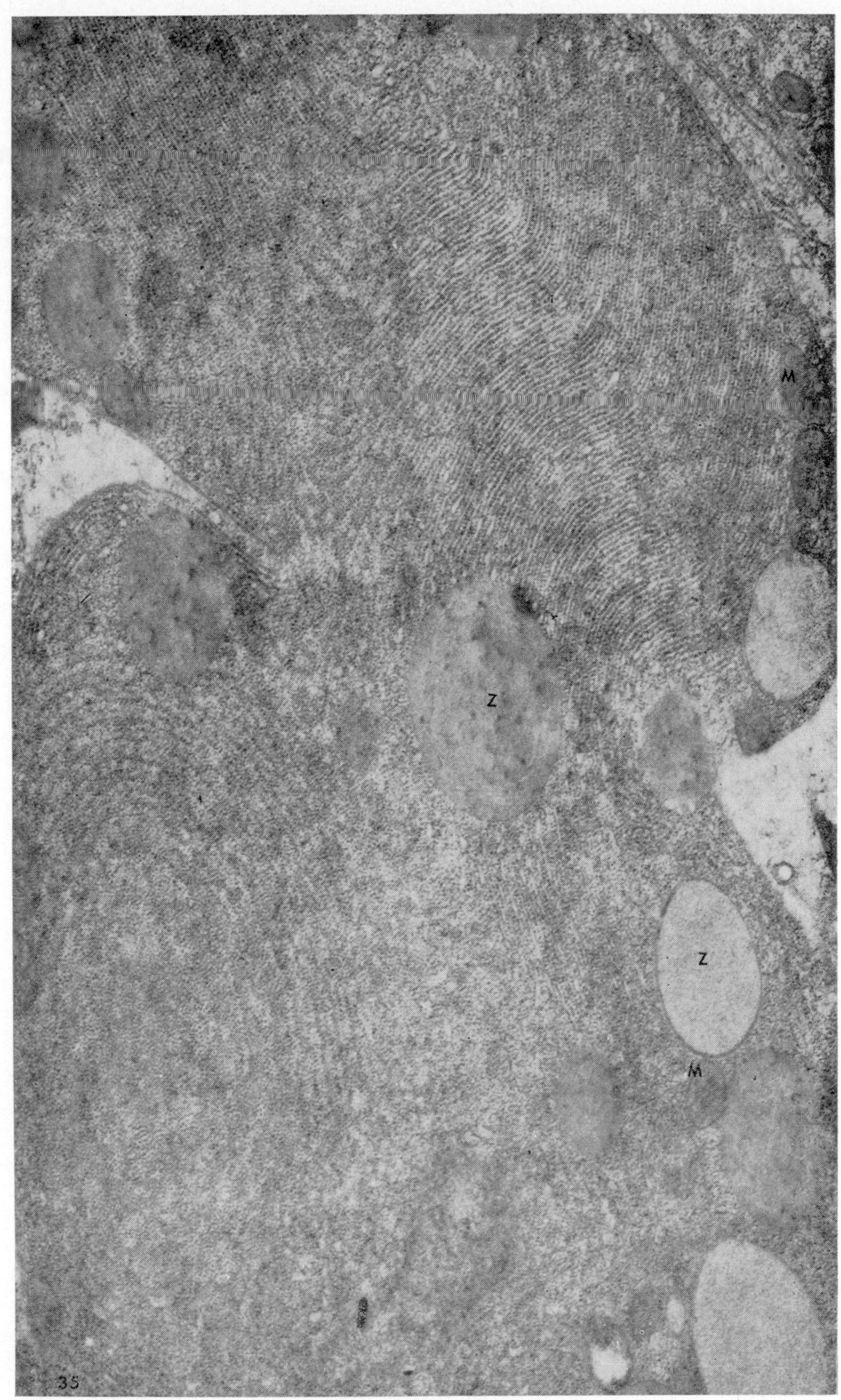
M
Z
Z
M
35

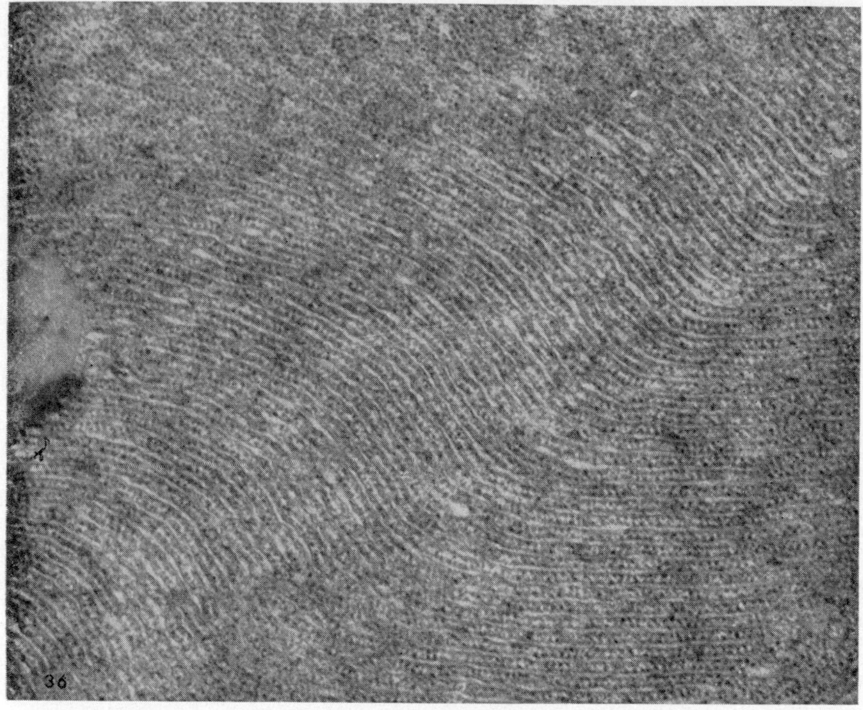

Fig. 36. An enlargement of a part of Figure 35. 41,000X.

DISCUSSION

HAND: Is it your impression that the tube forms outside the capsule of the nematocyst?

SLAUTTERBACK: Yes. I think the fact that the Golgi complex remains associated with the tip of the forming tubule makes it difficult to imagine that this is a prematurely fired tube. Furthermore, it is difficult to imagine a situation where every time the tube fired inside the cytoplasm it would end up with its tip in immediate association with the Golgi complex.

ROSS: Isn't there a big volume change in the cnidoblast as it develops?

SLAUTTERBACK: I haven't done any very accurate measurements, but I would say no, there is not. I think after it's fired there seems to be quite an enlargement.

LOOMIS: Do you picture the tube starting to be made at the mouth of the capsule, and then progressing out, smaller and smaller?

SLAUTTERBACK: That's right, except that this capsule at first is only a sort of crescentic shell or cup. It has not yet formed a full flask-shape structure.

LOOMIS: The tip, then, is the last part made?

SLAUTTERBACK: Yes.

LOOMIS: Is there anything like a hypostome or ring of production around the capsule lip, so that the tip would be the first part made as in a tentacle?

SLAUTTERBACK: No sir, not at all. In fact, completely the opposite.

LANE: Would you like to speculate about the mechanism of withdrawal of this externally formed tubule?

SLAUTTERBACK: Maybe Dr. Fawcett would like to speculate on that.

FAWCETT: No, I would not. I am content to regard it as the reverse of the mechanism of firing!

This is a minor point, but it may be of interest that the contents of the nematocyst are not only highly diverse from one kind to the other, but even the operculum is quite characteristic of the particular type of nematocyst. In this slide (Fig. 1) is one quite different from the one in Figure 2 and from any that Dr. Slautterback showed, in that the operculum has an interesting laminated structure. I have no idea as to what the significance of this lamination is.

HAND: Do you know what nematocyst that is that you showed on the slide?

FAWCETT: No, I do not.

WOOD: Hasn't the presence of some type of an intracapsular at-

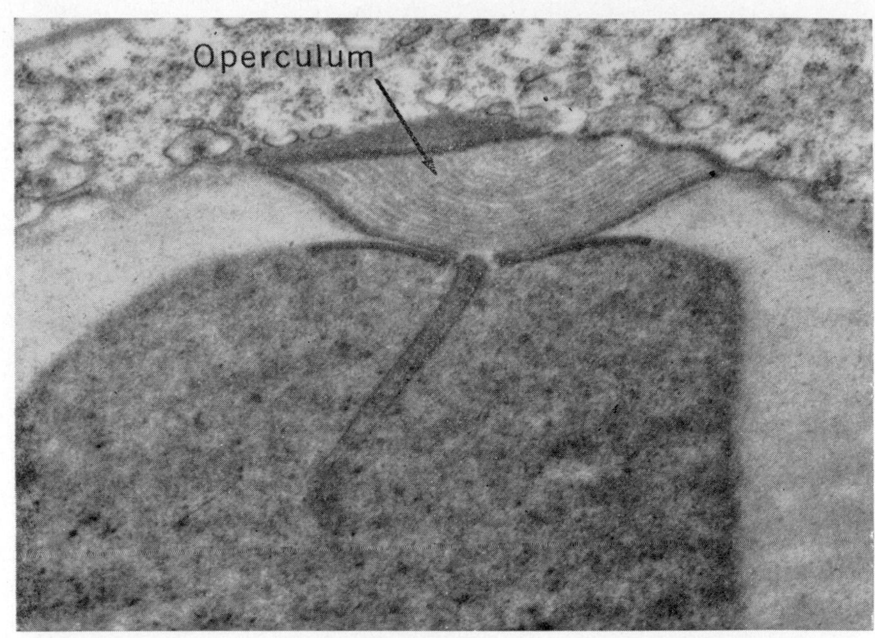

Fig. 1.

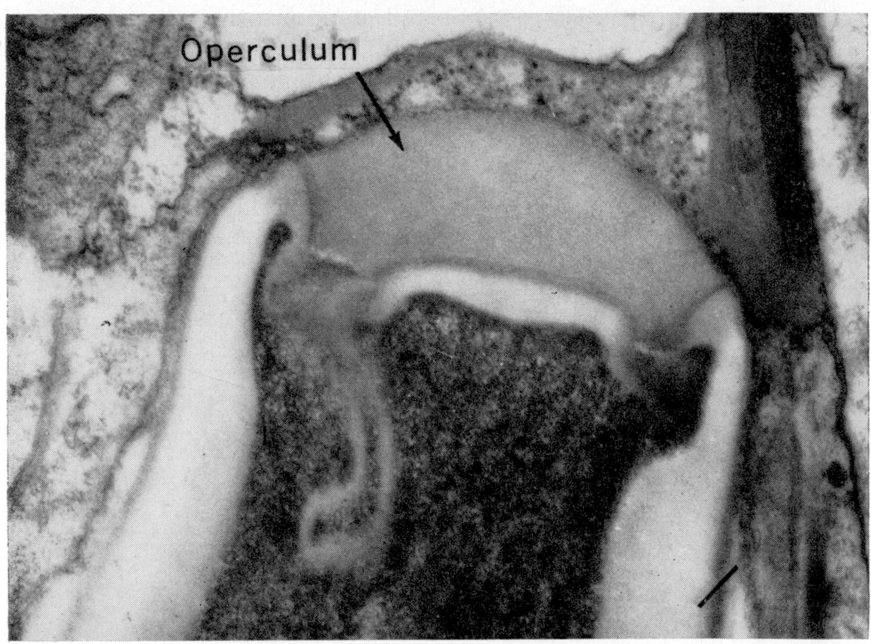

Fig. 2.

tachment region at the opposite pole from the operculum been described in the light microscope literature? Wasn't this interpreted as being important in retracting the tube after it had been formed? I seem to recall something of this sort. I have seen electron micrographs of nematocysts that show a specialized area at the opposite end from the operculum. I wonder if you would comment on this?

SLAUTTERBACK: Yes, I understand that such structures have been described around the outside of the capsule. I have never seen these.

HAND: Cutress described such a structure inside the microbasic mastigophore in his paper on anthozoan nematocysts, but he did not suggest that it was used to withdraw the thread.

SLAUTTERBACK: I have never seen anything inside that didn't obviously belong to the tubule itself, and these would be everted with it: spines, thorns, and things of that sort. George, did you want to speak about that?

CHAPMAN: I was wondering if Dr. Wood was referring to the plug in the basal capsule pore that Kepner and his colleagues described.

SLAUTTERBACK: Of the capsule itself?

CHAPMAN: A dense mass of material which they originally described as being a plug in the pore in the basal portion of the capsule. The function of it is not understood. It was thought to be the end of the spiral tube and to be converted to magma just prior to discharge.

SLAUTTERBACK: Have you seen such a structure?

CHAPMAN: Yes, I think one of our pictures of a few years ago presented it rather vaguely.

SLAUTTERBACK: I haven't seen it.

The Fine Structure of the Stenoteles of Hydra[1]

George B. Chapman
Department of Anatomy, Cornell University Medical College, New York, N. Y.

In the more than two hundred years which have passed since Leeuwenhoek (9) and Trembley (13) first referred to the nematocysts of hydra, these structures have been the subject of a great number of anatomical, biochemical and physiological investigations. As is usually the case, as many questions were raised as were answered. Recently, in an attempt to answer some of these questions, Hess *et al.* (6), Slautterback and Fawcett (12) and Chapman and Tilney (3, 4) studied ultrathin sections of nematocysts in the electron microscope. It goes without saying that these studies have contributed appreciably to our knowledge of nematocyst structure, development and function. Incidentally, the studies have reviewed rather thoroughly the extensive literature in this field. This report, therefore, omits such a review and refers to the previous work only where it is pertinent to the discussion of the most recent observations.

It is especially gratifying that the nematocyst, a structure worthy of study solely on the basis of its morphology, should also provide valuable information on cellular differentiation and synthesis, as Slautterback and Fawcett (12) have so clearly shown. Thus, once again, resort to the study of a classic animal has provided new data —in this case, concerning the role of the Golgi apparatus and endoplasmic reticulum in the production, by the cnidoblast, of an elaborate and highly specialized cell inclusion. Furthermore, evi-

[1]This work was supported by United States Public Health Services research grant E-3517.

dence exists which suggests that the new findings are generally applicable to problems of cell growth and cell differentiation.

The present report will be limited to some recent observations pertaining to the structure of stenoteles, the largest of the four types of nematocysts of *Hydra*.

MATERIALS AND METHODS

Entire *Hydra* (*H. vulgaris* and *H. littoralis*) were fixed for 1 to 2 hours at 2° to 5° in 1 per cent osmium tetroxide buffered to a pH of 7.6 with acetate-veronal buffer. The fixative also contained about 0.7 per cent sodium chloride and a few drops of 0.11 *M* calcium chloride.

Following fixation, the specimens were washed, dehydrated through a graded ethyl alcohol series and were embedded in Epon according to a schedule developed in Dr. H. Stanley Bennett's laboratory by Drs. J. H. Luft and R. L. Wood (1).

Sections were cut with a Servall Porter-Blum ultramicrotome using glass knives prepared in the laboratory. The sections were floated onto distilled water and were picked up on collodion-coated grids (Fullam #2001). Staining with uranyl acetate for 1 to 2 hours was carried out according to the method devised by Watson (14). Electron microscopy was accomplished with an RCA electron microscope, type EMU-2D, equipped with a 0.015 inch externally centerable (Canalco) platinum condenser aperture and a 50μ copper objective aperture in the standard objective pole piece.

OBSERVATIONS AND DISCUSSION

The present studies of stenotele fine structure have revealed several interesting new features. Figure 1, a sagittal section of a very nearly mature stenotele, shows, in addition to the structures previously described by Chapman and Tilney (1959b), *viz.*, capsule (C), operculum (O), invaginated capsular wall (ICW), stylets (ST), spines (S), matrix (M) and tubules (T), what appears to be a most fortuitous section through the enlarged "head" of the tubule

(HD). Distal to the head, may be seen a narrowed extension of the tubule ending in a hook (HK). Just proximal to the head, the longitudinal section reveals a rather fluted contortion suggesting why the cross sections of tubules often appear as three-bladed propellers. The enlarged head of the tubule is of particular interest for it is the only non-structural portion of the capsular content which is distinct in its texture from the matrix. One could speculate that this small packet of material might possibly represent the location of the venom of *Hydra*. It might further be speculated that the minute (approximately 150 Å in diameter) dense granules in the tubule head represent the 5-hydroxy tryptamine which Welsh and Moorhead (15) have suggested may be a constituent of coelenterate venom. Such a location for the venom would be most effective for the presence of the hook at the termination of the tubule suggests that the head portion of the tubule may be attached to the base of the invaginated capsular wall and thus be drawn out of the discharging nematocysts in advance of the rest of the tubule, thus causing the head to encounter the *Hydra's* prey at the earliest possible moment, thereby facilitating the utilization of the venom. If the enlarged head of the tubule does not contain the venom, it is difficult to imagine where the venom could reside save in the capsular matrix material. The latter possibility seems less satisfactory from an operational standpoint. (The head of the tubule may be projected rapidly to a distance of many microns from the body of *Hydra*, while the matrix material would have to depend largely on diffusion to reach the prey.)

The above observations thus tend to reopen the question of the nature of the tubule discharge mechanism. If eversion occurs, the contents of the tubule head could encounter the prey only when the tubule is fully everted. Prey located close to the surface of *Hydra* might be by-passed by the head of the tubule and any possible function of the contents wasted. If the head is discharged somewhat like a fishing lure is cast, it could quickly encounter prey located anywhere within its maximum range. The latter method of discharge, of course, raises the questions of how the head of the tubule could get outside of the invaginated capsular wall and how the contents of the head could be released. It is hoped that further study may clarify this intriguing situation.

Another structural feature of the stenotele not previously described is the occurrence on the base of each spine of a bulbous enlargement (arrow). This arrangement would seem to insure a firmer attachment of the spines to the invaginated capsular wall.

Figure 2 also illustrates, in a transverse section through the basal portion of a stenotele of a stage of maturity similar to that of Figure 1, the bulbous enlargement (arrows) of the bases of the spines. This figure is also interesting in that it includes a cross section through the enlarged head of the tubule (HD).

Figure 3, a transverse section through the apical portion of a stenotele, just below the level of the operculum, reveals the interlocking relationship of the stylets, previously described by Chapman and Tilney (ref. 4 Fig. 12). In the present figure, however, the stylets are closer together and no spines are included in the section.

In an earlier paper (4), following the lead of previous workers (*e.g.*, ref. 7), it was stated that the capsular wall consists of chitin or keratin. Since that paper was prepared, the author learned of the work of Lenhoff *et al.* (11), Johnson and Lenhoff (8) and Lenhoff and Kline (10), in which it has been shown biochemically and histochemically that nematocyst capsules contain protein which is probably a member of the collagen family of proteins. Since one of the prominent fine structural features of collagen is its characteristic periodicity, the electron micrographs of nematocyst capsules were scrutinized carefully to determine whether any indications of a periodic structure might be found. Figure 4, a transverse section through the basal region of a stenotele, reveals the presence, in the material of the invaginated capsular wall (ICW), of a periodic structure with a 160 Å periodicity. This is, of course, a value one-fourth that of the usual 640 Å period of collagen. It should be noted that no fibrillar elements were observed in the material of the capsule. Figure 5 shows a portion of the field of Figure 4 at higher magnification. It is not immediately clear why the invaginated capsular wall, which has been shown to be continuous with the capsule proper (4), should reveal this periodic structure when the capsule proper does not. Nor is it clear why this periodic structure is so rarely observed. It may be, however, that the preparative treatments usually fail to preserve this feature of the structure. Figure 4 also includes a section through the enlarged head of the tubule (HD).

Figure 6 includes portions of two interstitial cells (I) and a cnidoblast with a nearly mature stenotele. The cell at the lower left is considered to be the least differentiated of the three cells, using the criterion of sparse endoplasmic reticulum, as suggested by Slautterback and Fawcett (12). That cell is of great interest, however, because of the presence of a centriole (CE) with radiating spokes, a configuration reminiscent of, yet somewhat different from, that described in flagella by Gibbons and Grimstone (5). Although the angle of section through the cnidoblast is inappropriate, the centriole in the interstitial cell may be seen to bear a similarity to the section through the base of the immature cnidocil (CD). This figure is, then, considered to indicate a relationship between the centriole and cnidocil. Thus, the relationship between centrioles and cilia and flagella may be extended to include cnidocils. (More extensive evidence in support of the differentiation of centrioles into cnidocils will be presented elsewhere. However, it should be noted here that Bouillon *et al.* (2) believe the cnidocil to have a structure anatomically distinct from that of cilia and flagella.) Several elements of the outer supporting structures (SP_1) and inner supporting structures (SP_2) of the cnidocil, as described by Chapman and Tilney (3), are also visible in this figure.

Figure 7, an oblique section through the apical region of a stenotele and a nearly transverse section through the cnidocil, also reveals the similarity between the centriole and cnidocil base. Although the state of preservation of this particular cnidocil renders extensive discussion unwarranted, it may be stated that there appear to be nine peripheral groups of filaments, at least two of which are composed of two elements, and a central group of three filaments. In the original print, three circular profiles can just be distinguished in the core of the cnidocil, once again reminiscent of an appearance seen in flagella by Gibbons and Grimstone (5). It should be noted that, even in their extensive study of flagellar structure, Gibbons and Grimstone (5) apparently did not encounter this central configuration. It may, then, constitute one more variation from the basic pattern of filament arrangement in flagella and cilia. The dense granules (G) resemble closely the granules considered by Slautterback and Fawcett (12) to be glycogen.

SUMMARY

Electron microscopy of ultrathin sections of osmium-fixed and Epon-embedded intact *Hydra* have revealed several new aspects of stenotele fine structure. The internal tubule possesses an enlarged head containing dense granules which may represent a portion of the venom. The head has an extension ending in a hook. The spines are seen to posses a bulbous enlargement at their attachment to the invaginated capsular wall. Invaginated capsular wall material showed a 160 Å periodicity, possibly supporting the belief that nematocyst capsules contain protein related to the collagen family of proteins. A relationship is suggested between centrioles and cnidocils (because of the similarity in appearance of these two structures), thus extending the centriole–cilia, flagella relationship.

REFERENCES

1. Bennett, H. S. 1960. Personal communication.
2. Bouillon, J., P. Castiaux, and G. Vandermeerssche. 1958. Structure submicroscopique des cnidocils. *Bull. micr. appl.,* 8: 61.
3. Chapman, G. B., and L. G. Tilney. 1959. Cytological studies of the nematocysts of Hydra. I. Desmonemes, isorhizas, cnidocils, and supporting structures. *J. Biophysic. and Biochem. Cytol.,* 5: 69-78.
4. Chapman, G. B., and L. G. Tilney. 1959. Cytological studies of the nematocysts of Hydra. II. The Stenoteles. *J. Biophysic. and Biochem. Cytol.,* 5: 79-84.
5. Gibbons, I. R., and A. V. Grimstone. 1960. On flagellar structure in certain flagellates. *J. Biophysic. and Biochem. Cytol.,* 7: 697-716.
6. Hess, A. A., I. Cohen, and E. A. Robson. 1957. Observations on the structure of hydra as seen with the electron and light miscroscopes. *Quart. J. Micr. Sc.,* 98: 315-326.
7. Hyman, L. H. 1940. *The Invertebrates: Protozoa through Ctenophora,* New York, McGraw-Hill Book Company, 1-726.
8. Johnson, F. B., and H. M. Lenhoff. 1958. Histochemical study of purified hydra nematocysts. *J. Histochem. and Cytochem.,* 6: 394.

9. LEEUWENHOEK, A. 1702. In *Antony van Leeuwenhoek and his "Little Animals,"* by Clifford Dobell, Dover Publs. Inc., New York, 1960, p. 283.

10. LENHOFF, H. M., and E. S. KLINE. 1958. The high imino acid content of the capsule from *Hydra* nematocysts. *Anat. Rec., 130:* 425.

11. LENHOFF, H. M., E. S. KLINE, and R. HURLEY. 1957. A hydroxyproline-rich, intracellular, collagen-like protein of *Hydra* nematocysts. *Biochim. Biophys. Acta, 26:* 204-205.

12. SLAUTTERBACK, D. L., and D. W. FAWCETT. 1959. The development of the cnidoblasts of Hydra. An electron miscroscope study of cell differentiation. *J. Biophysic. and Biochem. Cytol., 5:* 441-452.

13. TREMBLEY, A. 1744. *Memoires pour servir a l'histoire d'un genre de Polypes d'eau douce, a bras en forme de cornes,* Leyden, J. and H. Verbeck, 1-324.

14. WATSON, M. L. 1958. Staining of tissue sections for electron microscopy with heavy metals. *J. Biophysic. and Biochem. Cytol., 4:* 475-478.

15. WELSH, J. J., and M. MOORHEAD. 1960. The quantitative distribution of 5-hydroxy tryptamine in the invertebrates, especially in their nervous systems. *J. Neurochem., 6:* 146-169.

Abbreviations used on Plates

C	capsule	MI	mitochondrion
CB	cnidoblast	N	nucleus
CD	cnidocil	O	operculum
CE	centriole	S	spine
G	granules, presumably glycogen	SP_1	member of group of nine outer supporting structures
HD	head of tubule	SP_2	member of group of inner supporting structures
HK	hook of tubule	ST	stylet
I	interstitial cell	T	tubule
ICW	invaginated capsular wall		
M	matrix		

In each figure, the magnification mark equals one micron.

Fig. 1. Sagittal section of a very nearly mature stenotele. Newly described structures are the enlarged head of the tubule (HD), hook of the tubule (HK) and the enlarged bulbous base of the spines (arrows). The unique appearance of the material in the tubule head should be noted. X17,000.

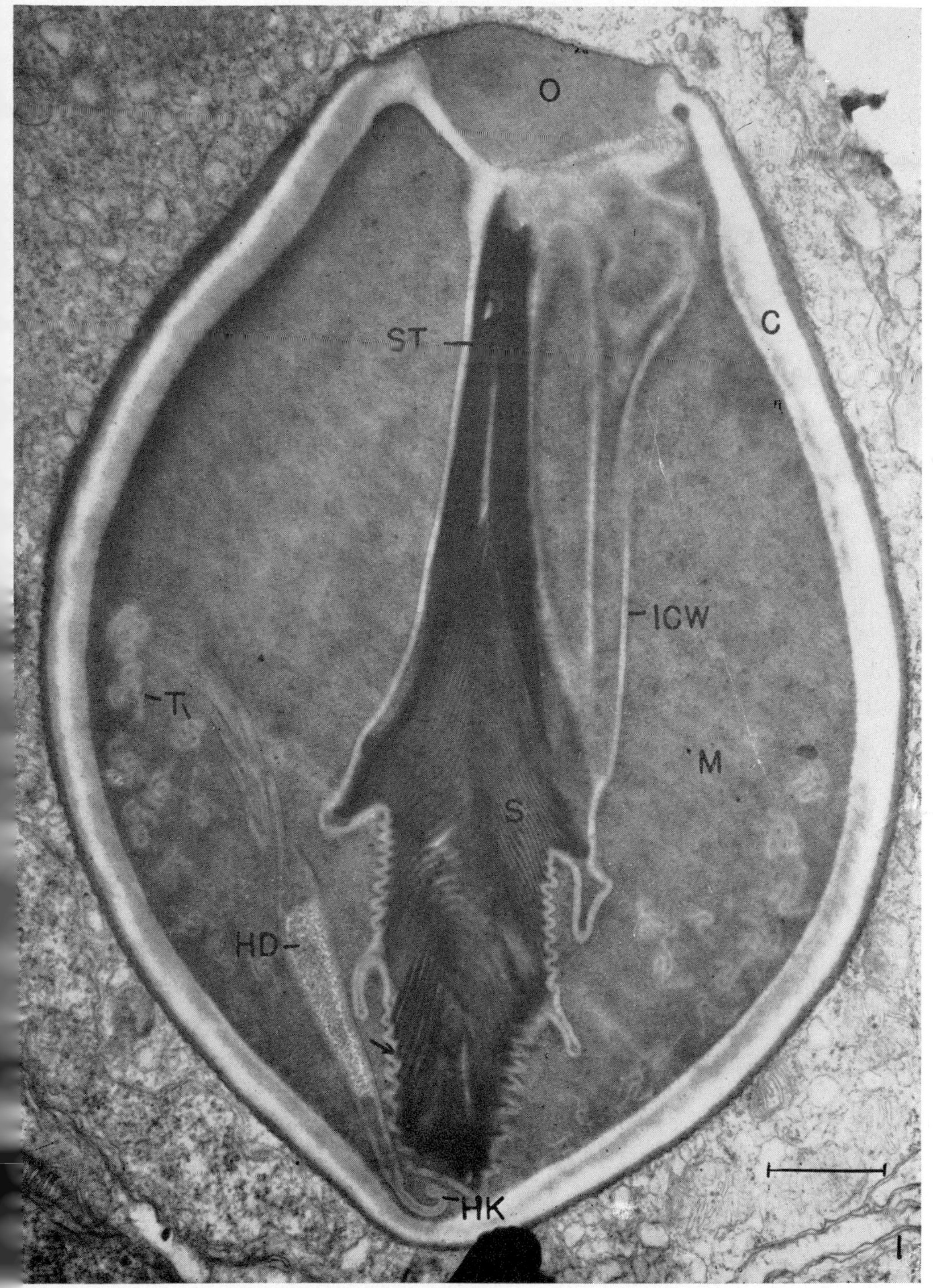
O
C
ST
ICW
T
M
S
HD
HK
I

Fig. 2. Transverse section through the basal portion of a stenotele. Bulbous enlargements of the bases of the spines are designated by arrows. A portion of the enlarged head of the tubule (HD) is included in the section. X15,600.

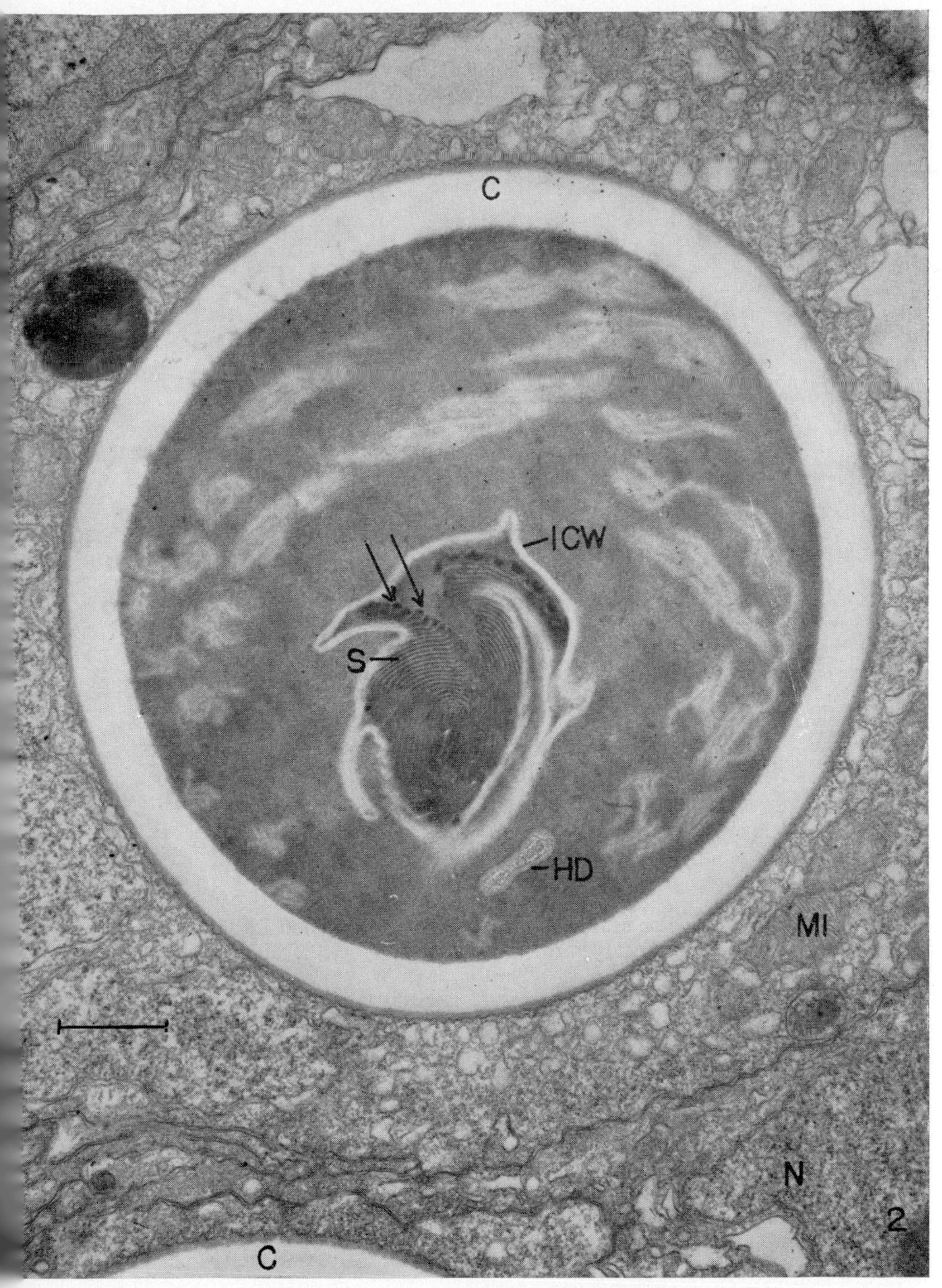
C
ICW
S
HD
MI
N
2
C

Fig. 3. Transverse section through the apical portion of a stenotele. The interlocking stylet arrangement is shown. X17,000.

Fig. 4. Transverse section through the basal region of a stenotele. The 160 Angstrom periodicity of the invaginated capsular wall material may be seen. The section also includes a portion of the head of the tubule. X29,000.

Fig. 5. An enlarged portion of Figure 4. X48,000.

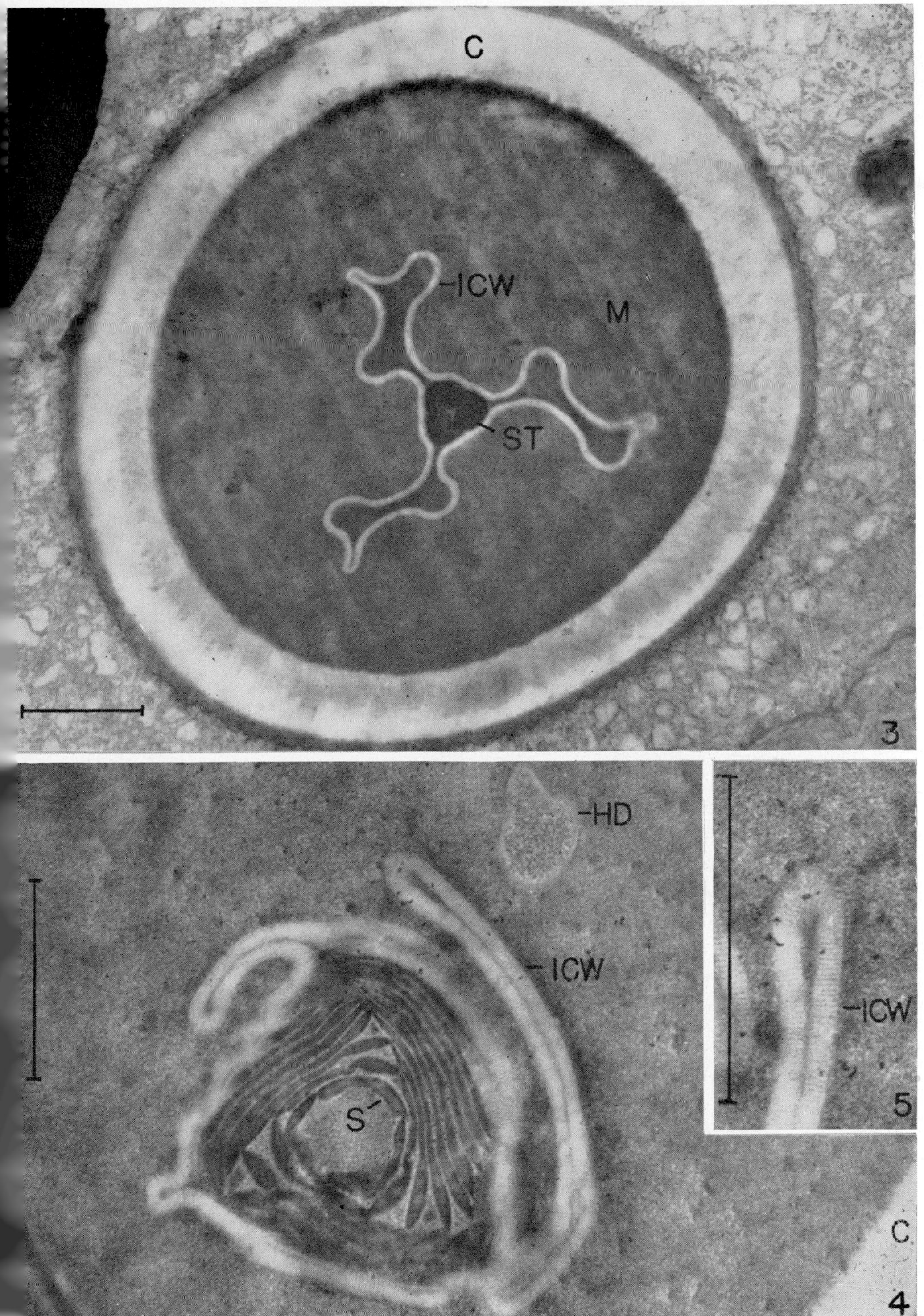
C
ICW
M
ST
3
HD
ICW
S
C
4
ICW
5

Fig. 6. Section through two interstitial cells (I) and a cnidoblast (CB) containing a nearly mature stenotele. A centriole (CE) may be seen in the interstitial cell at the lower left. Note the centriole's radiating spokes. Members of the outer (SP_1) and inner (SP_2) groups of cnidocil (CD) supporting structures may be seen. The cnidoblast cnidocil bears a resemblance to the interstitial cell centriole. X17,000.

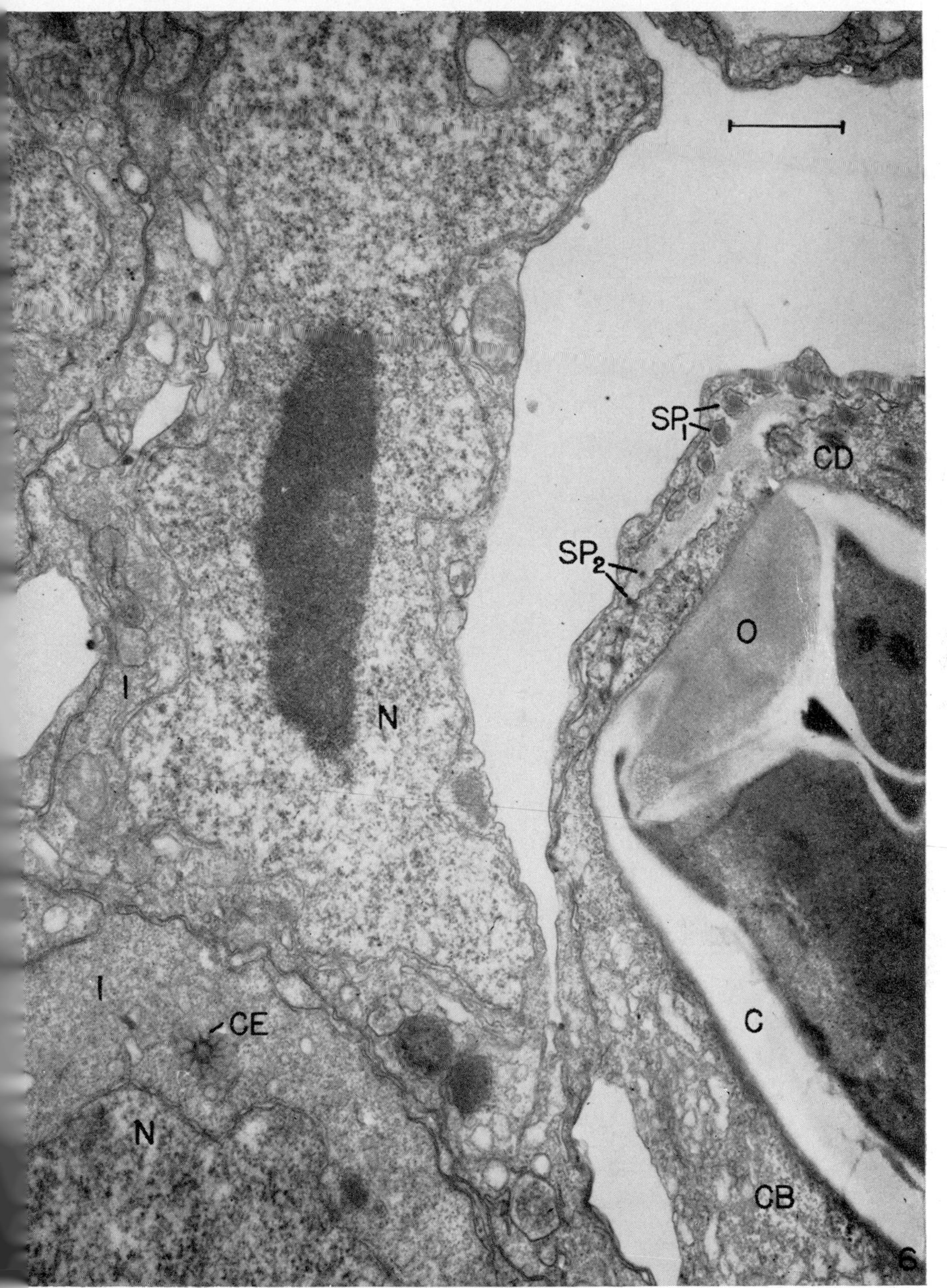
SP1
CD
SP2
O
I
N
C
I
CE
N
CB
6

Fig. 7. Oblique section through the apical region of a stenotele and a nearly transverse section through the cnidocil. The similar appearance between this cnidocil base and the centriole of Figure 6 should be noted. Granules, presumably glycogen, are designated G. X20,500.

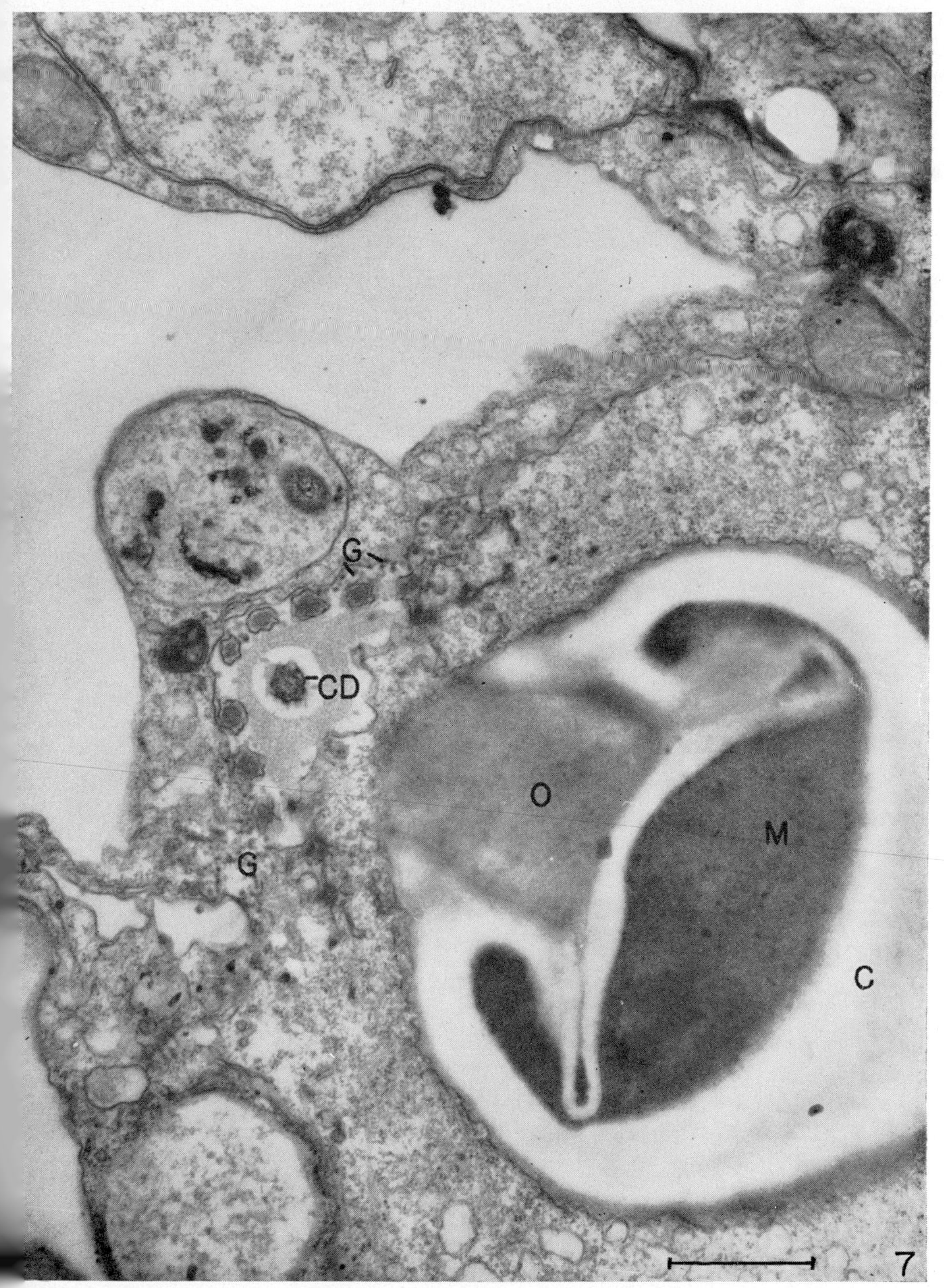
G
CD
O
M
G
C
7

DISCUSSION

WOOD: Have you seen a periodicity in the internal supporting structures which extend down past the capsule itself? I have seen this several times, a periodicity reminiscent of the periodicity of the ciliary rootlet found in other organisms but much narrower. I was curious whether you had made a similar observation.

CHAPMAN: I have not seen any periodic structure there.

FAWCETT: For the benefit of those who are not electron microscopists I would like to state that these pictures represent a notable technical achievement. I think they show very clearly what dramatic progress has been made in this field in a few years, largely as a result of the introduction of new imbedding materials. A few years ago, with all Dr. Chapman's skill, it was just impossible to get such fine pictures of this very difficult object. Now with epoxy resins, one can get beautiful micrographs of nematocysts and other cytological features of hydra.

With respect to the localization of collagen or collagen-like material—don't you feel that the very fine filaments found throughout the substance of the nematocyst capsule may be tropocollagen or collagen in such a state of dispersion that it would not be expected to exhibit any periodic structure? The area which you showed to have periodic cross banding may simply be a result of side-to-side aggregation of such macromolecular units of collagen that are more widespread than this limited occurrence of cross striated structure would suggest.

CHAPMAN: This is very possible.

LENHOFF: The "collagen" of *H. littoralis* nematocysts is different in many respects from vertebrate collagen. For example, there is much more hydroxyproline and proline and also less glycine in the nematocyst capsule than in classical collagens so that it is not surprising that the periodicity is different. In fact, we are very gratified that you find any periodicity at all.

WELSH: I wonder if this interesting structure that you show near the tip of the external tubule might conceivably be a supporting structure? I would seriously doubt that it was the toxin. Do you have any other evidence that the tips of the tubules attach to the prey rather than penetrate?

CHAPMAN: I don't think there is any other evidence. There is very little evidence on the structure of the tubule itself, because when tubules are fired they are hard as the dickens to find, and when they are not fired we don't often get such sections as this one.

HAND: How many times have you seen that hook?

CHAPMAN: Just once. But we have other sections showing that it is not an artifact.

HAND: You conclude that the tubule is not attached to the shaft and basal portion of the extruded nematocyst?

CHAPMAN: No. That section did not show the hook hooked on. It may never hook on. But it is suggestive. It's an interesting arrangement. Why form a hook if you're not going to do something with it?

MUSCATINE: Isn't it possible that the hook results from a tangential section through a twist in the tubule?

CHAPMAN: If one examines the negative or a good print of that particular figure very carefully, and specifically if one looks at the membrane limiting that tubule, I think it would be conclud-ed that the tubule had been cut very nearly sagittally and that it probably is indeed a hook. It seems to have been fortuitously cut precisely right. However, that is only an educated guess.

HAND: Which end of the thread is that really on?

CHAPMAN: It appears to be on the end that goes out first.

CROWELL: After the thread is fully discharged, which end is the hook on?

CHAPMAN: It would be on the end which is farthest from the stenotele.

HAND: Then you are proposing that that hook does not evert?

CHAPMAN: I am proposing that the tube which is coiled up inside, which has a propeller-shaped cross section, may not evert.

It may be fired out as a thread is fired out; as a flyline is fired out, if you will.

HAND: Then it is not a homolog of the tube of the holotrichous nematocyst such as Robson and Picken described?

CHAPMAN: I would agree.

HESS: I thought that it everted. Many previous investigators have suggested this.

CHAPMAN: I can't possibly imagine a tube which is many many microns long and is as narrow in diameter as that tubule is, completely everting in the sense of eversion of the capsule itself. I think it's almost impossible, even for a morphologist, to suggest anything like that.

FAWCETT: I can, I have that kind of an imagination.

CHAPMAN: OK, you explain it.

FAWCETT: I am not going to explain the mechanism, but direct your attention to the armament as it is folded within the nematocyst. You'll agree that the armament has to turn inside out in order to gain the position that it exhibits after the nematocyst is fired. After firing, the part bearing the spines is smoothly continuous with the wall of the tube and with the capsule. I think you'd have a serious problem to explain it any other way. If you think that only the base everts and the rest of it is flipped out like a flyrod, you would have to have a very different set of continuities than you find in the fired nematocyst. I do not see how you can have the base evert and the remainder flip out like a flyline. It has to be one way or the other. A combination of the two mechanisms is incomprehensible to me. I grant that it is difficult to visualize how this entire tubule could turn inside out, but if the morphological images suggest that this is true. I see no reason to doubt it simply because there is no ready physical or chemical explanation. The physical principals applicable to this problem may not have been worked out yet.

CHAPMAN: Yes, but the problem involved in turning the entire tubule inside out would be tremendous.

CROWELL: I have thought for many years, like Chapman, that this turning inside out of so fine a tubule probably violated the rules of hydraulics. It would be very nice to see a diagram of his interpretation, perhaps compared with the conventional interpretation.

CHAPMAN: I may have to get a flyrod out of my car.

SLAUTTERBACK: We have often seen these stenoteles when they have been interrupted by the fixative at various times during the firing process. It can be seen clearly that the narrow part of the tubule evaginates through the broad base, or butt, and expands in diameter as it does so. Our observations would support the elegant polarized light studies of Picken and Robson, whose interpretations ought not to be neglected in this discussion. Furthermore, since the base of the tubule is attached all the way around the orifice of the capsule I cannot imagine a route of exit if you propose to get it out sideways.

WOOD: Nematocyst discharge is probably pretty much the same for all nematocyst types. Using light microscopy, many people have observed the tubes coming out from the inside of the discharging holotrichs. To me, this is pretty strong evidence that the same sequence occurs in the other nematocyst types. I would agree with Dr. Slautterback.

CHAPMAN: My statements were made to explain how the tubule *might* be discharged *if* the hook and swelling did in fact serve the speculated functions. Most of the evidence supports the tubule eversion hypothesis even though this eversion would involve a nearly impossible physical feat.

Chemistry of Nematocyst Capsule and Toxin of *Hydra littoralis*

Edward S. Kline[1, 2]
Biochemistry Branch, Armed Forces Institute of Pathology, Washington, D.C.

Nematocysts are highly organized, complex, intracellular structures. They are vital for the survival of the animal. Much of the synthetic activity of the hydra is directed toward production of the functional nematocyst, a structure that is quickly lost in the course of its function in capturing the live animals upon which the hydra feeds. About 25% of the tentacle nematocysts are lost each time *H. littoralis* eats a meal of *Artemia*; these are rapidly replaced in about 48 hours from the store of differentiating nematocysts in the body (11). Because of this continual and active developmental process, nematocysts are an excellent system for chemical studies of biosynthetic and morphogenetic processes. It is toward an understanding of these processes that we hope to apply, as it accumulates, information regarding the chemical structure of these interesting organoids.

---

[1] Studies of the author on the nematocyst capsule were carried out in collaboration with Dr. H. M. Lenhoff, Howard Hughes Medical Institute, Miami, Florida; studies on the succinoxidase inhibitor were carried out in collaboration with Dr. V. S. Waravdekar, Chief of the Biochemistry Branch, Armed Forces Institute of Pathology; studies on serotonin were carried out in collaboration with Dr. H. Weissbach, Laboratory of Clinical Biochemistry, National Institute of Health, Bethesda, Maryland.

[2] Present address: Department of Chemistry, Indiana University, Bloomington, Indiana.

CAPSULE

Until recent years the nematocyst capsule was thought to be chitinous (2) With the advent of the controlled mass culture technique for the cultivation of *H. littoralis* (13) it became feasible to grow in the laboratory the large number of animals needed for chemical studies on these structures. Under most conditions employed to disrupt *Hydra* one finds that most of the nematocysts discharge. Advantage of this phenomenon was taken by Dr. Lenhoff, who, by a procedure of differential centrifugation, was able to isolate nematocyst preparations, largely discharged and free of the bulk of other tissue components (Table 1). When we chromatographed

TABLE 1
Isolation of discharged nematocysts from *Hydra*

1. Live animals disrupted in 10 kc sonic oscillator.
2. Suspension centrifuged 15 minutes at 160 g. Supernatant recentrifuged.
3. Whitish residues pooled and resuspended in water.
4. Residues centrifuged 20 minutes at 200 g.
5. Residue contained at least three types of nematocysts—penetrants, volvents, and glutinants – about 80% are discharged.

hydrolysates of such a preparation we found numerous amino acids, among them, one which was identified chromatographically as hydroxyproline (9). This compound, to my knowledge, has never been demonstrated in any protein other than collagen. The quantitative distribution of this compound between the protein of the whole *Hydra* and the nematocyst preparation shows that it is concentrated in the latter (Table 2). We have also found high amounts (over 20%) of the other imino acid, proline, in the nematocyst preparations (10). The absolute values obtained for the imino acid concentration in nematocyst preparations have shown some variation. More recent determinations of the hydroxyproline indicate that it is present in even higher concentrations than shown in the above table. These differences can be largely due to variations in the purity of different preparations. Since, in animals, high concentrations of these imino acids have been demonstrated only in collagens, we conclude that the capsule of the *Hydra* nematocyst

TABLE 2

Hydroxyproline content of whole *Hydra* and of nematocyst protein (From ref. 9)

Fraction	Hydroxyproline (mg.)	Nitrogen (mg.)	g. Hydroxyproline per 16 g. N
Hot – TCA – precipitate from 6,800 hydranths	0.568	5.21	1.74
Nematocyst preparation	0.230	0.285	12.7

contains a protein belonging to this class of compounds. The isolated nematocysts exhibit birefringence, visually resist trypsin digestion, show extreme stability to autoclaving, stain blue with the Masson trichrome reagent, show metachromasia with toluidine blue, and stain positively with alcian blue (9, 3). Except for the heat stability exhibited by the nematocyst preparation, all of these properties are indicative of a collagen type structure. One of the best known characteristics of the classical collagens is its property of forming gelatin upon heating, yet the nematocyst capsule retains its morphology even after many hours in the autoclave at 121°. I do not know whether this is due to the presence of other material in the capsule that "holds it together" or to the intrinsic inertness of the hydroxyproline-containing protein. Other lines of evidence have led Phillips (16) to postulate that the capsule of the anemone, *Metridium senile*, contains a cartilaginous material.

TOXIN

In connection with the work carried forth in our laboratory, the word "toxin" is probably inappropriate. I use it, only for the lack of a better term, to denote any nonstructural material which we believe to be present inside the nematocyst. We have no definite information that these materials constitute a toxin or even part of a toxin.

Succinoxidase Inhibitor – In an attempt to correlate the activity of oxidative enzymes with the phenomenon of regeneration we found that succinoxidase activity is virtually absent in *Hydra* homogenates (Table 3). This observation led to the realization that *Hydra* extracts contain an inhibitor of this enzyme system (6). It seemed reasonable to look for the inhibitor in the nematocysts, since these structures could contain this substance and thus prevent it from affecting the succinoxidase of the intact *Hydra*.

TABLE 3

Demonstration of succinoxidase inhibitor in *Hydra littoralis* (from ref. 6)

Tissue homogenate	Succinoxidase activity
	Q_{O_2} (dry weight)*
Hydra	1
Mouse liver	88
	Q_{O_2} (wet weight)*
Mouse liver	32
Mouse liver plus extract from *Hydra*⁺	2.4

*Q_{O_2} = μl of O_2 consumed per hour per mg. of tissue.
⁺The extract was obtained from *Hydra* suspended in distilled water. The animals were disrupted in a 10 kc Raytheon sonic oscillator, and most of the nematocysts and nematocyst walls were removed by centrifugation.
In all reaction vessels 0.1 ml. of a 5% homogenate of liver was used.

A basic difficulty that has characterized nearly all of the studies connected with coelenterate toxins has been the unavailability of isolated, undischarged nematocysts. Most studies have been carried out on toxic material obtained either from the whole animal or from tentacles and acontia. At the time our study was performed we also were unable to isolate clean, undischarged nematocysts. Therefore, our evidence showing that we are dealing with nematocyst material is indirect. Rather than to compare the amounts of inhibitory material in the various parts of *Hydra*, we attempted to elicit nematocyst discharge from the live, intact animal and see whether inhibitory activity is present in the culture fluid surrounding the animals. Chemical compounds known to cause nematocyst discharge were ineffective in our hands. Generally, the concentrations needed to cause the response also caused great damage to the animals. We did find, however, that a shock from a dry cell battery would induce discharge without killing the animals and with considerably less visual tissue damage than is caused by the chemical agents. As a result of the electric shock, significant numbers of nematocysts are discharged and soluble material is released into the culture medium; material which inhibits succinoxidase of mouse liver (Table 4). The possibility exists that this procedure causes the release of soluble material other than that from nematocysts. A similar way of causing nematocyst discharge has been reported by Glaser and Sparrow (1). These workers also presented a procedure for the isolation of undischarged nematocysts from hydra and other coelenterates. More recently Phillips (16, 17) and Lane and Dodge (8) have presented procedures for the isolation of undischarged nematocysts from *Metridium* and *Physalia,* respectively. By modifications of their methods we are now able to collect undischarged nematocysts from *Hydra littoralis* and hope to study these soon.

We purified the inhibitor (Table 5) and attempted to learn something of its nature. The purified inhibitor is a macromolecule which appears as a slow-moving and apparently rapidly diffusing single peak in the ultracentrifuge (Fig. 1). Ultracentrifuge experi-

TABLE 4

Succinoxidase inhibition by material discharged from nematocysts by electric current (from ref. 6)

Material	Inhibition of enzyme activity %
Mouse liver homogenate plus *Hydra* medium before electric shock (0.4 ml.)	2
Mouse liver homogenate plus *Hydra* medium after electric shock (0.4 ml.)	27

There were 57 animals in 2.5 ml. of solution. Aliquots of the solution without *Hydra* were removed before the shock. The solution was then diluted to the original volume and a shock from a 45-volt dry cell battery was applied. Then another aliquot of the solution was removed. For the succinoxidase assay of 0.1 ml. of a 5% liver homogenate was used in the reaction vessel. Qo_2 (wet weight) of control liver = 25. The same overall effect can be repeated but the actual precentage of inhibition does vary, depending upon differences in experimental conditions, e.g., the time the shock is applied and the number of nematocysts that are discharged.

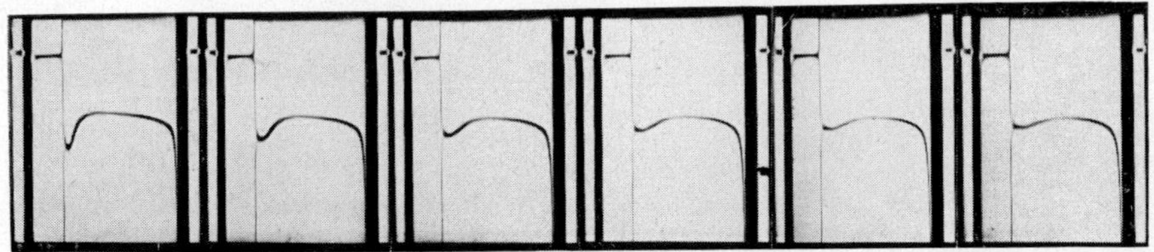

Fig. 1. Ultracentrifuge pattern of purified inhibitor at 59,000 r.p.m. (6).

ments indicate the molecular weight to be less than 50,000. Chemical tests show the presence of protein. The ultraviolet absorption spectrum (Fig. 2) is qualitatively very similar to that produced by proteins such as serum globulins. There are no peaks in the visible spectrum. All of our characterization studies affirm the presence of a protein in the purified inhibitor and, as

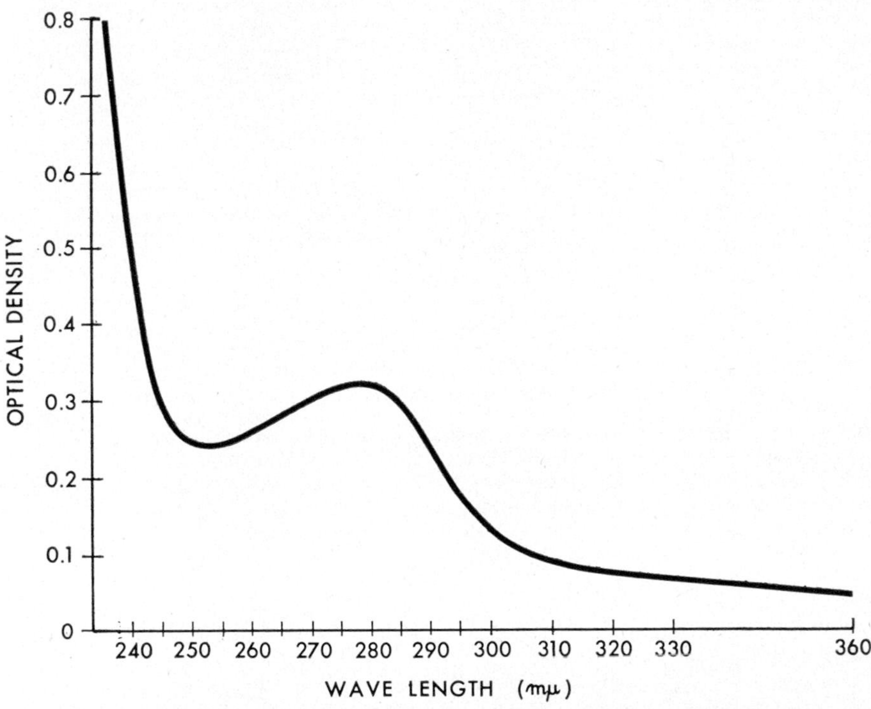

Fig. 2. The ultraviolet absorption spectrum of the purified inhibitor in phosphate buffer (6).

TABLE 5

Fractional separation of succinoxidase inhibitor from *Hydra* (from ref. 6)

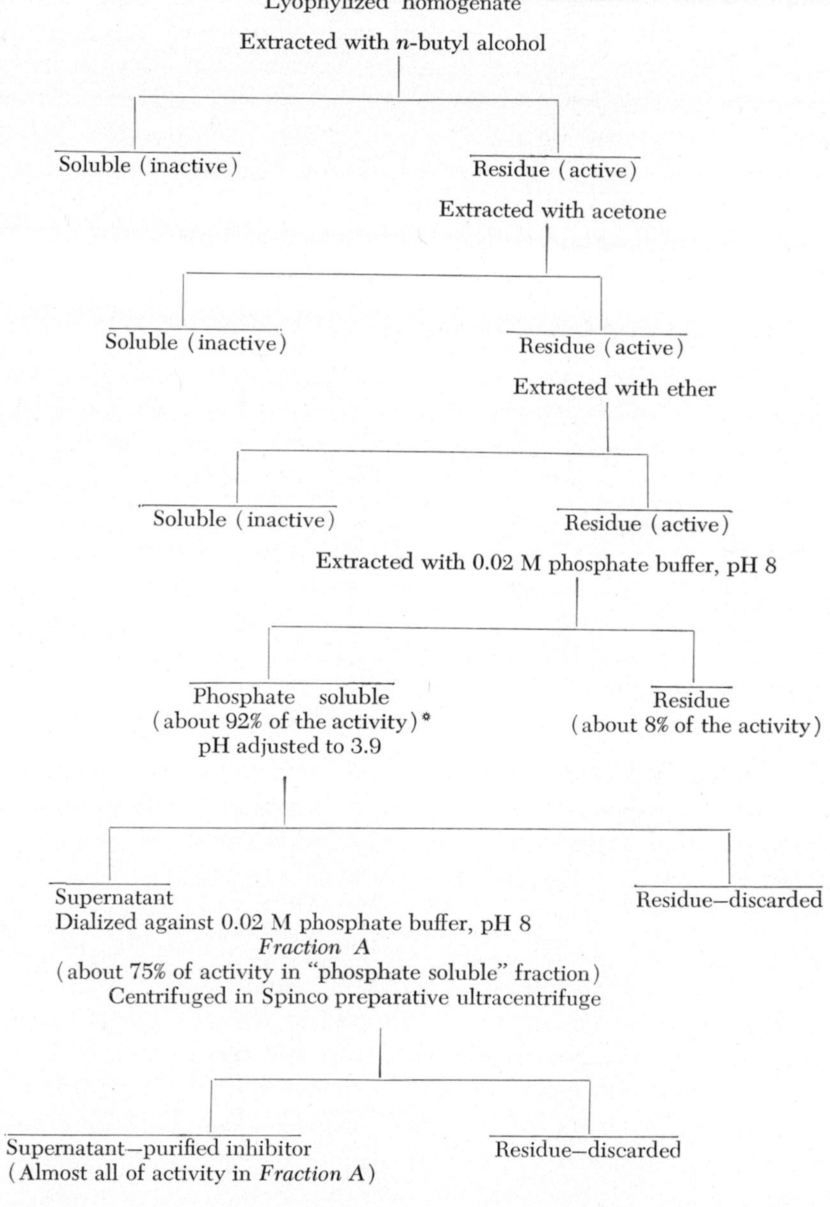

*Sample dialyzed before activity determination.

yet, we have not detected any other class of compounds. Next, we thought it of interest to determine whether the succinoxidase inhibitory activity is associated with the integrity of the protein. This was studied by incubating the purified inhibitor with the proteolytic enzyme trypsin to see whether digestion by this enzyme reduced the inhibitor's activity. After the incubation, soybean trypsin inhibitor was added to destroy the trypsin activity. The purified inhibitor, after such treatment, lost virtually all of its activity against mouse liver succinoxidase (6). From these studies we concluded that the inhibitor is a protein and that a high degree of the integrity of the protein is required for its activity.

At this stage of the study we became interested in the nature and mechanism of the succinoxidase inhibition produced by the *Hydra* protein. The next few experiments describe some of our findings in this area (7). The main parts of the succinoxidase chain, as it is now believed to exist, is shown in Figure 3. It is possible

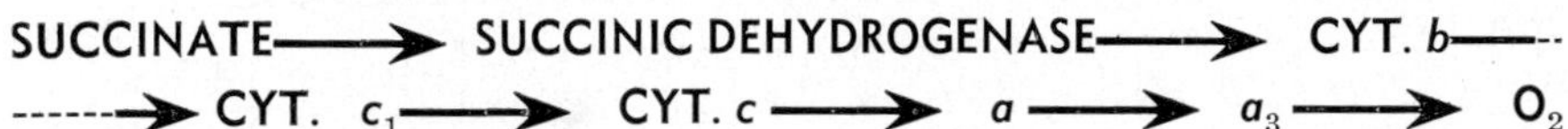

Fig. 3. A pathway for the oxidation of succinate. Not shown are the fat-soluble factors implicated in succinate oxidation. e.g., coenzyme Q, tocopherol and vitamin K.

by the use of specific assays to locate in this chain the general and perhaps the exact site at which an inhibitor acts. The quantitative effect of the purified inhibitor on succinoxidase is presented in Figure 4. These data show that the inhibition is linear to about the 50% level. The maximum level of inhibition is less than 100%, although, in other experiments the 100% level has been reached. The primary portion of the succinoxidase system, succinic dehydrogenase, does not appear to be the area in which the *Hydra* inhibitor operates (Table 6). Here, with 48 times the amount of material needed to inhibit succinoxidase 50%, there is less than 20% inhibition. The terminal portion of the succinoxidase chain, cytochrome oxidase, is not inhibited at all by 22 times the 50% inhibitory level for succinoxidase (Table 7). The next subsystem that we studied was succinate-cytochrome-*c* reductase. This system probably includes a

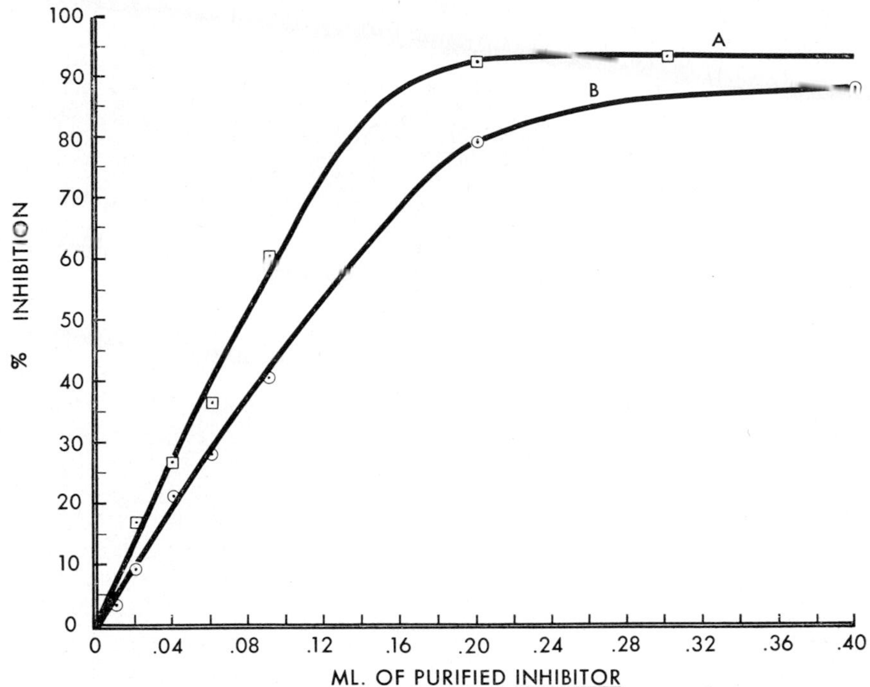

Fig. 4. The inhibitory effect of the purified inhibitor on the succinoxidase activity of mouse liver homogenate. In both Curve A and Curve B, the flasks contain 0.1 ml. of liver homogenate (5 mg. of wet tissue per flask) and the purified inhibitor (2.9 μg. of protein nitrogen per ml. of inhibitor). Total volume in all flasks: 3.1 ml. Each curve represents separate experiments (6).

TABLE 6

Effect of the purified inhibitor on succinic dedydrogenase

Material	Inhibitor to tissue ratio μg.: mg.	Succinic dehydrogenase activity Q_{O_2} (wet weight)	Inhibition %
Mouse liver homogenate	----	4.0	---
Mouse liver homogenate plus purified inhibitor (100 μg. protein N)	2.5 : 1	3.3	17.5

Each vessel contained 40 mg. of aqueous liver homogenate in final volume of 2.9 ml.

TABLE 7

Action of the purified inhibitor on cytochrome oxidase

Material	Inhibitor to tissue ratio µg.: mg.	Cytochrome oxidase activity Q_{O_2} (wet weight)	Inhibition %
Mouse liver homogenate	---	96	---
Mouse liver homogenate plus purified inhibitor (1.16 µg. protein N)	1.16 : 1	110	0.0

Each vessel contained 1.0 mg. of aqueous liver homogenate in final volume of 2.9 ml.

flavin moiety and components of the intermediary portions of succinoxidase, terminating at cytochrome *c*. The exact nature of this system in the enzyme preparation we used is not thoroughly understood. If the purified inhibitor is preincubated with the mouse liver homogenate, we find significant inhibition of succinate-cytochrome-*c* reductase. The inhibition, although less than with succinoxidase, is pronounced and occurs with the concentration of inhibitor which produces 50% reduction of succinoxidase (Table 8).

Our overall results in this area of the investigation lead us to postulate that the inhibition is specific [based on criteria of Keilin and Hartee (4) and Slater (22)] and that the reduction of cytochrome *c* is blocked, that is, the inhibition occurs on the substrate side of cytochrome *c*. Furthermore, since there is no evidence for

TABLE 8

Effect of the purified inhibitor on succinate-cytochrome-c reductase

Material	Inhibitor to tissue ratio µg.: mg.	Reductase activity (cyt. *c* reduction at 550 mµ) µ moles in 10 min.	Inhibition %
Mouse liver homogenate	---	0.0237	---
Mouse liver homogenate plus purified inhibitor (0.0116 µg. protein N)	0.058 : 1	0.0209	12
Mouse liver homogenate plus purified inhibitor (0.0309 µg. protein N)	0.174 : 1	0.0094	60

Aqueous liver homogenate preincubated with purified inhibitor for 30 minutes at room temperature. Each cuvette in assay had 0.2 mg. of homogenate. Volume in each cuvette = 3.0 ml.

direct inhibition of cytochrome *b* or any component preceding cytochrome *b*, we postulate that the inhibition occurs between cytochrome *b* and cytochrome *c*, (based on scheme in Fig. 3). This part of the system is not thoroughly characterized and I will not attempt to expand further on the above conclusions, except to add that these conclusions are similar in many ways to those drawn by Slater in his work with BAL (21, 22, 23), by Potter and Reif with antimycin A (18, 19, 20), and by Lightbown and Jackson with 2-heptyl-4-hydroxy-quinoline N oxide (12).

The purified inhibitor from *Hydra* has toxic effects on the mouse and the fiddler crab (5). When injected with the inhibitor (10 micrograms per gram body weight) most or all of the fiddler crabs became sluggish and about one-half of them lost their ability to right themselves, when placed on their backs. Eventually some of the animals died but most recovered. These effects were opposed to those of the boiled inhibitor, with which little or no adverse affects were noticed. We have done only a small number of experiments of this kind, with only 5 to 6 animals in each group, thus, we cannot really say much about the toxicity except that it occurs. Based on the amount of inhibitor required to elicit a discernible response in both the mouse and crab it does not appear that this material can account for more than a portion of the potent effect of toxic material present in *Hydra*. Welsh and Prock (25) have found tetramethylammonium in *Hydra littoralis*. If this compound is present in the nematocysts I expect that it may account for a large measure of the toxins potency.

Hydroxyindoleamines — Both hydroxyindoles and hydroxyindoleamines have been demonstrated in various coelenterates (14-17, 24, 26). One of these reports contained studies on *H. oligactis* (26). In it, Welsh showed the presence of significant amounts of 5-hydroxytryptamine (serotonin) in homogenates of this animal. Dr. Weissbach and I have found high concentrations of a 5-hydroxytryptamine in *Hydra littoralis*. We induced nematocyst discharge by electric shock and compared the amounts of 5-hydroxyindoleamine in the *Hydra* medium with that present in the whole animal (Table 9). This experiment showed that the discharged hydroxyindoleamine was present in more than 10 times the concentration than was found in the whole animals. Several attempts

TABLE 9

Hydroxyindoleamine distribution in fractions from *Hydra littoralis*

Preparation	Hydroxyindoleamine concentration	
	μg. per ml. of preparation	μg. per gram dry tissue
Whole *Hydra* homogenate	2.56	52
Hydra culture medium—before shock	0.011	57
Hydra culture medium—after shock	0.27	534

Conditions for the shock experiment similar to those used for experiment shown in Table 4.

were made to determine if the amine was serotonin. We have demonstrated a 5-hydroxyindoleamine by paper chromotography but as yet have not been able to obtain a sufficiently clean extract to determine precisely the identity of the compound. We do have indirect evidence that the compound is serotonin rather than bufotenine. This evidence consists of partition coefficients between ether and an alkaline aqueous phase. A 5-hydroxytryptophan decarboxylase is present in *Hydra* but this only shows that the animal can synthesize serotonin, not that serotonin is there. We are inclined to believe that serotonin is present in *Hydra littoralis,* but direct proof is still lacking.

CONCLUDING STATEMENTS

This study represents but a start toward the elucidation of the chemical composition of the nematocyst. It will be of interest not only to further characterize such preparations as the ones we have studied, but also to separate and compare the various types of nematocysts present in hydra, as well as the components of each nematocyst type. This information, coupled with the excellent morphology studies that are being carried out in various laboratories, could form the basis for an understanding of the manner in which these intriguing organoids develop and function.

REFERENCES

1. Glaser, O. C., and C. M. Sparrow. 1909. The physiology of nematocysts. *J. Exp. Zool. 6:* 361-382.
2. Hyman, L. H. 1940. *The Invertebrates: Protozoa through Ctenophora.* McGraw-Hill Book Co., Inc., New York, p. 382.
3. Johnson, F. B., and H. M. Lenhoff. 1958. Histochemical study of purified *Hydra* nematocysts. *J. Hist. Cytochem. 6:* 394.
4. Keilin, D., and E. F. Hartree. 1949. Activity of the succinic dehydrogenase – cytochrome system in different tissue preparations. *Biochem. J. 44:* 205-218.
5. Kline, E. S., and V. S. Waravdekar. 1959. Toxic effects of a material isolated from *Hydra littoralis. Amer. Soc. Pharmacol. Exp. Therap. 1:* 62.
6. Kline, E. S., and V. S. Waravdekar. 1960. Inhibitor of succinoxidase activity from *Hydra littoralis. J. Biol. Chem. 235:* 1803-1808.
7. Kline, E. S., and V. S. Waravdekar. 1960a. On the site of action of a succinoxidase inhibitor from Hydra. *Fed. Proc. 19:* 35.
8. Lane, C. E., and E. Dodge. 1958. The toxicity of *Physalia* nematocysts. *Biol. Bull. 115:* 219-226.
9. Lenhoff, H. M., E. S. Kline, and R. Hurley. 1957. A hydroxyproline-rich, intracellular, collagen-like protein of *Hydra* nematocysts. *Biochem. Biophys. Acta. 26:* 204-205.
10. Lenhoff, H. M., and E. S. Kline. 1958. The high imino acid content of the capsule from *Hydra* nematocysts. *Anat. Rec. 130:* 425.
11. Lenhoff, H. M., and J Bovaird. 1961. A quantitative chemical approach to problems of nematocyst distribution and replacement in *Hydra. Develop. Biol. 3:* 227-240.
12. Lightbown, J. W., and F. L. Jackson. 1956. Inhibition of cytochrome systems of heart muscle and certain bacteria by the antagonists of dihydrostreptomycin: 2-alkyl-4-hydroxyquinoline N-oxides. *Biochem. J. 63:* 130-137.
13. Loomis, W. F., and H. M. Lenhoff. 1956. Growth and sexual differentiation of hydra in mass culture. *J. Exp. Zool. 132:* 555-568.
14. Mathias, A. P., D. M. Ross, and M. Schachter. 1957. Identification and distribution of 5-hydroxytryptamine in a sea anemone. *Nature 180:* 658-659.
15. Mathias, A. P., D. M. Ross, and M. Schachter. 1960. The distribution of 5-hydroxytryptamine, tetramethylammonium, homarine, and other substances in sea anemones. *J. Physiol. 151:* 296-311.
16. Phillips, J. H. 1956. Isolation of active nematocysts of *Metridium senile* and their chemical composition. *Nature 178:* 932.
17. Phillips, J. H., and D. P. Abbott. 1957. Isolation and assay of the nematocyst toxin of *Metridium senile fimbriatum. Biol. Bull. 113:* 296-301.
18. Potter, van R., and A. F. Reif. 1952. Inhibition of an electron transport component by antimycin A. *J. Biol. Chem. 194:* 287-297.
19. Reif, A. F., and van R. Potter. 1953. Studies on succinoxidase inhibition: 1. Pseudoreversible inhibition by a napthoquinone and by antimycin A. *J. Biol. Chem. 205:* 279-290.
20. Reif, A. F., and van R. Potter. 1954. Oxidative pathways insensitive to antimycin A. *Arch. Biochem. 48:* 1-6.
21. Slater, E. C. 1948. A factor in heart muscle required for the reduction of cytochrome *c* by cytochrome *b. Nature 161:* 405-406.
22. Slater, E. C. 1949. The action of inhibitors on the system of enzymes which catalyze the aerobic oxidation of succinate. *Biochem. J. 45:* 8-13.

23. SLATER, E. C. 1949. A respiratory catalyst required for the reduction of cytochrome *c* by cytochrome *b*. *Biochem. J. 45:* 14-30.

24. WELSH, J. H. 1955. On the nature and action of coelenterate toxins. *Deep Sea Research,* Suppl. 3: 287-297.

25. WELSH, J. H., and P. B. PROCK. 1958. Quaternary ammonium bases in the coelenterates. *Biol. Bull. 115:* 551-561.

26. WELSH, J. H. 1960. 5-Hydroxytrytamine in coelenterates. *Nature 186:* 811-812.

DISCUSSION

WELSH: Were these serotonin values on a dry weight or wet weight basis?

KLINE: Dry weight basis.

WELSH: What do you say about the heat and pH stability of the succinoxidase inhibitor?

KLINE: It is stable at pH 5.8 and 8, and since one step in the purification of the inhibitor is a pH 4 precipitation it has appreciable stability even at this pH.

Heat stability is an interesting point. We felt that the inhibitor from *Hydra littoralis* could have been a phospholipase A. Phospholipase A's are heat stable and the succinoxidase inhibitor in snake venom is believed to be this enzyme. We heated separately some *Crotalus adamanteus* venom and our inhibitor at pH 5.8 in a boiling water bath for 15 minutes. The venom lost none of its effectiveness against succinoxidase while the purified inhibitor from *Hydra* lost about 75% of its activity.

EAKIN: What is its behavior on dialysis?

KLINE: Essentially all of the activity is non-dialyzable.

LENHOFF: Does the inhibitor do anything to mitochondria?

KLINE: We have done one or two preliminary studies and there seems to be some effect on the mitochondria, but as yet we have done too little to make any definite statements.

MARTIN: Have you ever tried to extract active substances from the nematocyst-poor parts of the *Hydra*? And if so, did they show any similarity with the nematocyst content?

KLINE: Which component? Serotonin?

MARTIN: Serotonin or the enzyme inhibitor.

KLINE: We have not done that. I believe that the best proof for the localization of these compounds will come when we can quantitatively isolate pure, undischarged nematocysts from the animal.

ROSS: I'm very interested and pleased to see your results with serotonin. But I'd like to hear your comments on some observations that Mathias, Schachter, and I made in London on the distribution of serotonin in sea anemones, because our results would indicate that we cannot extend this conception generally over a whole group from one species unless one looks at the distribution very carefully. We found extracts from tentacles separated from the column, or both separated from the tissues lining the coelenteron did not contain much serotonin in 3 of the 4 species of sea anemones that we used, *viz., Metridium senile, Actinia equina* and *Anemonia sulcata.* The only place where we found a significant amount of serotonin was in the "coelenteric tissue" of *Calliactis parasitica,* and there it was present in large quantities, 500-600 mg. per gram of freeze-dried matter. This was about 60 times the concentration found in the tentacles. Thus there seemed to be no correlation between the distribution of serotonin and nematocysts, or between different species. I wonder if you have any comment to make on that?

KLINE: I am aware of your work and it might appear that the findings in various laboratories are contradictory. But as you have said, we cannot necessarily extend results from one animal to another. I believe Phillips thought his hydroxyindoleamine was bufotenin rather than serotonin and that it was not localized in the nematocysts. Your group found serotonin in certain anemones and not in others and you feel that it is not concentrated in the nematocysts. Is this correct?

ROSS: Well, it's in a part of the animal where there are fewer nematocysts.

KLINE: Dr. Welsh's study with anemones points to it being serotonin and in the nematocysts. For the most part we all have been studying different animals with different approaches. As time passes I become more impressed by the variability between closely related animals.

PHILLIPS: Have you detected any hexosamines or uronic acids in the capsule?

KLINE: We have not looked for them.

STREHLER: What percentage of the total weight did you calculate would be collagen on the basis of this hydroxyproline content?

KLINE: Based on 20% hydroxyproline, the collagen-like protein represents about 10% of the total protein of *H. littoralis.*

Physalia Nematocysts and their Toxin

Charles E. Lane
Institute of Marine Sciences, University of Miami, Miami, Florida

Nematocysts in *Physalia* are widely distributed through the epithelium clothing most of the members of the colony. These organelles are formed in cnidoblasts by so far undescribed cytogenetic processes. The upper surface of the float and the proximal portions of the gastrozooids and of the fishing tentacles are relatively deficient in mature nematocysts. Over the surface of the fishing tentacle cnidoblasts are concentrated in the epithelium clothing the batteries. These are permanent structures distributed in bead-like fashion along the length of one edge of the tentacle, and they are illustrated in Figure 1, which shows a three-dimensional reconstruction of a segment of the fishing tentacle of *Physalia.* The batteries appear as discrete saccular enlargements along one edge. A longitudinal section through a portion of the tentacle, including a single battery cut equatorially appears in Figure 2.

The battery is lined by gastrodermis continuous with that lining the gastrovascular extension in the tentacle. The mesoglea is a thick band of fibrous connective tissue external to the gastrodermis. The epidermal layer bearing cnidoblasts clothes the entire structure. At the equator of the battery the epidermis thickens abruptly where the external hemisphere acquires its population of mature cnidoblasts. Perhaps the most outstanding histological characteristic of this epithelium is the regular distribution through it of nematocysts belonging to two different size groups. The total thickness of the epithelium is just sufficient to clothe the large nematocysts, which range from 25 to 30 microns in diameter.

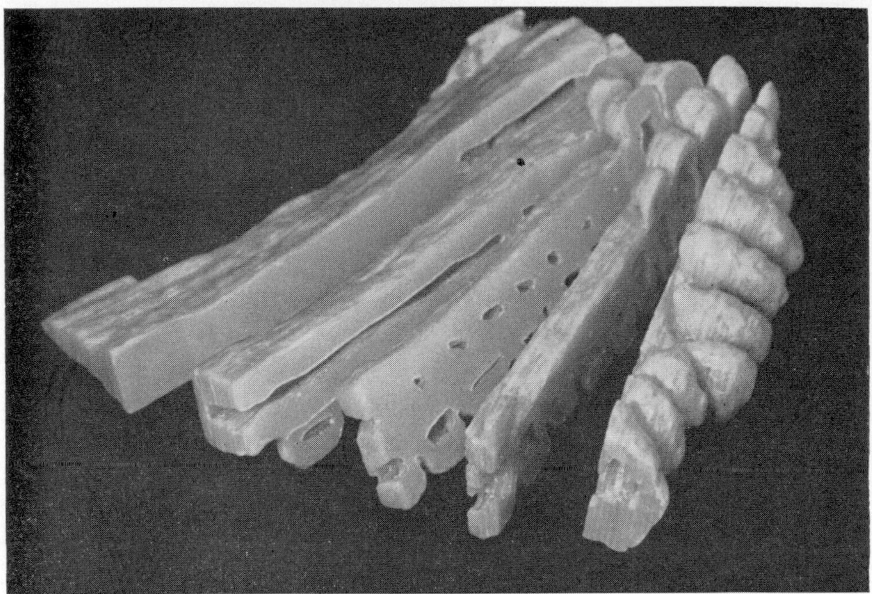

Fig. 1. Reconstruction in wax of a segment of the fishing tentacle of *Physalia*. The extension of the gastro-vascular cavity into the tentacle and the relationship between the cavities of the batteries and of the tentacle are clearly shown.

Regularly spaced between cnidoblasts bearing the large nematocysts occur small cnidoblasts whose capsules range from 7 to 15 microns in diameter. In favorable preparations each of the cnidoblasts may be seen to be provided with a *cnidocil,* projecting through the cuticular layer of the epithelium into the ambient water. The light microscope reveals a perinuclear basketwork of elastic fibers within the cnidoblast, which appears to surround the nematocyst. Other than this perinuclear network and the nematocyst capsule, the cytoplasm of the definitive cnidoblast appears to present very little structural specialization.

Cnidoblasts are regularly distributed throughout the epidermis of the external battery hemisphere, and there is also a repeating pattern of internal structure in adjacent nematocysts. The internal coiled thread, characteristic of the nematocysts of all Cnidaria, in each of the nematocysts originates at about the same point in the

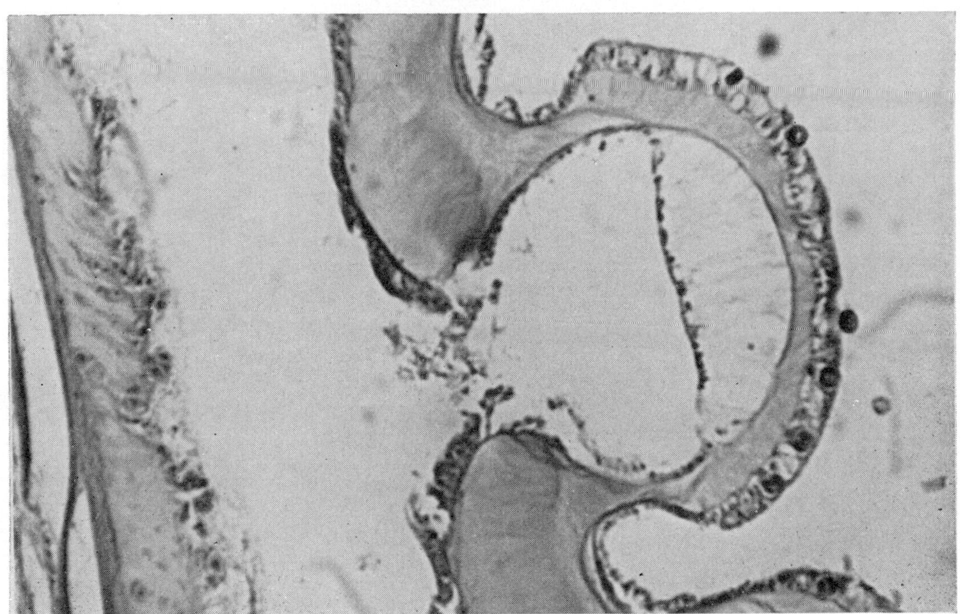

Fig. 2. Frontal Section through the fishing tentacle of *Physalia* X 200. The gastrovascular cavity of the tentacle communicates in the center of the field with the cavity of a single "battery." Hypertrophy of the gastrodermis begins at the equator of the battery.

capsule and coils in the same clock-wise direction in approximately the same plane.

If the surviving tentacle be stimulated by gradually increasing the concentration of solutes in the surrounding water, the nematocysts may be made to discharge. This is a dramatic, explosive process, the nematocyst threads being hurled from the capsule with sufficient force to penetrate the surface film. This observation explains our early experience of being severely stung even through a surgical glove.

In our laboratory we isolate surviving nematocysts by controlled autolysis at 4°, followed by screening, sieving, washing, and settling. The washing process is continued until the wash water is no longer toxic when injected into the hemocoele of the fiddler crab. This point may acquire some significance when one attempts to compare the activity and biochemistry of the toxin prepared in our laboratory with reports in the literature describing the activity of other *Physalia* toxin preparations. Earlier investigators, almost uniformly, have homogenized and extracted entire tentacle material. It will later appear that there are active extra-nematocyst substances present in the tentacle; however, the biochemistry and pharmacology of these materials has not been studied in our laboratory.

Isolated nematocysts may be concentrated by settling and decantation of the supernatant water. They do not survive centrifugation without discharge so it is necessary to permit them to settle by gravity alone. The putty-like concentrate resulting from our procedure is virtually free of tissue fragments and contains very few (less than 1%) discharged nematocysts. The concentrated nematocysts are frozen and stored in the deepfreeze where they retain their reactivity for periods of at least four years.

Surviving nematocysts are homogenized in an all-glass homogenizer in a minimum volume of distilled water for about twenty minutes, or until an aliquot shows no more than 10% unbroken capsules. The resulting brei is centrifuged at 4° in a refrigerated centrifuge at 15,000 $\times$ gravity; the residue is resuspended in a

TABLE 1

Amino acids in an acid hydrolysate of the crude toxin

Amino Acid	μM/Sample	Relative Concentration
Alanine	0.37	5
Arginine	0.12	1
Aspartic Acid	0.32	7
Glutamic Acid	0.85	20
Glycine	0.75	9
Histidine	0.05	1
Isoleucine	0.19	4
Leucine	0.25	5
Lysine	0.25	6
Phenylalanine	0.15	4
Proline	0.38	7
Serine	0.23	4
Threonine	0.07	1
Tyrosine	--------	------
Valine	0.21	4

minimum of water and recentrifuged. The supernatant solutions from these two centrifugations are combined and lyophilized.

The lyophilized "crude" toxin has regularly assayed between 15 and 16% nitrogen by micro-Kjeldahl. All tests for polysaccharide have been negative. A sample of crude toxin was hydrolyzed in 6*N* HCl, and the hydrolysate was analyzed on the Beckman Spinco amino acid analyzer with the results shown in Table I.

The lyophilized toxin is lethal to mice at dosage levels of 1.7 mg./kilogram.

When crude toxin was chromatographed one-dimensionally with 80% *n*-propanol as the solvent system, a series of nine spots appeared when the paper was developed with ninhydrin. Each of the spots was separately eluted and assayed for total activity in the fiddler crab, *Uca pugilator*. Four of the spots accounted for 95% of the total biological activity of the crude toxin.

The active regions on the chromatographic papers were eluted, hydrolyzed, and rechromatographed. Each was shown to contain more than one amino acid.

Since this chromatography had been accomplished in the presence of a solvent and at room temperature it was felt that considerable loss of activity may have occurred. Such an attenuation might be sufficient to mask activity in other fractions. Accordingly, the crude toxin was next fractionated on the Beckman refrigerated paper curtain electrophoresis apparatus, using phthallate buffer pH 5.8 at 2°. Four fractions were separated; after dialysis and lyophilization they were carefully diluted to their relative concentration in the original toxin and bioassayed on *Uca pugilator*. The results are shown in Figure 3.

One peptide nearly equals the activity of the original whole toxin, although representing less than 10% of its weight, and it therefore appears that some inert masking protein materials may have been removed by electrophoresis. *Physalia* toxin, therefore, appears to be a relatively simple protein consisting of only a few toxic peptides. Our future studies will seek to describe the precise molecular configuration of these peptides and to relate biochemical structure to pharmacologic activity.

I may be permitted to speculate briefly about the origin and synthesis of *Physalia* toxin. The gastrodermis lining the battery

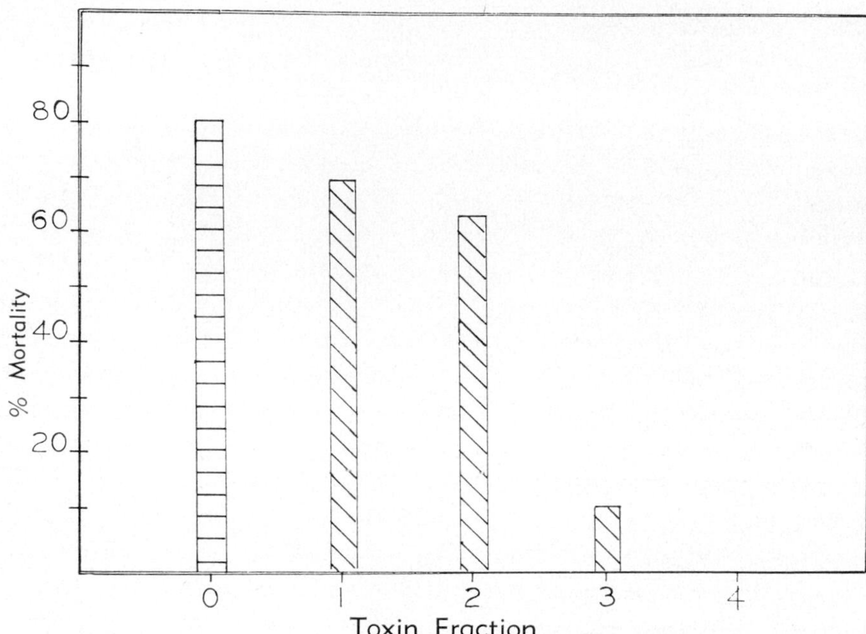

Fig. 3. Results of bioassay on groups of 10 *Uca pugilator* of: (0) whole crude toxin, and various fractions (1, 2, 3, 4) separated by electrophoresis from the crude toxin. Fractions were injected at levels approximating their separate concentration (by weight) in the crude toxin.

undergoes characteristic hyperplasia beneath that portion of the epidermis containing mature nematocysts. This histological change involves structural polarization, extensive vacuolation of the cytoplasm, and a change in the staining characteristics and chromatic density of the nucleus (see Fig. 2). The mesoglea separating the hyperplastic gastroderm cells from the nematocyst-containing epidermis is also modified. In preparations stained with Mallory's trichrome, the mesoglea shows discrete circular patches which stain differently from the rest of the mesoglea. These patches are always located between hypertrophied gastroderm cells and cnidoblasts in the surface epithelium.

We have shown the gastrovascular cavity of *Physalia* to contain and circulate a protein fluid. There is open communication between the gastrovascular cavity and the cavity of the battery. It is tempting to speculate that the modified gastroderm cells basal to the cnidoblasts absorb precursor materials from the circulating gastrovascular fluid and from these synthesize the toxin which they subsequently secrete through the mesoglea and into the cnidoblasts.

Slautterback and Fawcett have shown that the nematocyst thread in hydra originates from outside the nematocyst capsule and is subsequently introduced into the cavity of the nematocyst. If a structural component of the nematocyst may be formed external to the nematocyst capsule and subsequently introduced into it, it should not stretch our credulity too far to accept the suggestion that a soluble protein toxin may be synthesized outside the nematocyst and later may pass through it. One disturbing observation is that this would suggest or almost require that the nematocyst capsule be permeable to the toxin. We have repeatedly observed that the toxin does not leach from surviving purified nematocysts. Presumably, therefore, there is one stage in the morphogenetic history of the nematocyst when the capsule wall may be permeable to toxin but in the mature nematocyst these permeability relationships may be completely changed.

I suggest that *Physalia* toxin is synthesized by gastrodermal cells, passes through the mesoglea, and into the nematocyst during the morphogenesis of this structure.

DISCUSSION

CROWELL: Where are the nematocysts manufactured in *Physalia*? Where is the differentiation of the cnidoblasts taking place?

LANE: I can't answer because I don't know yet. I can tell you a few of the things we do know. In adult animals the float is generally free of cnidoblasts. The basal ends of gastrozoids are deficient in cnidoblasts. Cnidoblasts appear to be reasonably uniformly distributed throughout the length of the fishing tentacle. I have seen no clear histological evidence of interstitial cells such as we have heard about in hydra. Obviously they must be there, but I haven't seen them.

CROWELL: Is it possible that the whole tentacle is continuously growing so that it's always young basally and degenerating apically? If so, there is no need to replace the nematocysts along the length of the tentacle.

LANE: I think this is entirely possible.

CROWELL: Two other possibilities are that nematocysts are made all along the tentacles, and that they are built back in headquarters and are transported to the tentacles by unknown means.

LENHOFF: In the chromatograms you showed, were you running the entire fluid or a hydrolyzate of the fluid?

LANE: This was the entire material. We took the entire gastrovascular fluid without any treatment. I suspect we have amino acids and peptides. We are now analyzing this fluid using paper electrophoresis.

LENHOFF: What was the solvent?

LANE: *n*-propanol.

LENHOFF: In H. littoralis we find that the gastrodermis takes up mostly particles, and leaves behind the free amino acids in the gut. Your chromatogram looks somewhat like a normal pattern of free amino acids. Do you think *Physalia* does the same thing?

LANE: We'll know more about this very soon. We find that toxin peptides distribute very much like this and we have eluted, hydrolyzed, and rechromatographed them separately. We know they are peptides. So without actually having done it on this gastrovascular material, I feel fairly certain that these are peptides also.

WOOD: Do you have any real evidence that the gastrodermis extrudes materials into the mesogleal extracellular space, which are then picked up by the epidermal cells? I question this because it seems to me that it would be more efficient to transfer such materials directly. This bears on whether your specialized area in the mesoglea is cellular or is purely connective tissue?

LANE: That was the way we had interpreted it, but this is purely tentative and subject to change. Having seen the way in which both endodermal and ectodermal processes interdigitate and weave their way through the mesoglea in hydra, we could easily expect the same thing to take place here. It may be that these tremendously hypertrophied endodermal cells penetrate through the mesoglea in these regions.

MARTIN: I want to mention an experiment which supports Dr. Lane's hypothesis. We didn't work with *Physalia* or hydra, but with *Anthopleura elegantissima.* We separated the tentacles from the column and took the mesenteries out. Then we ground up the column and tentacles separately, made extracts and measured their toxicity by injecting them into mice and we found that the extracts of the nematocyst-poor column was as toxic as a crown, which is nematocyst-rich.

HAND: Did you remove the mesenterial filaments?

MARTIN: Yes.

HAND: Fine.

MARTIN: By the way, the mesenteric filaments were less toxic than the other two fractions.

HAND: That's quite contrary to what I would have expected, since they have the bulk of the internally located nematocysts.

SLAUTTERBACK: There is a mesogleal formation in hydra somewhat similar to the specialized areas you described. A great accumulation of mesoglea is sometimes seen under the pedal disk secretory cells. The predominant component here is amphorous. Whether it is the same material commonly found in the mesoglea has not been determined. The fine filaments and glycogen granules are not increased as much.

Also, is the greatly enlarged part of the hypertrophied gastroderm cells an enlarged "central vacuole"?

LANE: Yes.

SLAUTTERBACK: Were you ever able to fix anything in that vacuole?

LANE: We've tried a wide spectrum of fixatives on these vacuoles but they've always been clear.

BURNETT: Have you ever found nematocysts in the gastrodermal cells suggesting that there may be a migration through the gastrovascular cavity?

LANE: Yes, I've found them in gastrodermal cells, but they have been in cells which have incorporated this material from prey organisms.

BURNETT: Are they in a state of digestion?

LANE: That's right. Normally the nematocysts end at the lip of the gastrozoid. The lip is always identifiable by having cnidoblasts in its ectoderm, but none in its gastroderm.

Actually, we've had a great deal of trouble in keeping these animals in captivity. Probably the reason for this is that they have no protection against dragging their tentacles on the bottom. Whenever this happens the fragile surface epithelium is destroyed so that the next time the tentacle contracts, it squirts out some of this gastrovascular fluid. It's interesting that within an hour of placing a mature *Physalia* in an ordinary aquarium tank, the surrounding water becomes ninhydrin-positive. He loses much fluid. This is one reason why we have been unable to keep these animals in captivity long enough to feed them, and then study the distribution of digested food materials to the gastroderm.

LARSON What can you tell us about the pharmacological action of the toxin?

LANE: We haven't enough information on the pharmacology of the toxin to justify any statements.

GOREAU: Can rabbits be immunized against *Physalia* toxin?

LANE: Yes. The material is sufficiently antigenic to develop good titers. It is difficult, however, to differentiate between a lethal and an immunizing dose.

GORDEAU: That's the problem of anaphylactic shock which was discovered with *Physalia* toxin by Richet. If you could immunize an animal against the toxin and label the antibodies with suitable fluorescent groups it might be possible to find out whether there is transfer of toxin from the gastroderm through the mesoglea into the epidermal nematocyst batteries.

LANE: Yes, that would be an interesting experiment.

Compounds of Pharmacological Interest in Coelenterates

John H. Welsh
Biological Laboratories, Harvard University, Cambridge, Massachusetts

The nematocysts of coelenterates appear to serve two principal functions: one, a means of protection, the other, a role in feeding. A person once badly stung by *Physalia, Cyanea* or certain of the cubomedusae avoids contact with one of these a second time. It may be assumed that an animal that is stung and survives also may avoid future contact with a coelenterate if it is capable of learning. More important, perhaps, to the coelenterates, is the paralyzing or relaxing action of the contents of the nematocysts when injected into their prey.

Since the very early years of this century, efforts have been made to identify the substances in coelenterates that are responsible for the symptoms that result from their sting. In most of the earlier work, extracts of whole coelenterates or of nematocyst-bearing parts (tentacles and acontia) have been used. Therefore, it has not been possible to attribute an observed action to nematocyst contents. The recently developed methods of isolating clean nematocysts will obviate this difficulty if it can be shown that they lose none of their contents during the isolation procedure.

A condensed and incomplete summary of substances or fractions obtained from various coelenterates follows. Some of these derive from nematocysts; others, almost certainly, do not.

I. Early attempts to isolate toxic components of coelenterates by Richet and Portier (19, 20, 21) yielded three active extracts: "thallasin," "congestin" and hypnotoxin." None of these was chemically identified and each was doubtless a mixture of substances (see refs. 13, 22, 23, 25, for summaries of this and other earlier work).

II. Quarternary ammonium compounds:

Several nitrogenous bases have been isolated from various coelenterates, including the following:

	References
tetramethyl ammonium hydroxide or "tetramine"	4, 11, 17, 27
N-methylpyridinium hydroxide	5
homarine	2, 10, 17, 27
trigonelline	2, 27
γ-butyrobetaine	1, 27
zoo-anemonin	3, 6, 27

Of these bases, the only one that has marked paralyzing action is tetramine (4, 27). It is the only one found thus far in a fresh-water coelenterate (27). It is a known toxic component of certain molluscan tissues (7, 9). With the exception of zoo-anemonin, the other bases listed above are widely distributed among marine invertebrates where they may play a role in osmoregulation (10, 27).

III. 5-Hydroxytryptamine (serotonin, 5-HT):

This very potent pain-producer and histamine releaser has now been identified in a variety of coelenterates (17, 25, 26). It is present in the coelenteric tissues of *Calliactis parasitica* in very large amounts (17) but in other coelenterates it is most abundant in regions (tentacles and acontia) where nematocysts are concentrated (25, 26).

IV. Histamine and histamine releasers:

Histamine has been found in some coelenterates but not in others (17, 24). Potent histamine releasers have been extracted from a sea anemone (12) and *Cyanea* (24).

V. Active proteins:

Much evidence indicates that the paralyzing and edema-producing actions of coelenterate toxins are due, in large measure, to a protein component(s) (8, 13, 14, 15, 16, 21, 22, 23). There is some evidence that this component acts on cholinergic neurons in such a manner as to block conduction and/or transmission (17). The neutralizing action of certain acetylcholine blockers such as tetraethylammonium (TEA) on the paralyzing action of tentacle extracts supports this view (25).

Certain of the symptoms that follow a coelenterate sting such as pain, burning, itching, localized edema and hemorrhaging could result from injected 5-HT (a potent pain producer and histamine releaser), from histamine itself, and from other histamine releasers. These substances, however, cannot be responsible for the paralyzing action of the nematocyst contents. Many quaternary ammonium compounds do have a paralyzing action as junctional blocking agents. Of those listed above, only tetramine can qualify as a candidate for the paralyzing action. In the first place it is the only one that has been identified in hydra extracts, while most of the others are widely distributed among the marine invertebrates. In the second place, tetramine is an effective poison and is the toxic component of the salivary glands of certain marine gastropods (7, 9), while the others are surprisingly non-toxic (cf. 27). Furthermore, the earlier observed antagonism of coelenterate extracts by tetraethylammonium chloride or Banthine (25) strongly suggests that a methylated quaternary nitrogen compound is, in some way, involved in the paralysis resulting from a coelenterate sting. However, calculations may be made that indicate that there is not enough tetramine, in the extracts that we have used, to account for their paralyzing action, at least on arthropods.

Evidence has been accumulating over the years that the paralyzing factor in coelenterate toxins is a protein or group of proteins. Several recent studies show that toxicity remains after dialysis but is destroyed by boiling and by treatment with certain proteolytic enzymes (14, 15, 16, 18). The exact mode of action of the toxic protein(s) is not yet clear.

RÉSUMÉ OF SOME EXPERIMENTS THAT ARE CURRENTLY IN PROGRESS

We are, at present, comparing the actions of homogenates of *Metridium* acontia and whole *Hydra,* and of material discharged

from their nematocysts by electrical stimulation, on *Carcinus maenas, Uca pugilator* and several species of cockroaches. A brief résumé of some of the experiments and tentative results follows:
1) The minimum lethal dose of a homogenate of *Hydra americana,* in terms of the number of *Hydra* injected is between 5 and 10 *Hydra* for *Carcinus* weighing 20-30 gms.; 2-3 *Hydra* for *Uca* weighing 4-5 gms.; and about 5 *Hydra* for female *Bryostria* sp. (cockroach) weighing 4-5 gms. These are doses that usually kill in from 1 to 24 hours. The average dry weight of *Hydra americana,* reared in the laboratory, is about 35 μg. If the paralyzing factor constitutes something like 0.1% of the total dry weight, it appears that 0.2-0.4 μg. of toxic substance is lethal for a 20-30 gm. green crab.
2) Heating a *Hydra* homogenate for 30 min. at 100° results in complete or nearly complete loss of paralyzing action.
3) Electrical stimulation of numbers of *Hydra* (200-300) in a minimum volume of distilled water discharges many of the nematocysts. Injection of a small volume (0.05 ml.) of the fluid surrounding the *Hydra* into *Uca,* produces symptoms that are qualitatively like those seen when whole *Hydra* homogenate is injected.
4) *Hydra,* and *Metridium* acontia, have been homogenized in 1.0% tetraethylammonium chloride (TEA). When volumes are injected known to contain minimum lethal doses of *Hydra* or acontia, none of the characteristic symptoms develop and most test animals survive indefinitely. This agrees with earlier observations on the autotomy reflex in brachyurans when it was found that TEA very effectively antagonized the effects of coelenterate extracts (25). If the TEA is blocking the action of a toxic protein component, and not tetramine only, this may provide a clue to the mode of action of the toxin.

REFERENCES

1. Ackerman, D., 1927. Über die Identität des Atkinins mit dem γ-Butyrobetaine. *Zeitschr. f. Biologie, 86:* 199-202.
2. Ackerman, D., 1953. Über das Vorkommen von Homarin, Trigonellin und einer neuen Base Anemonin in der Anthozoa *Anemonia sulcata. Zeitschr. f. physiol. Chemie, 295:* 1-9.
3. Ackerman, D., 1954. Richtigstellung: "Zoo-Anemonin" statt Anemonin. *Zeitschr. f. physiol. Chemie, 296:* 286.

4. Ackerman, D., F. Holtz, and H. Reinwein, 1923. Reindarstellung und Konstitutionsermittelung des Tetramines, eines Giftes aus *Aktinia equina. Zeitschr. f. Biologie, 79:* 113-120.
5. Ackerman, D., F. Holtz, and H. Reinwein, 1924. Über die Extraktstoffe von *Aktinia equina. Zeitschr. f. Biologie, 80:* 131-136.
6. Ackerman, D., and P. H. List, 1960. Zur Konstitution des Zooanemonins und des Herbipolins. *Zeitschr. f. physiol. Chemie, 318:* 281.
7. Asano, M., and M. Itoh, 1960. Salivary poison of a marine gastropod, *Neptunea arthritica* Bernhardi, and the seasonal variation of its toxicity. *Ann. N.Y. Acad. Sci., 90:* 674-688.
8. Cantacuzène, J., and A. Damboviceanu, 1934. Caractères physico-chimiques du poison des acconties d'*Adamsia palliata. C. R. Soc. Biol., Paris, 117:* 138-140.
9. Fange, R. 1960. The salivary gland of *Neptunea antiqua. Ann. N. Y. Acad. Sci., 90:* 689-694.
10. Gasteiger, E. L., P. S. Haake, and J. A. Gergen, 1960. An investigation of the distribution and function of homarine (N-methyl picolinic acid). *Ann. N. Y. Acad. Sci., 90:* 622-636.
11. Haurowitz, F., and H. Waelsch, 1926. Über die chemische Zusammensetzung der Qualle *Velella spirans. Zeitschr. f. physiol. Chemie, 161:* 330-317.
12. Jacques, R., and M. Schachter, 1954. A sea anenome extract (thalassine) which liberates histamine and a slow contracting substance. *Brit. J. Pharmacol., 9:* 49-52.
13. Kaiser, E., and H. Michl, 1958. *Die Biochemie der tierischen Gifte.* Franz Deuticke, Vienna.
14. Lane, C. E. 1960. The toxin of *Physalia* nematocysts. *Ann. N.Y. Acad. Sci. 90:* 742-750.
15. Lane, C. E., and E. Dodge, 1958. The toxicity of *Physalia* nematocysts. *Biol. Bull., 115:* 219.
16. Martin, E. J., 1960. Observations on the toxic sea anenome, *Rhodactis howesii* (Coelenterata). *Pacific Science, 14:* 403-407.
17. Mathias, A. P., D. M. Ross and M. Schachter, 1960. The distribution of 5-hydroxytryptamine, tetramethylammonium, homarine, and other substances in sea anenomes. *J. Physiol., 151:* 296-311.
18. Phillips, J. H. Jr., and D. P. Abbott, 1957. Isolation and assay of the nematocyst toxin of *Metridium senile fimbriatum. Biol. Bull., 113:* 296-301.
19. Richet, C. 1902. Du poison pruritogène et urticant contenu dans les tentacules d'Actinies. *C. R. Soc. Biol., Paris, 54:* 1438.
20. Richet, C., 1903. Des poisons contenus dans les tentacules des Actinies, congestine et thalassine. *C. R. Soc. Biol., Paris, 55:* 246.
21. Richet, C., and P. Portier, 1936. Recherches sur la toxine des coelentérés et les phénomènes d' anaphylaxie. *Résultats des campagnes scientifiques, Monaco 95:* 3-24.
22. Sonderhoff, R., 1936. Über das Gift der Seeanemonen. I. Ein Beitrag zur Kenntnis der Nesselgifte. *Liebig's Ann., 525:* 138-150.
23. Thiel, M. E. 1935. Über die Wirkung des Nesselgiftes der Quallen auf den Menschen. *Ergebnisse u. Fortschr. der Zoologie, 8:* 1-35.
24. Uvnas, B. 1960. Mechanism of action of a histamine-liberating principle in jellyfish (*Cyanea capillata*). *Ann. N.Y. Acad. Sci., 90:* 751-759.
25. Welsh, J. H., 1956. On the nature and action of coelenterate toxins. *Deep Sea Research, 3(suppl.):* 287-297.
26. Welsh, J. H., 1960. 5-Hydroxytryptamine in coelenterates. *Nature, 186:* 811.
27. Welsh, J. H., and P. B. Prock, 1958. Quaternary ammonium bases in the coelenterates. *Biol. Bull., 115:* 551-561.

DISCUSSION

HAND: The extra serotonin that you find in the acontia seems reasonable in view of some very simple observations that one can make on *Metridium* and other acontiate anemones. They commonly eat small worms, copepods, and things of this nature. If you get a small transparent anemone, you can see that after the food is swallowed the prey is still kicking, wriggling and squirming. It gets into the coelenteron and the acontium coils around the animal, presumably the nematocysts of the acontium discharge, and this very quickly subdues it. It quivers a couple of times, and then stops. The acontia, of course, are rich in nematocysts.

ROSS: Do you think that the amounts of serotonin that you find in the acontia, ca. 1 μg./g., is significant? Compared with the amounts that we found in other parts of anemones, they seem so small that we would have dismissed them.

WELSH: Well, I think if I may say so, it was unfortunate that you looked at *Calliactis* first. I think if you had looked at other anemones you would have viewed this situation differently.

ROSS: Not at all.

WELSH: Let me put it this way. If you go out and catch a vicious stinging wasp, you can get out of its venom a perfectly tremendous amount of serotonin. You measure it as 6 to 20 milligrams per gram of venom. Now if you do its nervous system, you get a few tenths of a microgram. I believe that the serotonin in the nervous system is just as important in the life of the wasp as the serotonin in its venom. The most we have in any part of our nervous system is 0.4 micrograms per gram of hypothalmus. And if the tranquilizer reserpine is doing what they say its doing, releasing serotonin, then this brings this down to a 10th of that, and here we're working in the 10ths and hundredths of micrograms per gram range. This is less than the concentration range of serotonin that one finds in acontia.

ROSS: We found 600 times as much in the lining of the coelenteron in *Calliactis,* so this made us think it couldn't possibly be associated with nematocyst poisons.

WELSH: But when you looked at other parts, you found that the tentacles were richer than the body wall?

ROSS: A bit, but on the borderline.

LENHOFF: Couldn't we view the tetramethylammonium compounds not as toxins, but as part of the normal nervous system transmitters of coelenterates since tetramine is present in all of the tissues assayed? I ask this question because when glutathione activates the feeding response in *H. littoralis,* some of the few substances that enhance the response are certain tetramethylammonium compounds. Possibly the transmission of the glutathione stimulus goes through a tetramine-mediated pathway rather than through an acetylchloline-mediated pathway?

WELSH: I think it is entirely possible. We have no evidence on the tetramine one way or the other. However, tetramine does occur in a number of venoms; it occurs in the salivary glands of some marine gastropods in large amounts. And, of course, other choline esters, and other quaternary ammonium compounds occur in certain molluscs. But that tetramine may be taking the place of acetylcholine in the coelenterate nervous system is a good possibility.

HESS: Do these animals have choline esterase or acetylcholine?

WELSH: There is choline esterase.

PASSANO: I suspect that the acetylcholine esterase system is not significant in the functioning of the scyphozoan nervous system, and we know that 5-hydroxytryptamine also fails to have any effect. Could it be that the use of these substances, toxic to other animals as nematocyst toxins, might be valuable to the coelenterates because they would avoid the danger of self-inflicted paralysis? Is this even why their neuropharmacology is different from that of other animals?

WELSH: Venomous animals are generally successful in keeping their venoms away from themselves.

PASSANO: Well I would like to ask then, in other people's experience in studying the feeding responses of nematocyst-bearing animals, are the nematocysts always prevented from penetrating the animal that possesses them? The independent effector is quite different from the effector at the end of a wasp; it is not so neatly controlled. The tentacle of a coelenterate coils around its prey. There is a great chance for nematocysts to be discharged into a tentacle. This would obviously create difficulties if the tentacle was paralyzed by its own poison.

BURNETT: It is common for hydra to pierce its own tissues with nematocysts during feeding.

PHILLIPS: I think the experiments of Dr. Ross, and of Dr. Martin and the ones that I did on *Metridium* suggest that caution should be employed in the interpretation of work using whole tissue extracts. Sometime ago, when I was working on the toxin, I detected a 5-hydroxyindole compound, which at that time I thought corresponded more closely to bufotenin. On purification I noticed that the level of 5-hydroxyindole compounds decreased steadily. In fact, pure suspensions of nematocysts contained no detectable 5-hydroxyindole compounds at all, yet the nematocysts were still capable of discharging and still possessed toxicity.

WELSH: In that connection, I would be interested to know if the 5-hydroxytryptamine washed out of the nematocyst. It's a small, soluble molecule that diffuses readily through some cell surfaces.

PHILLIPS: This is a possibility. But the nematocyst suspensions after purification still should show toxicity.

WELSH: I don't think that the serotonin is really toxic. You can put a large amount of serotonin into a crab and it gets very nervous and jittery. An hour later it is normal.

PHILLIPS: Diffusion from the nematocyst during purification, of course, is always a possibility. At the same time, nematocysts are still susceptible to osmotic discharge, so that gross permeability changes do not seem to have occurred.

LOOMIS: How do you keep your nematocysts from discharging while you separate them?

PHILLIPS: With high concentrations of sucrose.

Present State of Nematocyst Research: Types, Structure and Function

CADET HAND
Department of Zoology, University of California, Berkeley, California

I want to start by quoting an admirable passage from the Introduction of the recent paper by Burnett and colleagues (1). On page 247 they state "One of the most structurally complex and certainly one of the most enigmatic organelles in the animal kingdom is the nematocyst of coelenterates. For nearly a century hosts of scientists, too numerous to mention, have concentrated their attentions on the mode of formation, the migration pathways, the mechanism of discharge, and the chemical nature of these unusual structures. . . ." These same authors go on to make the statement that ". . . none of these subjects of investigation has been resolved to any degree of satisfaction." In many ways this statement is accurate and acceptable, but I think in many ways I would disagree with the generality. A good deal is known about each of the subjects they cite and I for one have found considerable satisfaction in the numerous papers on nematocysts that I have examined. I also want to acknowledge that some of my satisfaction has come from reading the papers of Burnett and his co-workers.

I want to talk today about types, structure and function of nematocysts. I also want to make it clear that I do not work *on* nematocysts, I work *with* them. My interests in them are twofold. First, nematocysts are a truly valuable systematic tool and many coelenterates can be positively identified by their nematocysts alone. Not only this, but nematocysts are useful in relating higher taxa such as genera, families or even orders, and in the broad view even classes. Second, as a student of coelenterates I am interested in the biology of these animals, and the nematocysts are intimately involved in numerous aspects of the lives of coelenterates.

There have been several attempts to classify nematocysts and some of the results of these have come down to us in the form of such useful and descriptive names as penetrants and glutinants. However, it was not until the elaborate system of Weill (10) was published that any real uniformity of nomenclature of nematocysts was arrived at. With the introduction of Weill's terminology some people complained that the system was too clumsy and the names too long to be useful. For example the commonest penetrant of many anthozoans could be called a hoplotelic microbasic mastigophoric rhabdoidic heteronemic stomocnidic nematocyst, or a stenotele could be called a stenotelic rhopaloidic heteronemic stomocnidic nematocyst. In common practice, and as Weill's terminology is being applied, the names microbasic mastigophore (or just mastigophore) and stenotele suffice. Weill's system is only forbidding when one first meets it, but it is a defined system which makes possible far greater accuracy in communication than any other so far devised. To use the full nomenclature, as in the examples I cited, is just as absurd as to start the name of some species with the phylum name, add in the names of the class, order and family and finally tack on the specific binomial.

Weill's system recognizes two categories of cnidae, spirocysts and proper nematocysts. Spirocysts are restricted to the zoantharian anthozoans while all coelenterates have nematocysts. The structure and function of spirocysts are obscure. Weill (10) believes that spirocysts have but a single layered wall and it is extremely rare to see a spirocyst which has everted its thread. Cutress (5) has argued rather convincingly that spirocysts are nematocysts and from his comments one could conclude that they represent a form of holotrichous nematocyst. The test of this conclusion will undoubtedly come when a study of these cnidae is carried out with an electron microscope.

The nematocysts proper have two major subdivisions, *astomocnidae* whose tubes are closed and *stomocnidae* with tubes open at the tip. The astomocnidae are divided in turn into two categories, the familiar *desmonemes* or volvents, and the much less familiar *acrophores* and *anacrophores* of the Siphonophora, which are collectively called *rhopalonemes* and have a sac like tube rather than the coiled or corkscrew tube of the desmonemes.

The stomocnidae show much more variety in form. They can be divided into the *haplonemes,* whose tube has no enlarged basal portion or butt, and the *heteronemes* which have a butt. Among the haplonemes we find the familiar armed *holotrichs* and unarmed *atrichs,* as well as partially armed forms we call *basitrichs.* These haplonemes have a thread or tube of constant diameter and are technically *isorhizic.* A second type of haploneme has an anisodiametric tube which may taper or be slightly swollen near the base. These are the *anisorhizic* nematocysts of various siphonophores and *Tubularia.*

The heteronemes, which you recall have a butt, can be divided into the *rhabdoides* whose butts are isodiametric and the *rhopaloides* whose butts are anisodiametric. The rhabdoides can in turn be subdivided into *mastigophores* with a terminal thread and *amastigophores* which have no terminal thread, while the rhopaloides may be subdivided into *euryteles* whose butts are dilated at their distal ends and *stenoteles* whose butts are dilated at their bases.

Further subdivisions of a number of the nematocyst categories mentioned above were proposed by Weill (10) but it is not necessary to review them further here. Weill's system described a total of eighteen different nematocyst categories, and in fact made it possible by applying the terms *hoplotelic* for armed threads and *anaplotelic* for unarmed threads to distinguish two sub-types within most of the subdivisions of the heteronemes.

Working from Weill's system still other kinds of nematocysts have been described. Carlgren (2) divided mastigophores into *b-mastigophores* and *p-mastigophores,* based on the appearance of the end of the inverted butt. The p-mastigophore was the type Weill (10) had described and the b-mastigophore was a new category which in its unexploded condition looked like a basitrich but when exploded looked like a mastigophore.

Another worker, Cutress (5), using the light microscope described two further categories of nematocysts, *q-mastigophores* and *macrobasic p-mastigophores,* and proposed the elimination of *amastigophores* (microbasic and macrobasic amastigophores of Weill). Cutress also made a number of claims about nematocysts, some of which are wrong and others certainly are questionable. Unfortunately we have not yet progressed far enough in our study to analyze critically all of the structural details of all nematocysts, and until electron microscope studies have been extended to many more types of nematocysts, a number of suggestions Cutress has made cannot be proven or disproven.

One of Cutress' suggestions is that the shaft or butt of mastigophores is folded within itself as well as being inverted before explosion. This would bring the point of the butt to the tip of the capsule, would keep the point in the lead as the basal half of the butt everts, and he claims the thread is attached to this leading tip of the shaft. The tread would evert after the shaft has completely emerged. Miss Jane Westfall of the Department of Zoology at the University of California at Berkeley has been examining a number of nematocyst types with the electron microscope and has been particularly interested in mastigophores. Her studies have not yet progressed to a point where publication seems warranted, but we can comment on Cutress' suggestion. Both cross and longitudinal thin sections have been examined as well as whole exploded nematocysts. The material has been primarily the nematocysts of the acontia of our West Coast *Metridium senile fimbriatum.* Cross sections of microbasic amastigophores, microbasic b-mastigophores and basitrichs (sensu Weill and Carlgren, refs. 2, 10) show clearly that the shaft is not folded on itself and contains only the spines. The spines are blades, as was shown so clearly by Robson (8), and are oriented with their tips toward the open end of the capsule. Longitudinal sections of amastigophores also show that the notch seen in the light microscope at the distal end of the shaft of amastigophores and p-mastigophores is the result of this being the end of the armored region of the shaft. Moreover, there is no thread within the shaft as Cutress has proposed. From these observations we conclude that Cutress is wrong, as were certain earlier workers who proposed folded as well as inverted shafts. It also should be noted that from the work of Picken (7) and Robson (8) that Cutress' claim that the holotrichs of *Corynactis,* which he calls macrobasic p-mastigophores, has an inverted and folded shaft is wrong.

The proposal of Cutress (5) to eliminate the categories microbasic and macrobasic amastigophores also is not acceptable. It is true that there frequently is a short thread on many amastigophores, but this thread is apparently sometimes entirely absent. In our electron microscope studies we have failed to find more than a wisp of a thread at the end of the shaft of these nematocysts in *Metridium* and in thin sections we have not been able to verify, as Cutress suggested, that this thread is attached to the inner capsular wall near the end of the shaft. Studies such as Cutress', which were based on the light microscope alone, cannot resolve problems such as this and we must await definitive electron microscope studies.

The new category of nematocysts, microbasic q-mastigophores, which Cutress described may indeed be a valid type although this too is open to question. I and other workers have noticed dart-like structures which characterize q-mastigophores lying among exploded nematocysts. Weill (10) reports a number of such occurrences and reviews some older accounts. These darts, which Cutress says are unattached discrete structures, occur within the shafts of certain microbasic mastigophores of acontiate anemones. Cutress reports them from the genera *Metridium* and *Aiptasia,* to which I can add *Diadumene.* It was my conclusion that the darts in *Diadumene franciscana* were nothing more than the mass of spines which should have armed the shaft. These spines are tightly curled within the shaft as we have seen in electron micrographs (unpublished) and are commonly sloughed off soon after eversion of the shaft as many workers have noted. Little would be required for this mass of spines to stick together, lose their contact with the shaft and form the dart. Whether this happens accidentally or as a normal process is not known. In *Diadumene franciscana* the darts could usually be found lying near a mastigophore with no spination on the shaft. Cutress, however, figures darts emerging from mastigophores with spined shafts and associated with nematocysts with spined shafts. If these are accurate observations, the recognition of a special nematocyst, the microbasic q-mastigophore, certainly is called for. It is unfortunate that Cutress did not choose some other name than dart for the organized structure contained in his q-mastigophores. This name, dart, had already been used by Picken (7) to describe the tip of the packed spines as they emerge from the everting thread. Both structures would appear to be for penetration, and both may be the same if Cutress' interpretation is wrong. If, however, Cutress is correct two things would seem apparent. First with such a large structure as Cutress' dart seems to be, the spines of his mastigophore cannot be as large as those figured by Robson (8) nor as seen in Miss Westfall's micrographs because there would not be space for both. In Miss Westfall's unpublished electron micrographs the spines completely fill the shaft, and Cutress figures spines which would appear to be normal, at least as we see them in the light microscope (see ref. 5, p. 132, Fig. 7b and c). Second, it will continue to be confusing if two dissimilar parts of nematocysts have the same name and Picken's use of the word dart has priority.

Another difficult point in Cutress' work concerns basitrichs. It is his contention that the category of nematocysts Weill (10) identified and defined as basitrichs are in fact for the most part better assigned to the category microbasic b-mastigophore. Cutress is correct when he notes the difficulty in solving the problem with the light microscope because the basic problem here is to determine whether one is dealing with isodiametric isorhizas or with heteronemes with a butt. The magnitude of the difference between butt and thread may be as little as 0.1 microns Cutress notes, and this is not a readily resolvable difference with a light microscope. Cutress solves the problem by arbitrarily deciding that when one sees a straight inverted shaft, as in Weill's basitrich, this means the *tube* of this portion is differentiated as a shaft, is greater in diameter than the thread and that the tube itself is stiffer than the thread. The fact that this portion of the tube, the straight part carrying the armature, may be stiffened and not coiled only because it is packed with spines seems not to have occurred to Cutress. Cutress suggests we restrict basitrichs to certain nematocysts which so far are known only from anthozoans and have no stiffened or straight part in the inverted tube. These nematocysts, as he shows in his Figure 3, are basitrichs in every sense. In our electron microscope work we have examined uneverted basitrichs. The wall of the spined portion is not thicker than the wall of the thread. We cannot comment on diametric relationships since it would be the everted, not uneverted picture which should be examined and we have not done this. These basitrichs look structurally very much like the much larger microbasic b-mastigophores we have looked at in the same tissue, the acontia of *Metridium.* Cutress may be correct in writing "It may be presumptuous to state that the man who defined almost the entire system of cnidae classification failed to recognize his own categories" (ref. 5, page 126), but it seems "presumptuous" to me for Cutress to have done this on what appears to be spurious logic which assumes a shaft, rather than on factual evidence such as the electron microscope could have produced. At any rate, the evidence is not in yet and whether most basitrichs, as we have known them from the literature, are in fact b-mastigophores remains to be seen. If Cutress is correct the identification of microbasic b-mastigophores will be much easier than it is today.

My last comments on Cutress concern his new category of macrobasic p-mastigophores. By definition this category is said to have the undischarged shaft inverted and folded back on itself. This certainly is not so as I noted earlier, nor do I believe that this category includes the holotrichs of *Corynactis* as Cutress states. In our *Corynactis californica* the holotrichs are good isorhizas, that is the thread is isodiametric. The category Cutress proposes would include the former macrobasic amastigophores, and again I would say that the shortness of the thread, if it exists at all, is good reason for keeping the amastigophore separate from the p-mastigophore. It also seems reasonable that macrobasic p-mastigophores do exist, but they differ strikingly in their appearance from the microbasic p-mastigophore which has the obvious long coiled terminal thread within the capsule.

The comments I have made so far concern both structure and types of nematocysts and I do not intend to review the details of fine structure which are so well known to so many and which we are adding to almost daily as new electron micrographs are examined. The work of Chapman and Tilney (3, 4) stands out as the best work to date on the fine structure of fully formed nematocysts, and the work of Slautterback and Fawcett (9) on the development of nematocysts is clearly the best on this subject to this date. That this elegant work is being done on hydra is little wonder when one considers how easy this beast is to handle in the laboratory, primarily as a result of Loomis' studies. What are needed are studies of many different coelenterates so that all of the types may be fully explored rather than merely the limited cnidom of hydra.

I would like to briefly explore one other aspect of nematocysts, namely their function and functioning. We have not yet arrived at a point where any single explanation can be had as to how a nematocyst discharges nor do we understand the meaning of diversity in nematocysts. Diversity in some microscopic structures such as lepidopteran scales and perhaps some sponge spicules seems not to be adaptive. This is, they all perform the same function and as long as a given size or distribution is maintained, variation in shape and ornamentation apparently can occur without selective forces coming into action.

In nematocysts we do know that some of the diversity is adaptive. There is little doubt as to the role of stenoteles and desmonemes in hydra and the recent work of Burnett, Lentz and Warren (1) has shown that the desmonemes respond before the stenoteles, trap the prey and hold it till the stenoteles discharge and kill it. Also, it appears clear from the work of Ewer (6) that the atrichs discharge against smooth surfaces and presumably are sticky, or are glutinants. Ewer also showed that foodstuffs or extracts from food inhibited the atrichs while enhancing the discharge of stenoteles. Anyone who has worked with nematocysts has soon discovered that not all types respond to all stimuli, and some types like atrichs and spirocysts are very difficult to discharge under most conditions. However, with all the work that has gone on we still can identify only three functions for nematocysts as far as the biology of the animal is concerned, namely adhering, entangling and penetrating, although Ewer (6) has suggested that the holotrichs of hydra may be purely defensive. The penetrating types are all assumed to deliver toxins and poison to the prey or foe but this has not been proven. We have no described or specific function for most nematocyst types and in fact our knowledge is limited in that what is known about function comes entirely from hydra. The work on the nematocysts of other types of coelenterates has concerned itself with biochemical problems, with studies of discharge mechanisms, the toxins and the makeup of the capsule rather than the function of the many varied types. Thus we are left with about twenty types of nematocyst of which we known the function of three. It would appear that all the heteronemic stomocnidae are penetrants, but the functions of most haplonemic stomocnidae are not known though we may assume they are adhesive. Among the astomocnidae we find the entangling desmonemes, but what of the rhopalonemes? As well as being in doubt of the function of most nematocysts we are again faced with diversity for which it is not easy to see adaptive values. Cleverly contrived experiments may be able to answer many of these questions, but the possibility exists that nematocysts may be another example of variation without functional significance. At the moment it is difficult for me to imagine what functional differences one could ascribe to a series of mastigophores with no threads, short threads or long threads. Such variations exist, however, and in discrete places and patterns, that is one species may have one type in one tissue, another in some other tissue, while a second species will show only one type in one place. Certainly types deserves attention.

The problem of how nematocysts discharge is a complicated one and one to which many authors have addressed themselves. The cnidocil, which is so characteristic of at least some nematocysts of hydra, is not known to be associated with most nematocyst types, and in fact has been reported only in hydrozoans. When and if a final relationship between cnidocil and discharge in stenoteles and desmonemes is worked out we still will have to resolve the problem of how other nematocysts are related to what is found here. We have seen no signs of cnidocils in *Metridium* acontia.

What the operculum is, or even if it exists in most nematocysts is a difficult problem. There seems to be little doubt that some sort of a plug or structure exists at the point on a capsule where the thread or tube starts everting. In stenoteles the operculum is a real structure as demonstrated by the electron microscope studies of Chapman and Tilney (4). In Miss Westfall's studies of nematocysts no operculum has yet been seen, although the material has not made optimum observation on this point possible to date.

The mechanism of discharge has been analyzed by many people and I do not feel a detailed summary is called for here. The recent summary of Chapman and Tilney (3) cites the conclusions of the various authors and I would single out the reports of Picken (7) and Robson (8) as those which are most significant. New information will be added as we gather more information on fine structure and as further chemical and biochemical studies are carried out. One could suggest from observations on available electron micrographs such as those of Yanagita and Wada (11), Chapman and Tilney (4) and unpublished ones of Miss Westfall's that the shaft of some heteronemes is folded accordion style. If to this we add the fact that the capsule contracts on explosion, we could imagine that the shaft of these nematocysts unfolds as it everts. This may account for the full eversion of heavily armed shafts and only later would uptake of water play a role in eversion. This suggestion can be at least partly tested by critical analysis of the length of the sculptured or folded outline of uneverted shafts as compared with the full length of everted ones.

It is a rare field of biology where one can say the last word has been said and one wonders if such a field exists, but the study of nematocysts seems clearly to be in its infancy and there is little chance of running out of problems (or words). I do feel, however, that with the renewed interest in these intriguing and complicated structures which has appeared in recent years there is high hope that many of our problems will be solved. I look forward with excitement to the time in the future when we have enough knowledge to talk about the types, structure and function of nematocysts rather than what is not known.

REFERENCES

1. Burnett, A. L., T. Lentz and M. Warren, 1960. The nematocysts of hydra (Part I). The question of control of nematocyst discharge reaction by fully fed hydra. *Ann. Soc. Royal Zool. Belgique 90:* 247-267.
2. Carlgren, O. 1940. A contribution to the knowledge of structure and distribution of cnidae in the Anthozoa. *Kungl. Fysiog. Sällskapets Handl. N. F. 51:* 1-62.
3. Chapman, G. B. and L. G. Tilney, 1959. Cytological studies of the nematocysts of Hydra. I. Desmonemes, isorhizas, cnidocils, and supporting structures. *J. Biophysic. and Biochem. Cytol. 5:* 69-78.
4. Chapman, G. B. and L. G. Tilney, 1959. Cytological studies of the nematocysts of Hydra. II. The Stenoteles. *J. Biophysic. and Biochem. Cytol. 5:* 79-84.
5. Cutress, C. 1955. An interpretation of the structure and distribution of cnidae in the Anthozoa. *Systematic Zoology 4:* 120-137.

6. Ewer, R. F. 1947. On the functions and mode of action of the nematocysts of *Hydra. Proc. Zool. Soc. London 117:* 365-376.
7. Picken, L. E. R. 1953. A note on the nematocysts of *Corynactis viridis. Quart. Jour. Micros. Sci. 94:* 203-227.
8. Robson, E. A. 1953. Nematocysts of *Corynactis*: The Activity of the filament during discharge. *Quart. Jour. Micros. Sci. 94:* 229-235.
9. Slautterback, D. L. and D. W. Fawcett, 1959. The development of the cnidoblasts of Hydra. An electron microscope study of cell differentiation. *J. Biophysic. and Biochem. Cytol. 5:* 441-452.
10. Weill, R. 1934. Contributions a l'étude des Cnidaires et de leur Nématocystes. *Trav. Stat. Zool. d. Wimereux Tome 10, 11.* Paris.
11. Yanagita, T. M. and T. Wada, 1959. Physiological mechanism of nematocyst responses in sea-anenome VI. A note on the microscopical structure of acontium, with special reference to the situation of cnidae within its surface. *Cytologia 24:* 81-97.

DISCUSSION

GOREAU: To those of us who swim in reefs and sometimes come into painful contact with *Millepora complanata* and similar stinging species, it would be of interest to know what nematocysts produce the burning sensation and the erythema.

HAND: Four categories have been described: atrichs, basitrichs, macrobasic mastigophores and stenoteles. One could guess that the stenoteles and macrobasic mastigophores give you the kick.

MUSCATINE: Has anyone observed the extrusion of substances from the end of nematocyst threads?

HAND: Yes, I think there is a lot of information about material being extruded, and one of the places this is most readily visible is in the big holotrichs that corallimorpharian anemones and some corals have. First, there is an uptake of methylene blue. Then there is eversion of the thread as Picken and Robson have explained so beautifully. And then real droplets of the material leave the terminal end of the thread. One can see this happening in a fresh preparation. Whether or not this is the toxin, and what relation this has to the total picture, is not at all clear. But certainly there is something leaving the capsule. And the total volume of the everted system is in general greater than the uneverted system. In order to create this, something has had to move into the system or expand within it.

ROSS:[1] I would like to report some work which is partly on the point of Dr. Hand's talk.

By chance, a few months ago, I stumbled on a phenomenon that I think has some bearing on the specialized function that certain nematocysts can perform. The sea anemone, *Calliactis parasitica,* which I mentioned earlier today, lives on shells of hermit-crabs in British and Mediterranean waters. About 2 years ago I found that the anemone gets on the shell by a rather interesting behavior pattern (Fig. 1). It will transfer from another surface to the shell by a maneuver which begins with the adhesion of the tentacles to the shell; subsequently the animal detaches the pedal disc which then

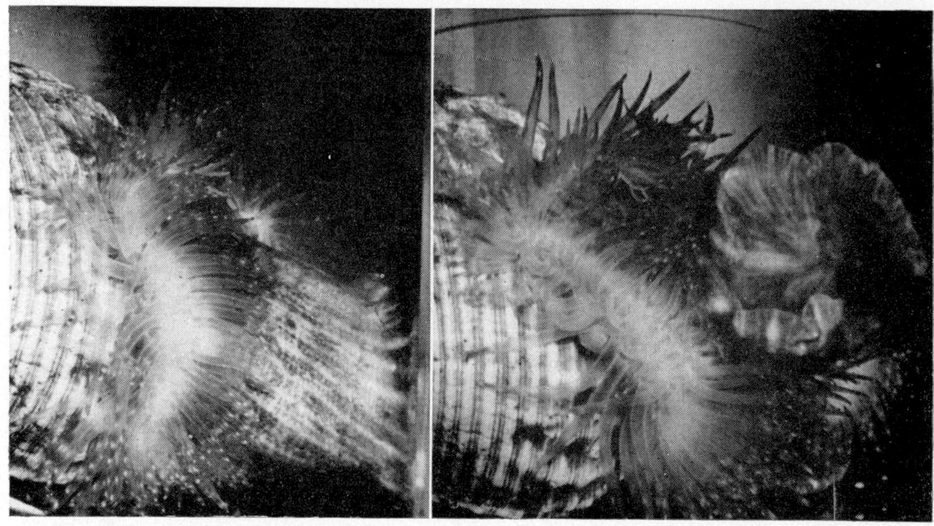

Fig. 1. ***Calliactis parasitica*** **adhering to shell by tentacles and (a) detaching pedal disc from plastic plate and (b) swinging detached pedal disc over towards shell for eventual settling. 4 min. between (a) and (b).**
(From Ross, D.M. 1960. ***Proc. Zool. Soc. London, 134:*** **43-57. Reprinted by the courtesy of the Society)**

swings over and settles on the shell (Ross, D.M. (1960). *Proc. zool. Soc. Lond. 134:* 43-57). But the important point to which I wish to draw attention is this initial response of the tentacles when

[1]Dr. Donald Ross, Department of Zoology, University of Alberta, Edmonton, Alberta, Canada.

they adhere to the shell. A few months ago, working at Banyuls on the French Mediterranean Coast, D. Davenport, L. Sutton and I looked at this phenomenon and satisfied ourselves that this initial sticking of the tentacles was due to the discharge of nematocysts (Davenport, D., D. M. Ross, and L. Sutton. 1961. *Vie et Milieu,* in the press). I don't know what kind of nematocyst was involved so I can't add anything about particular nematocyst types and their functions, but certainly it was a nematocyst response to the shell. Now that raises a puzzling point, because these tentacles of *Calliactis* stick very readily to shells when the anemone itself is not on a shell; but if you pass a shell over the tentacles of a *Calliactis* that is already on a shell, its tentacles do not stick. In other words, these nematocysts seem, at any rate from this first observation, to be affected by whether the anemone's foot is on the shell or not.

We did some experiments to extend this observation. We had 20 *Calliactis*; 10 of them were settled on shells and 10 were lying unattached on the floor of a tank. By taking a test shell and touching it to single tentacles around the disc, one can get a score of the number of tentacles that stick. When the anemones are on the shell, one gets a score of the order of 5 or less "tentacle-sticks" in 100 shell-tentacle contacts. With the animals lying prone in the tank, one gets a score of the order of 50 or more "tentacle-sticks" using the same shell. In our experiments we transferred these same animals, allowing those that had been unattached to settle on shells and stripping off those that were attached so that the experiment could be done in reverse. And then we got a good reversal of the scores; the animals which were now on shells, which when unattached had given scores of the order of 50, had now dropped to 5 or less, and the other group, which when attached had given scores of 5 or less, had now climbed up to about 50 "tentacle-sticks" per 100. To my mind this phenomenon raises a crucial point as to whether nematocysts are independent effectors or not. I say this because the only change made in the experiment is that in one case the anemone has its pedal disc attached to the shell, and in the other case the pedal disc is free and unattached. So this observation forces one to conclude that the threshold for this kind of nematocyst discharge could be affected by some form of remote control which in this case seemed to originate in the pedal disc.

HAND: I'd like first just to applaud this work and say this is exactly what I was asking for, except that you must find out what these nematocysts are!

CROWELL: About how long did you wait before you retested?

ROSS: A few hours. The anenomes, when you strip them off, take at least an hour to open up and relax. The other anemones will also take about an hour to settle securely on the shells. One has to wait until all are open and all are settled. So several hours always elapsed between the two sets of observations in our reversal experiments. But we did several such experiments, and each time obtained clear evidence of big differences in the threshold of nematocyst discharge as measured by "stickiness" of tentacles to shell.

GOREAU: There is a matter which may be important in connection with what Ross just said. Not too long ago we observed at a depth of about 70 feet a large anemone, probably *Bartholomea annulata,* which has living amongst its tentacles a small red fish and several shrimp of the genus *Periclimenses.* This shrimp moves freely amongst the tentacles, climbs around on them or hovers just in front of them, waiting for small fish to come along. As soon as a fish is in position, the shrimp climbs aboard and proceeds to remove ectoparasites from the head and mouth. Once finished with the job, the shrimp returns to its host anemone. Neither the shrimp nor the commensal fish living among these tentacles excite any sort of feeding reflex on the part of the anenome. The questions I'd like to ask are these: "What protects these commensals against the nematocysts of the host anemone? Do the nematocysts fail to discharge into the animals at all, or are they immune to the action of the nematocysts?" The observations made by Ross seem to indicate that there is complete failure to discharge any menatocysts. In other words, commensal animals living among the tentacles of anemones can probably do so because they somehow inhibit nematocysts discharge and do not trigger off any sort of feeding reflex. That's the thing I don't understand, because I know that such anemones react instantly to any bits of meat dropped on the tentacles. This immediately sets off a feeding reaction resulting in flexion of the tentacles and opening of the stomodeum.

ROSS: From my experience, I think this is a failure of the nematocysts to discharge. Anemones are usually very active when they are responding to chemical stimuli and discharging their nematocysts. If nematocysts were being discharged, in this case, one would expect signs of this in the anemone's behavior.

HAND: Davenport and Norris (*Biol. Bull. 115,* 1958) working with the anenome *Stoichactis* and the fish *Amphiprion,* which I believe were Philippine in origin, concluded that the nematocysts were not discharging. When a single scale was rcmoved, however, then the fish gets it fast. As soon as the mucous layer is broken the nematocysts respond and the animal is in trouble.

MARTIN: In the experiment which Dr. Ross described, I wonder if you are sure if the reaction of stickiness is a virtue of the nematocysts or of the epithelium of the tentacles?

ROSS: We managed to induce a nematocyst discharge by offering small pieces of shell to tentacles, and observing under the binoculars that a large number of nematocyst threads were attached to the piece of shell. We also found that nematocysts were discharged into "Cutex" impregnated with tiny shell fragments, but not into "Cutex" alone used as a control. We were satisfied that it was a nematocyst discharge when we witnessed the following pheneomenon: You can present a shell to a *Calliactis* by bringing it up very carefully to a single tentacle. If it sticks, that tentacle adheres so strongly at the tip that you can lift up the whole animal by lifting the shell. It is impressive to see one of these large anemones hanging from the shell and attached only by the tip of a single tentacle. I cannot conceive of anything other than a powerful local nematocyst discharge that could produce this particular effect.

MUSCATINE: Have you ruled out a mucous adhesive?

ROSS: We satisfied ourselves by direct observation that they were not adhering by mucous strands, but that the tentacle was sticking directly to the shell at definite points of contact and not over the whole surface.

BURNETT: Perhaps your animals which did not adhere to the shell were still discharging nematocysts? We have found that satiated hydra still discharge nematocysts when an *Artemia* strikes the tentacle, but the nematocyst is quickly released from the tissues of the hydra and the *Artemia* falls to the bottom of the culture dish. If satiated with food, the hydra makes no effort to hold its prey. Perhaps in your experiments, the nematocysts discharged but were not retained by the cnidoblasts.

ROSS: I only refer to the original observation which was that when an animal is on a shell you can brush another shell across it and there is not the faintest sign of a response. The tentacles are just brushed aside; they don't stick to it in any way. Yet you have this phenomenal behavior which is elicited when the animal is off a shell; it practically pounces on the test shell. Starting from that observation, we went on and did this other experiment. I wouldn't say that this is the complete answer, but I think it raises the whole question of nematocyst control very sharply, even though more investigation is required to clear it up. You certainly have a very different type of behavior depending whether the animal's foot is on a shell or not. It seems to us that this behavior, when it occurs, begins with nematocyst discharge.

LOOMIS: Do you think it might be a matter of the shell transmitting calcium to the tentacle and making it sticky?

ROSS: I've tried a good many models of shells and also shells boiled in alkali to remove organic material. The anemone does not respond to these; cleaning the shells destroys the activity. If you present *Calliactis* with a perfect plaster of Paris model of the shell, it shows no interest. The rest of the story (I haven't time for the evidence here) is that some substance in the mollusc shell, and not derived from the crab but from the mollusc, triggers the nematocyst discharge and the subsequent behavior pattern. It is not responding to the calcium of the shell, or to any other inorganic constituent, or the characteristically sculptured surface of the shell. In fact, the anemone gets on the shell occupied by the hermit-crab by responding to the ghost of the long-dead mollusc that used to live there. It has nothing to do with the crab as such.

SLAUTTERBACK: Does anyone care to go into metaphysics further? If not, I declare this meeting adjourned.

Activation of the Feeding Reflex in *Hydra littoralis*

HOWARD M. LENHOFF

Laboratories of Biochemistry, Howard Hughes Medical Institute, and Zoology Department, University of Miami, Miami, Florida

Throughout this talk, I will often speak of experimenting on *Hydra* as if these animals were systems of purified enzymes. I speak in these terms more confidently today than I could have a few years ago when I first tried to adapt my former training in enzymology to experimentation with live *Hydra.* In enzymology I was able to treat a relatively simple experimental system in a limited number of ways, and the results were usually clear and unambiguous. I soon found, however, that *Hydra* could be treated in virtually an unlimited number of ways and that the measurable responses of the animal were more difficult to interpret correctly.

During a rewarding apprenticeship with Dr. Loomis, I was introduced to his method for rearing *Hydra* in the laboratory in solutions of known composition (16), a development that has enabled investigators to experiment with hydra using the same rigorous controlled conditions which are applicable to simpler systems. These first discoveries of Loomis opened the door wide to contemporary hydra research.

His selection of *Hydra* for use in quantitative studies of cellular problems was a happy one because of at least three intrinsic properties of the animal. First, genotypic constancy is practically guaranteed by using animals descended from a single individual by budding. Second, their small size and lack of skeleton lend them to many of the quantitative techniques (7, 14) applicable to simpler systems. But perhaps the feature of hydra which makes them so remarkably adaptable to quantitative study is their lack of a definite self-regulated internal extra-cellular fluid. In place of this fluid is their culture solution, a solution regulated by the investigator. Once the environment is controlled, individual variation between hydra is minimized and thus the results are rendered less ambiguous.

Working on the assumption that the intact *Hydra* can be treated with the same controlled conditions that we normally employ with an enzyme in solution, we find that in order to get reliable results with the glutathione-*Hydra* system, we must control precisely and within restricted limits the following factors, some of which I will report on today: pH, nature of the buffer, ionic strength, the nature of both the cations and anions, temperature, presence of trace metals, amount of aeration, concentration of glutathione or related compounds, presence or absence of proteases or glutamic acid, and length of time since previous exposure to glutathione or since last feeding. Undoubtedly, there are other factors that are as yet unknown.

Of course, when studying developmental phenomena, more complex problems are met with. At present such phenomena as regeneration, budding, and cell migration have none of the convenient environmental chemical "handles" (comparable to glutathione and pCO_2) which have so often provided the means of attacking a problem. Yet certainly many of the environmental factors affecting the feeding reflex also influence developmental phenomena. For example, *Hydra* grown in a culture solution low in sodium have smooth short tentacles and few nematocysts. At even lower sodium concentrations the ectoderm thickens, developmental abnormalities occur, and often cellular areas begin to disintegrate. These abnormalities never occur in a medium of the proper sodium content (11).

Research with a whole animal challenges the quantitative biologist. When he treats hydra with the same precision that he treats an *in vitro* system, he will find that much of the mystery surrounding the animal disappears and that the excitement of a new understanding beckons.

Now let us consider the activation of the feeding reflex in *Hydra littoralis* by the tripeptide reduced glutathione. We owe the discovery of this phenomenon to two independent studies: one, by Helen Park, who, while studying the effects of radiation on *Hydra,* observed that the anti-radiation compound reduced glutathione caused the *Hydra's* mouth to open (20); the other by Loomis, who, in a systematic search, identified reduced glutathione as the substance present in crustacean extracts that activated the feeding reflex in *Hydra* (17).

The significant aspects of this discovery are many. From an evolutionary viewpoint, data on the distribution of the glutathione-activated response has been used to deduce the sequence in geological time that the feeding mechanisms of some coelenterates evolved (6, 15, 17). On the whole animal level, the feeding response is an example of an elaborate behavioral pattern controlled by a single environmental compound. At the cellular level, the glutathione-activated feeding reflex is a clear example of chemoreception specific for only one molecule.

This morning I would like to dwell on a fundamental subcellular aspect: the mechanism by which glutathione combines with and activates the glutathione-receptor.

DESCRIPTION OF THE NORMAL FEEDING REFLEX

All measurements are based on *Hydra's* characteristic feeding movements, described earlier by Ewer (4) and Loomis (17). The drawings in Figure 1 illustrate each of these steps. A *Hydra* in the absence of the glutathione has its mouth closed, and its tentacles outstretched and relatively motionless. After the addition of glutathione, the tentacles begin to writhe and sweep inwards toward the longitudinal axis of the animal (Fig. 1A). Next, the tentacles bend toward the mouth, and the mouth opens (Fig. 1B). Shown in this composite drawing (Fig. 1B) are the various positions that a tentacle takes before contracting. These movements, culminating in mouth opening, usually all take place within half a minute. Figure 1C shows how a *Hydra* looks during the greater portion of the feeding reflex, its mouth open wide and the tentacles in various phases of contraction. Frequently, the tips of the tentacles are observed within the *Hydra's* mouth, as shown in Figures 1B and 1C.

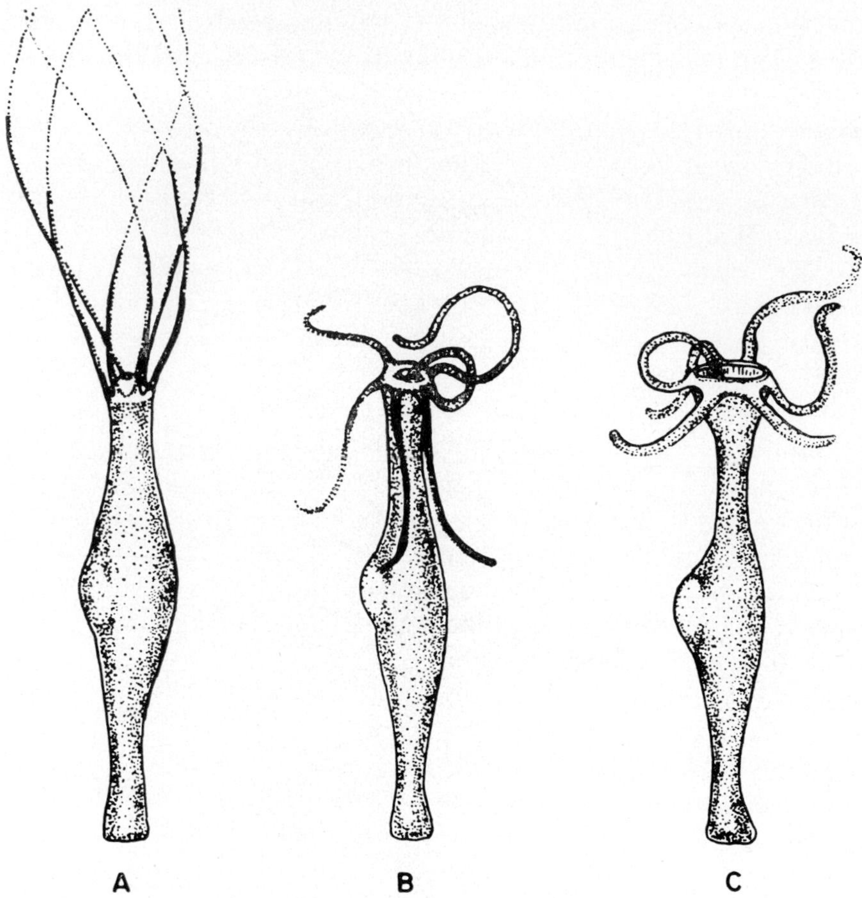

Fig. 1. Stages of the feeding reflex (see text) (From Ref. 8).

A QUANTITATIVE ASSAY

Requisite for quantitative studies of any biological phenomenon are accurate and reliable measurements. Therefore, special emphasis is placed on the assay procedure which has as its basis the visual measurement of the mechanical process of mouth opening.

Meaningful measurements of the feeding reflex require *Hydra* that respond to glutathione in a quantitatively reproducible manner. Large numbers of such experimental animals were obtained by starving for one or two days mass cultures of *Hydra littoralis* (18) that had been reproducing asexually in a solution consisting of 10^{-3} M $CaCl_2$ and 10^{-4} M $NaHCO_3$ in deionized water. Special care was taken to remove most of the organic waste products from the cultures twice daily (18). The animals in each tray were not allowed to reach a density of over two or three thousand hydranths per 1500 ml. of culture solution.

The assay procedure used in most of these experiments was as follows: Five starved *Hydra* obtained from the mass cultures were rinsed three times in 30 ml. portions of a solution lacking glutathione and consisting of 10^{-3} M $CaCl_2$, 10^{-4} M NaCl, and 10^{-3} M histidine chloride buffer, pH 6.2. The five *Hydra* were then transferred in one drop of the solution into 2 ml. of the same solution containing glutathione (Sigma, St. Louis, Mo.). (Reduced glutathione is not readily oxidizable at pH 6.2.) This glutathione solution was in the spherical concavity (36 mm. diam. x 5 mm. deep) of a Maximov tissue culture slide. The *Hydra* were immediately observed through a binocular dissecting microscope set at a magnification of 19.5. The time intervals between the moment the *Hydra* were placed in the glutathione solution and the initial and final (t_i and t_f) times that the mouth of each animal was open were recorded. The magnitude of the feeding reflex is expressed as the average time (t_f-t_i) during which the mouths of the *Hydra* remained open in response to glutathione.

In Table 1 are shown the results of four different experiments (a-d) which were carried out in excess glutathione. In these experiments each *Hydra* opened its mouth within 0.4 to 1.0 minutes (t_i) after being placed in the glutathione solution. Under optimal conditions, the variations observed in the opening time t_i were small when compared to t_f, and did not significantly alter the overall time during which the mouth was open (t_f-t_i).

The closing time (t_f) for the individual *Hydra* in each experiment (Table 1, expts. a through d) was about 35 minutes. Because the standard deviations were small in comparison to the total length of the response, they were not routinely calculated.

At sub-optimal concentrations of glutathione (Table 1, expt. e), or in the presence of a compound known to compete with glutathione for the glutathione-receptor (13) (Table 1, expt. f), some *Hydra* took as long as 6 minutes to open their mouths, while others did not carry out the feeding reflex at all. In these cases, the standard deviation is large relative to t_f-t_i. Data of this type are similarly expressed as the average time (t_f-t_i) during which the mouths of the five *Hydra* tested remained open regardless of the number that responded positively.

TABLE 1

Method of expressing the duration of the feeding reflex

Expt.	Glutathione concentration	t_i(min.)	t_f(min.)	t_f-t_i(min.) Mean ± S.D.
(a)	10^{-5} *M*	0.43, 0.46, 0.60, 0.78, 1.33	33.00, 35.36, 38.08, 39.71, 41.00	36.71 ± 2.95
(b)	10^{-5} *M*	0.50, 0.53, 0.71, 0.88, 0.91	32.80, 33.16, 36.25, 36.43, 38.11	34.64 ± 2.10
(c)	7.5 × 10^{-6} *M*	0.43, 0.46, 0.58, 0.68, 0.96	28.21, 36.50, 36.50, 38.30, 43.45	35.97 ± 5.30
(d)	5 × 10^{-6} *M*	0.48, 0.50, 0.61, 0.78, 1.05	26.88, 35.25, 37.41, 42.00, 43.41	36.31 ± 6.36
(e)	5 × 10^{-7} *M*	0.68, 2.33, 2.63, 4.75, ∞	5.08, 16.25, 22.50, 25.60,–.	11.81 ± 9.29
(f)	2 × 10^{-6} *M* (+10^{-4} *M* glutamine)	2.45, 3.75, 6.00, ∞, ∞	6.41, 13.45, 22.91, –, –.	6.11 ± 7.23

Hydra starved for two days were used in all experiments.
Data from reference 8.

The values for t_f-t_i at excess glutathione concentrations are usually within the range of 25 or 35 minutes, depending upon whether the *Hydra* were starved one or two days preceding the experiment. This fact should be borne in mind when comparing data from different sets of experiments. (It now also is known that small changes in temperature influence t_f-t_i significantly as shown in Table 7.)

These data, in addition to providing a basis for the assay, give insight into central problems concerning the mechanism by which glutathione elicits the feeding reflex. The values given for t_i must include the time required for at least two major processes to occur: (a) the union of glutathione with its receptor, which in experiments a-d is probably rapid (i.e., within a few seconds), and (b) all of the subsequent events leading to mouth opening. The values for t_i (0.4 to 1.0 minutes) may represent, for the most part, the latter events.

Large values of t_i (those greater than 2.0 minutes) indicate that the experimental conditions for the feeding reflex are not optimal. For example, it takes longer for the mouth to open at low glutathione concentrations (Table 1, expt. e) or in the presence of a competitive inhibitor (Table 1, expt. f) than at excess glutathione concentrations under optimum conditions. Similarly, cellular poisons, such as N-ethyl maleimide or heavy metals, also cause an increase in t_i (9). Further, *Hydra* in distilled water take longer to respond than do *Hydra* in distilled water containing added calcium (10). In the cases mentioned here, it would appear that the large values of t_i result from the interference with the activation of a sufficient number of functional receptor sites needed to elicit an optimally rapid response. Another cause of a delay in mouth opening might stem from interference with some of the cellular events initiated by the combination of glutathione with its receptor.

At sub-optimal concentrations of glutathione (Table 1, expt. e, and Fig. 3 at concentrations less than 5×10^{-6} *M* glutathione) the t_f-t_i values were small in comparison to those obtained at higher glutathione concentrations. These results show that graded responses can occur when conditions are not optimum. In addition, it is generally observed that the larger the value of t_i, the smaller the value of t_f-t_i.

EFFECT OF GLUTAMIC ACID AND GLUTATHIONE ANALOGS

Using glutathione analogs, we have undertaken a study of the size and configuration of the glutathione molecule necessary for activation of the response. The results, summarized in Table 2, show that the glutathione-receptor has a most unusual specificity compared to proteins which react with glutathione (13). The receptor (a) is not dependent upon the sulfhydryl moiety of glutathione for activation, (b) has a high order of specificity for the structure of the tripeptide "backbone" of glutathione, and (c) is inhibited by glutamic acid.

TABLE 2

Activators and inhibitors of the feeding reflex

A	B	C
	R | CH_2 |	
$^{-}O_2C\text{-}CH\text{-}CH_2\text{-}CH_2\text{-}CO\text{-}$ | $^{+}NH_3$	$NH\text{-}CH\text{-}CO\text{-}$	$NH\text{-}CH_2\text{-}CO^{-}_2$
A γ-glutamyl -	B alanyl	C - glycine

Activators	Inhibitors (tripeptide)	Inhibitors (others)
$R = -H$	$R = -SO_2H$	glutamic acid
$R = -CH_3$	$R = -SO_3H$	glutamine
$R = -SH$	$R = -S-COCH_3$	cysteinylglycine
$R = -S-CH_3$	$R = -S(N-\text{ethylsuccinimido})$	
	$R = -S-SG$	
	$R = SH$ and $A = {}^{-}O_2C-CH-CH_2CO-$ | $^{+}NH_3$	

In confirmation of Cliffe and Waley (3), we were able to extend their striking results demonstrating that the sulfhydryl group is not necessary for the action of glutathione on *Hydra* and that this group can be altered within certain limits. These workers obtained a positive response in *Hydra* exposed to the lens tripeptide ophthalmic acid (γ-glutamyl-α-amino-*n*-butyryl-glycine). This tripeptide, as well as nor-ophthalmic acid, activates the feeding reflex in *Hydra*. Both peptides are identical to glutathione except that they have respectively a methyl or a hydrogen atom instead of the sulfhydryl. We further show that the S-methyl analog of glutathione also activates the feeding response (13).

On the other hand, substitution of large groups for the sulfhydryl moiety leads to analogs which do not have the right configuration to activate a response. Rather, such analogs (γ-L-glutamyl-L-sulphi-alanylglycine, γ-L-glutamyl-L-sulpho-alanylglycine, S-acetyl glutathione, S-succinimido glutathione, and oxidized glutathione) when at high concentrations inhibit the action of glutathione (3, 13). These inhibitions are overcome by increasing the glutathione concentration. Thus, those analogs which retain the tripeptide backbone of glutathione act as competitive inhibitors in the activation of the feeding reflex.

Another tripeptide which acts as a competitive inhibitor is asparthione (β-aspartylcysteinylglycine) (13). This compound is nearly identical to reduced glutathione except that it lacks one methylene group, having aspartic acid substituted for glutamic acid. Loomis first showed that asparthione fails to activate the feeding reflex (17). These characteristics of asparthione point out the importance of the γ-glutamyl moiety of the tripeptide for the activation process, as well as providing additional proof that the presence of a sulfhydryl group on a tripeptide similar to glutathione is not sufficient for activity. Contrastingly, glyoxylase, another glutathione-requiring system, functions with asparthione (1).

Further evidence that the γ-glutamyl moiety is of special importance in the active structure of glutathione is the action of both glutamic acid and glutamine as competitive inhibitors of glutathione, while neither cysteine nor glycine have this effect (13). The importance of the α-amino group of the glutamyl moiety is emphasized by the failure of α-keto glutaric acid and of glutaric acid to inhibit. Also, as might be anticipated, neither aspartic acid nor asparagine were inhibitory (13).

These data indicate that the receptor has a high affinity for the γ-glutamyl group, that the sulfhydryl group is important only in that it conforms to certain size limitations, and that the glycine is needed to complete the fit of the tripeptide into the receptor (Loomis has shown that γ-glutamylcysteine does not activate a response. Ref. 17). As more analogs become available, we hope to determine the exact structural requirements for the stimulatory activity of glutathione. In addition, it should be possible by comparing the K_i's of the different inhibitors to determine the relative affinities of the receptor for the different parts of the glutathione molecule.

No other system known to require glutathione has such exacting requirements for the peptide backbone of glutathione. Regardless of this remarkable specificity and of the ample glutathione in the fluids emitted from *Hydra's* captured prey in nature, the possibility remained that some unknown trace factors present in these fluids are the natural activators of the feeding reflex.

To examine this possibility, the following series of experiments were carried out (Table 3): a diluted aqueous extract (30μg.) from homogenized *Artemia* elicited a 37 minute feeding response in *Hydra* (expt. 1). A similar extract containing 10^{-4} *M* added glutamic acid gave only a 7 minute response (expt. 2). The glutamic acid was presumably competitively inhibiting the glutathione in the *Artemia* extract because, if in addition to 10^{-4} *M* glutamic acid, 10^{-5} *M* glutathione, was also included, then the inhibition was reversed (expt. 3). The inhibition was also reversed by increasing the amount of shrimp extract (expt. 4). Further evidence that the glutamic acid was acting competitively and was not irreversibly

TABLE 3

The inhibition by glutamic acid of the feeding reflex induced by *Artemia* extracts, and the reversal of that inhibition by glutathione

Expt.	Test Solution	t_f-t_i (min.)
1.	30 μg. *Artemia* extract.	37.3
2.	30 μg. *Artemia* extract and 10^{-4} *M* glutamic acid.	7.4
3.	30 μg. *Artemia* extract, 10^{-4} *M* glutamic acid, and 10^{-5} *M* reduced glutathione.	40.6
4.	140 μg. *Artemia* extract and 10^{-4} *M* glutamic acid.	26.5
5.	*Hydra* from expt. 2 in 10^{-5} *M* reduced glutathione.	29.1
6.	10^{-5} *M* reduced glutathione	42.1

Hydra starved for two days were used in all experiments.

poisoning the *Hydra* was shown in experiment 5 where the inhibited animals from experiment 2 were washed and then immediately placed in a fresh glutathione solution; these inhibited *Hydra* responded again for an additional 29 minutes. These experiments leave little doubt that reduced glutathione emitted from the prey is the major natural substance activating the feeding reflex in *Hydra littoralis.*

EFFECT OF ENVIRONMENTAL CATIONS AND ANIONS

As emphasized earlier, the *Hydra's* external aqueous environment takes on a special importance when studying the feeding reflex. This fluid serves a dual role: it conveys glutathione from the prey to *Hydra,* and it bathes both the receptor and the ectodermal effector cells which are involved in part of the contractile processes of the feeding reflex. Therefore, before directly investigating the mechanism by which glutathione activates the response, it is necessary to consider the influence on the feeding reflex of the ions in the media bathing the animals. Knowledge of the effects of these ions might be useful in gaining insight into the mechanisms involved

TABLE 4

Ionic requirements for the activation of the feeding reflex

Cations			Anions		
Expt.	Text Solution	t_f-t_i (min.)	Expt.	Test Solution 10^{-3} *M*	t_f-t_i (min.)
1.	10^{-5} *M* EDTA	0	1.a.	$CaCl_2$	28.5
2.	10^{-5} *M* EDTA and 10^{-3} *M* $CaCl_2$	28.5	2.a.	$CaBr_2$	23.0
			3.a.	CaI_2	9.2
3.	10^{-5} *M* EDTA and 10^{-3} *M* $SrCl_2$	6.8	4.a.	$Ca(NO_3)_2$	8.3

Hydra starved for one day used in all experiments.
All ions were dissolved in a solution of 10^{-4} *M* $NaHCO_3$.
Data from reference 10.

in the feeding reflex in addition to defining the experimental limits within which the ionic composition can be varied.

Summarized in Table 4 are data concerning the ionic requirements for the feeding reflex (10). *Hydra* placed in a 10^{-4} *M* solution of the chelating agent ethylenediamine tetraacetic acid (EDTA) lost their ability to respond to glutathione (expt. 1). Since EDTA is known to chelate calcium ion, one of the two environmental cations required for the growth of *Hydra,* 10^{-3} *M* $CaCl_2$ was added to this same solution, and the *Hydra* responded normally (expt. 2). No other cation would replace calcium to any degree in reversing the inhibitory action of EDTA except strontium (expt. 3). Since this metal behaves chemically like calcium, experiment 3 strengthens the evidence that calcium is required to effect the feeding reflex.

Further evidence for the calcium requirement was obtained

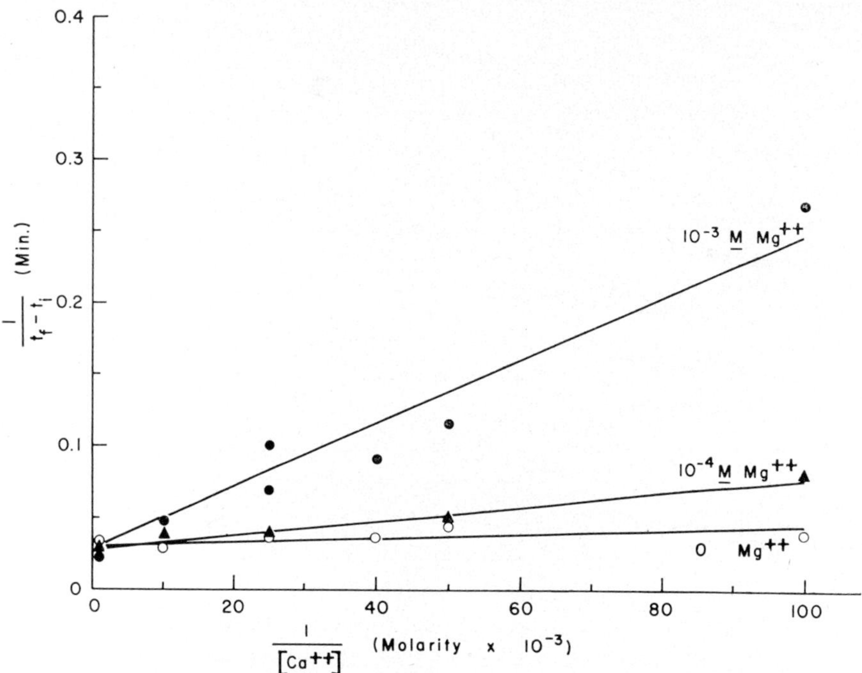

Fig. 2. The inhibition of the feeding reflex by magnesium ions, and its reversal by calcium ions.

using magnesium ions, an ion known to compete with calcium in many biological systems. To show the competitive nature of the magnesium inhibition, our data is expressed in a fashion analogous to the Lineweaver-Burke plot. Here (Fig. 2) we plot the reciprocal of the duration of the feeding reflex against the reciprocal of the calcium concentration. These experiments were carried out in the absence of magnesium, or in 10^{-4} *M* $MgCl_2$, or in 10^{-3} *M* $MgCl_2$. The data show that the higher the concentration of magnesium, the greater is the inhibition. Furthermore, as the calcium concentration is increased, the magnesium inhibition is completely reversed. These experiments leave little doubt that magnesium is interfering with the normal function of calcium ions in the feeding reflex. Sodium ions also exhibit similar competitive inhibitory effects (9). However, for a comparable inhibition higher concentrations of sodium ions are necessary.

At present there is little evidence as to whether the calcium functions at the glutathione-receptor, or in the effector system. (It appears that the trypsin activation of the feeding reflex, which will be described later, also requires environmental calcium, thus favoring the involvement of calcium in the effector system.)

Anions were also found to influence the feeding reflex (Table 4). Holding the calcium content constant, the order of effectiveness of the anions in increasing the duration of the feeding reflex was: $Cl > Br > I = NO_3$ (10). The relationship of this order to the lyotropic series suggests that these ions influence the state of some proteins involved in the feeding reflex.

From a practical viewpoint, these results point out the necessity of controlling precisely the ionic environment for the quantitative study of the feeding complex.

COMBINATION OF GLUTATHIONE WITH THE RECEPTOR

Most of the data just described concerns environmental chemistry. Now we have to ask questions about the first physiological event of the feeding reflex, the combination of glutathione with the receptor.

TABLE 5

Time required for mouths to close on removal of glutathione

Time in Glutathione (min.)	Time to Close (min.)
5.0	0.94
10.0	0.92
12.5	0.99
15.0	0.76
20.0	0.72
22.5	0.44
25.0	0.41

All experiments were carried out using *Hydra* starved for one day, and at excess glutathione (10^{-5} M).

Data from reference 8.

The following simple experiment demonstrated that glutathione did not act as a "trigger," if a triggered response is defined as one that continues after the initial stimulus is removed. Groups of *Hydra* were incubated in 10^{-5} M glutathione for periods varying from 5 to 25 minutes (Table 5). At the end of each incubation period, the animals in one drop of glutathione solution, were placed in 30 ml. of a solution of the same composition but lacking glutathione. In all cases the mouths closed in less than one minute (Table 5). The results indicate that glutathione had to be constantly present during the total time of the feeding reflex in order for the response to continue. In addition, since the mouths close repidly on removal of glutathione it is concluded that the equilibrium between glutathione and the receptor is rapidly attained.

This observation that the continued presence of glutathione is required for the activation of the feeding reflex allows us to formulate a hypothesis on how glutathione activates the receptor. We visualize the receptor as an inactive protein on the surface of certain *Hydra* cells. When that protein combines with glutathione, its tertiary structure is altered, rendering the receptor protein physiologically active. The active protein is then capable of either initiating, or allowing to go on to completion, the events involved in the receptor-effector system.

These data also indicate that the longer *Hydra* were exposed to the glutathione, the sooner the mouths closed when glutathione was removed. The time that it took for the mouths to close probably represent the time required both for the dissociation of the glutathione and for the cessation of the cellular events involved in the receptor-effector system. The observations that mouth closure was more rapid the longer *Hydra* were exposed to glutathione may imply that bound metabolic intermediates or cofactors, postulated to be released by and to take part in this system (12), become depleted as the feeding reflex nears completion.

When considering the quantitative aspects of the union of glutathione with the receptor, we found that the data were more meaningful if they were treated according to concepts borrowed from enzymology. Therefore, we investigated the effect of glutathione concentration on the "activity" of the receptor-effector system, the "activity" in this case being expressed as the duration of the feeding reflex (Fig. 3). For each concentration of glutathione, duplicate groups of five animals were used. In experiments employing *Hydra* starved for two days (solid curve), a maximum response was observed at concentrations of 5×10^{-6} *M* and greater. No further increase in the duration of the feeding reflex occurred at higher glutathione concentrations. At lower glutathione concentrations, the duration of the feeding reflex increased in nearly direct proportion to the amount of glutathione added. However, at these smaller values there was greater variation in the response of the individual *Hydra*, some not responding at all, as indicated by the symbols used in Figure 3. The similarity of this plot (Fig. 3) to the Langmuir adsorption isotherm, and to a curve illustrating the saturation of an enzyme by its substrate is apparent. Accordingly, the results (Fig. 3) are interpreted as indicating that at glutathione concentrations greater than 5×10^{-6} *M* all of the glutathione-receptors are saturated. In these experiments we have not been able to demonstrate that the glutathione is metabolized in a manner analogous to the metabolism of a substrate by its enzyme. But rather it appears as if the glutathione continues to activate all of the receptor-effector systems until the response ceases. At subsaturation levels of glutathione, the animal does not respond to its fullest capacity (see also Table 1, expt. e).

Another useful concept, analogous to the Michaelis constant, or K_M, used in enzymology, is the concentration of glutathione eliciting a half-maximum response. For the glutathione-*Hydra* system this value, ca. 10^{-6} *M*, probably closely approximates a true dissociation constant because of the apparent absence of glutathione metabolic products. A rough mass law treatment using the method of Scatchard (21) indicates that this constant can be measured within a factor of 2. The significance of this constant is threefold: First, its smallness indicates that the receptor has a high affinity for glutathione. Second the value of 10^{-6} *M* is within the physiologically active range expected to occur under natural conditions of feeding. And, third, this number provides a means of characterizing the receptor; that is, the glutathione receptor can be said to have a constant of 10^{-6} *M*. This constant has been found to be a characteristic of the receptor and to be nearly the same no matter what the nutritional state of the *Hydra*. For example, Figure 3 demonstrates that *Hydra* starved for two days respond to higher concentrations of glutathione for a greater period of time than do *Hydra* starved for one day (lower curve). Nonetheless, the concentration of glutathione eliciting a half-maximal response on both sets of *Hydra* was 10^{-6} *M*.

The difference in the maximum response observed in *Hydra* starved one or two days (Fig. 3) become understandable if another comparison is made with enzyme systems. Just as the maximum activity of an enzyme reaction is dependent on the quantity of enzyme present and is not a specific property of the enzyme, in a similar manner the duration of the reflex at concentrations eliciting the maximum response is dependent upon the quantity of completed[1] receptor-effector systems of the *Hydra*. The maximum response is not an intrinsic property of the receptor or of *Hydra* as is the K_M. Thus, *Hydra* starved for one day are interpreted to have fewer completed receptor-effector systems than *Hydra* starved for two days.

As emphasized in the above comparison, just as the total enzyme activity at saturating concentrations of substrate is proportional to the amount of enzyme, so the total maximum response of *Hydra* to

[1] A completed receptor-effector system is defined as one containing all of the components necessary for it to function when in combination with glutathione. When all the receptor-effector systems are completed, the *Hydra* is capable of carrying out a maximum response.

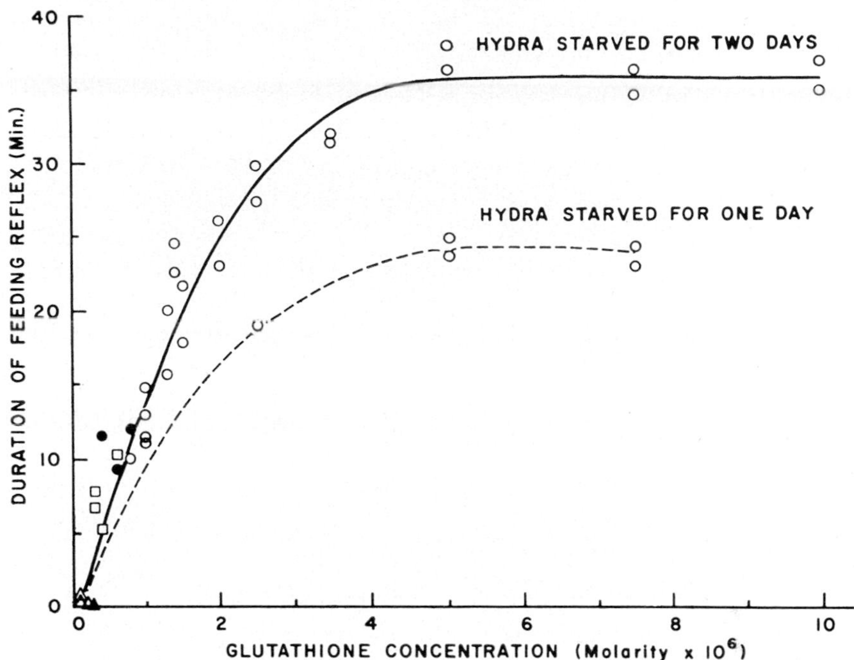

Fig. 3. Effect of glutathione concentration on the duration of the feeding reflex. Each point represents the mean for five *Hydra*. The type of symbol used indicates the number of *Hydra* in the group of five responding to glutathione: i.e. ○, five; ●, four; □, three; △, two; and ▲, one. (From reference 8).

excess glutathione is proportional to the number of active receptor-effector systems in each *Hydra*. Thus, in order to get comparable results, it is imperative in experiments using excess glutathione concentrations (10^{-5} *M*) that each *Hydra* possess approximately the same number of such systems. Since it is impossible to know beforehand the number of completed receptor-effector systems per *Hydra*, the only criterion for obtaining quantitatively reproducible results is to select *Hydra* reared under nearly identical laboratory conditions. We repeatedly find that the standard deviation of the response of *Hydra* to excess glutathione is low if these animals come from the same mass culture (Table 1, expts. a-d). Therefore, one should not compare experiments employing *Hydra* taken from different mass cultures. Variation might result either from differences in the following factors: the time elapsed since the previous exposure to glutathione, the ratios of environmental cations or anions, the temperature of the experiment, or to some presently unidentified factors.

EVIDENCE FOR AN INTRINSIC LIMIT TO THE RESPONSE

The data in Table 1 and Figure 3 show that the feeding reflex is limited to 25-35 minutes, depending upon the conditions of the experiments. In order to determine whether this mouth closure resulted from some intrinsic change within the *Hydra*, or from the oxidation or alteration of glutathione in the culture solution the following experiment was performed: A group of 5 *Hydra* were exposed to 2 ml. of 10^{-5} *M* glutathione until their mouths closed (Table 6). The same glutathione solution was then transferred to

TABLE 6

Response of different groups of *Hydra* exposed to the same solution of excitatory compound used three times

	DURATION OF FEEDING REFLEX t_f-t_i (min.)		
Group of *Hydra*	Glutathione 10^{-5} *M*	Ophthalmic Acid 10^{-5} *M*	S-Methyl Glutathione 10^{-5} *M*
1	27.1	27.6	29.5
2	19.8	23.1	26.2
3	28.1	24.0	21.7

All *Hydra* were starved for one day.
Data from reference 8.

another group of 5 *Hydra;* this latter group of *Hydra* opened their mouths for 27 minutes, indicating that sufficient glutathione remained to elicit a near-maximum response. This transfer process was repeated, and again the *Hydra* responded positively, although for a somewhat shorter time. Using the p-mercuribenzoate procedure of Boyer (2), parallel experiments were run in which the respective solutions were assayed for sulfhydryl groups after the *Hydra* had closed their mouths. No perceptible decrease in the sulfhydryl content of the solution occurred.

Similar experiments were carried out using the glutathione analogs ophthalmic acid and S-methyl glutathione, compounds that activate the feeding reflex and are not auto-oxidizable. As shown in Table 6, these analogs like glutathione, retain much of their activity after several exposures to *Hydra*. It can be concluded from all the experiments summarized in Table 6 that the feeding reflex normally ends as a result of some other cause than the oxidation, disappearance, or alteration of the glutathione molecule; also it does not end because of the accumulation of inhibitors in the culture solution.

Further examination of Table 6, however, does indicate some shortening of t_f after using the same glutathione solution on three successive groups of *Hydra*. Thus, it appears that either the glutathione concentration was in some manner slightly lowered, or that some inhibitory factor gradually accumulated in the environment.

It is not necessary to assume that the glutathione or glutathione analogs are altered or destroyed when combining with the receptor. There are known instances in which a biological response is initiated by a molecule (non-coenzymic in function) combining with a specific site without being metabolized. For example, thiogalactoside induces the adaptive formation of the enzyme β-galactosidase without being hydrolyzed (19).

Thus, from the data in Table 6, we might postulate as one result of glutathione activation, the consumption of some substance in the receptor-effector system, the concentration of which limits the duration of the feeding reflex to 25-35 minutes. If this postulate is true, then one might expect that after the *Hydra* have carried out a maximum response, there will be a period during which they give no further response to a fresh solution of glutathione. Secondly, there will be another period in which they regain their ability to respond maximally. This proved to be the case as shown in Figure 4. In this experiment large numbers of *Hydra* were exposed to glutathione for forty minutes. The animals were then washed with and placed into the glutathione-free culture solution, and, at intervals, exposed to a fresh solution of glutathione. The results show that

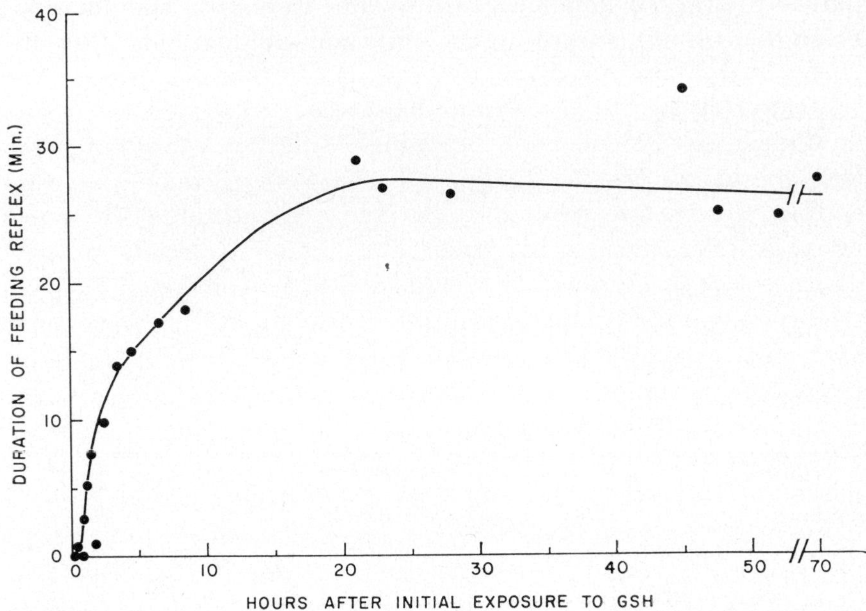

Fig. 4. Time for recovery of the ability to respond to glutathione (see **text**).

during the first hour, the animals give little if any response. By the tenth hour, however, the *Hydra* had regained their ability to respond for about 15 minutes, and after one day, responded maximally. Extending the interval between exposures to over 70 hours did not result in any further increase in the length of their response to fresh glutathione.

This lag and gradual resumption in the ability of *Hydra* to respond to a fresh stimulus of glutathione is interpreted to signify the period for the resynthesis of some substance, called "X," which we postulate to be limiting in the receptor-effector system. This view places a greater emphasis on the state of the receptor-effector system than on the physiology of the whole animal.

EFFECTS OF TEMPERATURE

The effects of temperature on the feeding response were studied primarily to provide more evidence concerning limiting substance X and information concerning its role in the execution of the response. These experiments are still in the notebook stage and will be summarized here only in order to show you some of the directions our research is taking.

If the reactions of the feeding reflex (Fig. 5) are depicted as involving the conversion of limiting substance X to Y, then one might expect two major results of lowering the temperature. First, a small lowering in temperature should lower the rate of all the thermochemical reactions. However, by slowing down the reaction converting the X to Y we should therefore slow down the rate at which the supply of X is depleted, and thus increase the length of time that the mouth remains opened. This proved to be the case as shown in Table 7 where, as the temperature approaches 15°, the *Hydra* respond for nearly 100 minutes.

TABLE 7

Effect of temperature on the duration of the feeding reflex

Temperature	t_f-t_i (min.)	Temperature	t_f-t_i (min.)
6.2°	5.9	18.1°	86.9
8.9°	36.4	18.6°	55.0
10.3°	59.8	19.7°	59.2
12.5°	70.7	20.6°	55.0
14.5°	60.0	21.9°	35.1
15.4°	88.6	24.1°	29.4
16.3°	99.7	25.3°	21.5
		27.7°	19.7

All *Hydra* were starved for two days.

As a second effect of lowering temperature, the limiting reaction may go so slowly that the optimum (threshold) conditions necessary for the feeding reflex are not maintained. Thus, when the *Hydra* are held below 15° they are observed to open their mouths for a few minutes, then close, open, etc. until they finally stop responding. The total duration of the responses below 15° becomes progressively less until the *Hydra* barely respond (Table 7). In fact, when the temperature is lowered from 20° to 5°, the mouth takes longer to open (Table 8). These results (Table 8) are interpreted to mean that as the temperature is lowered, it takes longer for the completion of all the reactions (including the limiting one) leading to mouth opening.[2]

TABLE 8

Effect of temperature on time of mouth opening

Temperature	$1/t_i$ (min.)
5.2°	0.10
7.9°	0.35
9.5°	0.62
13.0°	1.11
16.3°	1.72
18.5°	1.56
20.1°	2.56

All *Hydra* were starved for two days.
Each value is the mean for 25 animals.

ACTIVATION BY PROTEOLYTIC ENZYMES

Recently we have been carrying out some experiments in activating the feeding response in the absence of added glutathione by using certain proteolytic enzymes. Although still in the preliminary stage, these experiments may help illucidate the sequence of events taking place in the receptor-effector system, and thus are of sufficient interest for some of them to be reported here.

We have previously shown that papain, ficin, and trypsin activate a feeding response in *Hydra* (12). This proteolytic activation was shown not to be the result of any toxic action of the enzymes for the *Hydra* were intact and alive after one day's exposure to the proteases. Dialyzed ficin, like papain (Table 9), did not activate a response unless cysteine was added to render the enzyme active. The boiled enzymes could not be activated by cysteine. The action

[2]At temperatures below 13° *Hydra* vary greatly in their response, some animals not responding at all. Therefore, the data are expressed as $1/t_i$ rather than as t_i because in cases where there was no response, the t_i values would range to infinity.

of trypsin was inhibited by trypsin inhibitor (Table 9). Thus, the response seems to be a result of the proteolytic activities of these enzymes. Of twenty other purified proteins, only chymotrypsin gave a significant (8 min.) response (12). It does not seem likely that the proteases are acting by releasing reduced glutathione from *Hydra* because γ-glutamyl linkages are rare in proteins, and because furthermore glutamic acid, a specific inhibitor for glutathione (13), does not inhibit the action of trypsin (9).

The possible effects of proteases on a whole animal are so numerous that it would be difficult at this time to single out any one action that would explain their effect on *Hydra.* Nevertheless, the important fact remains that proteases do activate a response, and thus a study of their effects might help in arriving at an understanding of the actual mechanism. For example, trypsin can activate only an 18-minute response; if glutathione, however, is added to the same *Hydra,* they respond an additional 17-18 minutes. In contrast, after a 35 minute response initiated by glutathione, the addition of trypsin has no effect. A mixture of excess glutathione and excess trypsin, interestingly enough, elicits a response equal only to that initiated by glutathione alone. Thus, these preliminary experiments indicate that the protease probably activates a series of events common to those activated by glutathione and involving the consumption of limiting substance X (9). Therefore, in Figure 5, the arrow indicating the site of action of the protease is drawn

TABLE 9

Activation of feeding reflex by proteases

Expt.	Test Solution	t_f-t_i (min.)
1.a.	20 μg./ml. papain	0.1
b.	20 μg./ml. papain + 10^{-3} *M* cysteine	19.8
c.	20 μg./ml. papain + 10^{-3} *M* cysteine, boiled 5 min. at 100°	0
2.a.	0.1 mg./ml. trypsin	17.8
b.	0.1 mg./ml. trypsin + 0.1 mg./ml. trypsin inhibitor	0

All *Hydra* were starved for two days.
Data from reference 12.

somewhere between the receptor and before the reaction involving the consumption of X.

The activation by proteases has also been useful in determining the relative site at which calcium functions. Since the presence of environmental calcium ion is required for the activation of both glutathione (10) and proteases (9), we feel that calcium plays a role in the effector system rather than in the combination of glutathione with the receptor.

A recent development which places added importance upon the activation of the feeding reflex by proteases is the discovery by Fulton (6) that proteases also activate the feeding reflex in *Cordylophora.* His results are striking in that he has also shown that *Cordylophora* do not carry out the feeding reflex in response to the peptide reduced glutathione, but rather to the single imino acid proline (5). Thus, although *Hydra* and *Cordylophora* have different specific excitatory compounds, the feeding reflex in both animals can be activated by proteases. In addition, *Physalia* gastroozoids, which normally respond to glutathione (15), also are activated by proteases (12). All of these results suggest that the protease is acting on some step which is common to the feeding reflex of all these organisms irrespective of the excitatory compound involved.

SUMMARY AND CONCLUSIONS

With the aid of the simplified scheme shown in Figure 5, I would like to summarize the present state of knowledge concerning the mechanism by which glutathione combines with and activates the glutathione-receptor of *Hydra* to elicit the feeding reflex. The activity of the glutathione resides in the size and configuration of the γ-glutamylalanylglycine backbone of the tripeptide, and not in the reducing properties of the molecule (3, 13, 17). Concentrations of glutathione greater than 5×10^{-5} *M* activate all of the receptor-effector systems (Fig. 3), which are probably localized in the area immediately around the mouth and on the tentacles (8). The concentration of glutathione eliciting a half maximum response is 10^{-6} *M* (Fig. 3). In order for a response to take place, the glutathione must be constantly present at the receptor site (Table 5). The association of glutathione with the receptor is rapidly attained (Table 5); the affinity of the receptor for glutathione is high (Fig. 3). After glutathione combines with the receptor, it takes about 0.5 minutes for all the events necessary for mouth opening to occur (Table 1). Once the reflex begins, it will continue for 25 to 35 minutes (Tables 1, 3, 4 and 6; Figs. 3 and 4). The response does not stop because of any alteration in the glutathione molecule (Table 6), but rather because of some inherent property of *Hydra*. The duration of the response is probably directly related to the conversion of some limiting substance X to its product Y (Tables 1, 3, 4 and 6). Lowered temperatures increase the duration of the feeding reflex, probably by decreasing the rate at which the supply of X is exhausted (Table 7). It takes about 24 hours for X to be resynthesized either from Y or anew (Fig. 4). The response can be stimulated in the absence of glutathione by certain proteases (12). The protease probably acts before the step involving the consumption of X. Furthermore, the presence of small amounts of calcium ion in the medium surrounding *Hydra* are required in order that a response may occur (10). The calcium appears to be involved in steps occurring between the site of activation by proteases and the effector system.

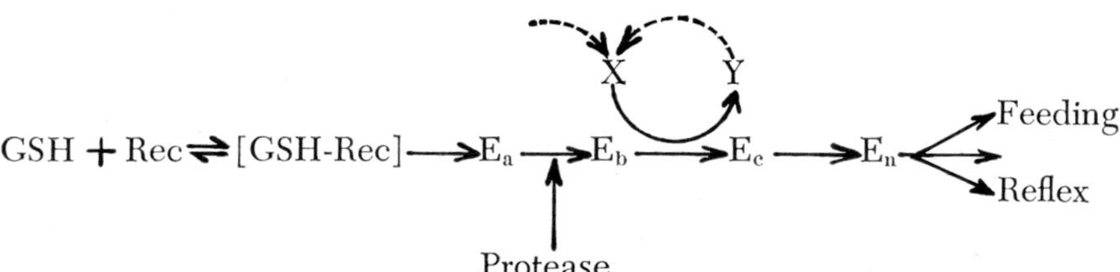

Fig. 5. Schematic outline of the glutathione receptor-effector system. Rec represents the receptor; E_a, E_b, E_c and E_n, enzymes; X, the limiting substance; and Y, its metabolic product.

These results are concerned with a single biological system in which a specific excitatory compound combines with its receptor to activate a coordinated response. Activations by an excitatory compound comprise the common step in many basic biological phenomena such as chemoreception and hormone action. Some of the results described here on the interaction of glutathione with the *Hydra* receptor may bear a relation to the functioning of some of these other systems.

ACKNOWLEDGEMENTS

It is a pleasure to acknowledge the superb assistance that Mr. John Bovaird has provided throughout this study. The criticisms of this manuscript by Drs. J. F. Woessner, Jr., A. Phillips, E. L. Chambers, and W. D. Dandliker are greatly appreciated.

REFERENCES

1. Behrens, O. 1941. Coenzymes for glyoxylase. *J. Biol. Chem. 141:* 503-508.
2. Boyer, P. D. 1954. Spectophotometric study of the reaction of protein sulfhydryl groups with organic mercurials. *J. Am. Chem. Soc. 76:* 4331-4337.
3. Cliffe, E. E., and S. G. Waley. 1958. Effect of analogues of glutathione on the feeding reaction of hydra. *Nature 182:* 804-805.
4. Ewer, R. F. 1947. On the function and mode of action of the nematocysts of *Hydra. Proc. Zool. Soc. London 117:* 365-376.
5. Fulton, C. 1960. The biology of a colonial hydroid. Ph.D. Thesis. The Rockefeller Institute.
6. Fulton, C. (in press). The growth and feeding of *Cordylophora* and other hydroids. In *The Lower Metozoa: Comparative Biology and Phylogeny,* edited by M. B. Allen. Academic Press, Inc., New York.
7. Lenhoff, H. M., 1961. Digestion of protein in *Hydra* as studied using radioautography and fractionation by differential solubilities. *Exptl. Cell Research 23:* 335-353.
8. Lenhoff, H. M. (in press). Activation of the feeding reflex in *Hydra littoralis.* I. Role played by reduced glutathione, and quantitative assay of the feeding reflex. *J. Gen. Physiol.*
9. Lenhoff, H. M. Unpublished observations.
10. Lenhoff, H. M. and J. Boviard. 1959. Requirement of bound calcium for the action of surface chemoreceptors. *Science 130:* 1474-1476.
11. Lenhoff, H. M. and J. Bovaird. 1960. The requirement of trace amounts of environmental sodium for the growth and development of *Hydra. Exptl. Cell Research 20:* 384-394.
12. Lenhoff, H. M. and J. Bovaird. 1960. Enzymatic activation of a hormone-like response in *Hydra* by proteases. *Nature 187:* 671-673.
13. Lenhoff, H. M. and J. Bovaird. 1961. Action of glutamic acid and glutathione analogues on the *Hydra* glutathione-receptor. *Nature 189:* 486-487.
14. Lenhoff, H. M. and W. F. Loomis. 1957. Environmental factors controlling respiration in hydra. *J. Exp. Zool. 134:* 171-182.
15. Lenhoff, H. M. and H. A. Schneiderman. 1959. The chemical control of feeding in the Portuguese man-of-war, *Physalia Physalis* L. and its bearing on the evolution of the Cnidaria. *Biol. Bull. 116:* 452-460.

16. LOOMIS, W. F. 1954. Environmental factors controlling growth in hydra. *J. Exp. Zool. 126:* 223-234.
17. LOOMIS, W. F. 1955. Glutathione control of the specific feeding reactions of hydra. *Ann. N. Y. Acad. Sci. 62:* 209-228.
18. LOOMIS, W. F. and H. M. LENHOFF. 1956. Growth and sexual differentiation of hydra in mass culture. *J. Exp. Zool. 132:* 555-574.
19. MONOD, J. 1956. Remarks on the mechanism of enzyme induction. In *Enzymes: Units of Biological Structure and Function,* edited by O. H. Gaebler. Academic Press, Inc., New York, pp. 7-28.
20. PARK, H. D. 1953. In W. F. Loomis, reference 17, p. 211.
21. SCATCHARD, G. 1949. The attraction of proteins for small molecules and ions. *Ann. N. Y. Acad. Sci. 51:* 660-672.

DISCUSSION

LANE: Would you care to speculate about the nature of the glutathione-receptors, and their location?

LENHOFF: I can only guess that the receptor is a very specific protein, probably a lipoprotein on the cell membrane. The evidence is not too good concerning the location of the receptors on *Hydra*. Experiments using isolated parts of *Hydra* show that some are located on the tentacles, and others on the hypostome. We tried to localize the receptor by radioautography using glutathione. But the glutathione washes readily off.

SLAUTTERBACK: Aren't you inhibiting the oxidative enzymes severely when you get down to 6 degrees and thus reduce the general motility of the animal?

LENHOFF: No doubt we are slowing down many reactions by lowering the temperature, but the limiting reaction is the one that we think causes this delay in mouth opening.

SLAUTTERBACK: Are these animals still moving around actively?

LENHOFF: Yes. In assaying the feeding reflex, we observe mouth opening, tentacle waving and contraction. All these movements seem normal as does contraction after a mechanical stimulus.

BURNETT: Maybe you could explain this preliminary experiment. We placed hydra in a 10^{-5} *M* solution of glutathione and waited until all of them had closed their mouths and discontinued their feeding response. At this time we offered the hydra several hundred brine shrimp. The hydra readily captured, killed, and ingested the shrimp.

LENHOFF: I can give some explanation. When a *Hydra* punctures a shrimp, all sorts of new and unknown substances present in the body fluids of the shrimp flow into the media. There is a possibility that these emitted fluids contain substances which enhance the feeding reflex. In fact, we have some preliminary indications that phospholipids present in serum do just this. Since I think that the initial activation takes place on the cell membrane, it is possible that the phospholipids act there.

BURNETT: I suppose it is enhancing something already present.

LENHOFF: Yes. The point I want to emphasize is that it is very hard to know what is happening since you do not know what is present in the fluids coming out of the shrimp. So many factors affect the feeding reflex, as I have shown you already.

Chandler Fulton also shows that *Cordylophora* respond somewhat to shrimp after they no longer respond to proline. This may be a similar phenomenon.

GOREAU: Have you tried amino acids? I ask because we recently noted that small amounts of methionine caused corals to extrude mesenterial filaments. The entire colonies become covered with tangled white masses of filaments that stayed out as long as the methionine (2 μg/10 ml) was in the medium. Extrusion of masenterial filaments is a typical response of some corals when feeding in the presence of thick plankton swarms, but I have never seen such a strong sustained reaction with other stimulants, including clam juice, as with methionine.

LENHOFF: I haven't tried methionine, although I doubt whether it would cause *Hydra* to respond. I fully agree that other compounds may work on other organisms. Fulton, for example, has shown that proline activates the feeding reflex of *Cordylophora*.

GOREAU: Glutathione seems to have little effect on those corals on which it was tried. Zooplankton swarms probably secrete detecable amounts of all kinds of organic substances which activate chemoreceptors to trigger the corals' feeding posture. Corals feed any time there is plankton around. The classic story that reef corals expand only at night is untrue. In fact, we have frequently seen corals feeding on swarms of zooplankton in the middle of the day irrespective of light intensity, using tentacles and extruded mesenterial filaments to catch and entangle their prey.

LENHOFF: It would be nice to see whether methionine analogs will inhibit this response in corals elicited by clam juice. This would provide strong evidence that methionine is the active compound in the clam juice.

STREHLER: Langdon found that the reduced chain of insulin is a competitive inhibitor of glutathione-TPN reductase. Have you tried reduced insulin?

LENHOFF: We have not tried insulin or reduced insulin yet. But Langdon's finding places this experiment high on our list.

Another point I find exciting is that Langdon calls insulin a "prohormone." That is, he suggests that insulin will not work unless it is first split, although here it is split by reduction. Thus, insulin may represent a case of an excitatory compound being activated by the unmasking of an essential group. We think that unmasking phenomena (possibly proteolytic) may operate in control systems generally.

BURNETT: Did you repeat the experiments of Balke and Steiner showing that lactic and ascorbic acids elicited a feeding reflex?

LENHOFF: Yes. I found neither lactic nor ascorbic acid to work. However, I still wouldn't be surprised if under certain conditions other compounds also activate. For example, they may act, like the proteases, along the chain of reactions involved in the feeding reflex. Perhaps lactic acid, under their conditions affected some step of the response. And there still remains the possibility that *Hydra* has more than one receptor. All I can say is that in *Hydra littoralis* all the factors that I mentioned in my talk influence the response, and that there is no question that reduced glutathione is a natural activator.

BURNETT: We once found that dilute concentrations of bovine testes hyaluronidase stimulated the feeding response. At that time we assumed that our enzyme preparation was contaminated with glutathione. A more recent preparation consisting of crystals quite different from our original preparation was not effective.

LENHOFF: These are factors that you have to consider. First you must dialyze to remove endogenous glutathione. For example we found some of our enzyme preparations elicted a response before dialysis but not afterwards.

KLINE: Some compounds may cause the mouth to open without producing the true feeding reflex.

LENHOFF: Definitely. You can get mouth opening, but not the true feeding reflex from many compounds, usually toxic ones. As Dr. Loomis pointed out in his original paper, the best proof that a compound can initiate the feeding reflex is to give the *Hydra* some *inert* material impregnated with the compound you are testing. If the *Hydra* ingests the inert material, then a true feeding reflex was elicited by that compound.

The Nutrition of *Hydra*[1]

David L. Claybrook
Dept. of Physiology & Pharmacology, Wayne State University College of Medicine, Detroit, Michigan.

The study of hydra nutrition is in its infancy. In fact, we are not aware of any investigation of specific nutrient requirements prior to our own. I suspect that the absence of such studies has been due to the complexity of the problem rather than to a lack of appreciation for its importance. The laboratory culture of hydra was more of an art than a science until Dr. Loomis' fundamental research defining environmental conditions for optimal growth (12). The number of environmental variables was then greatly reduced to the point that the rate of growth could be directly controlled by limiting the food supply.

The hydra's apparent refusal to ingest non-living food made it essentially impossible to feed a formulated diet. When the glutathione control of the feeding reaction was revealed (3), it offered a means for feeding to the animals particulate preparations of the experimenter's choice. With these possibilities in mind, we began a study of hydra nutrition.

We undertook this investigation for two main reasons. First, we wanted to know to what extent the hydra's requirements were similar to and different from those of other animals. With the exceptions of the protozoa and insects, very little work has been devoted to the nutrition of invertebrates. Information on coelenterate nutrition would contribute significantly to our knowledge of comparative biochemistry.

The second, and primary purpose of the project was to increase the usefulness of the hydra as a biological material for the

[1]In part from a dissertation submitted to the Graduate School, The University of Texas, in partial fulfillment of the requirements for the degree of Doctor of Philosophy, August, 1960.

chemical study of development and differentiation processes – a field to be discussed by Dr. Eakin. Since the nutritional state of an animal affects all of its physiological processes to some extent, it is desirable to be able to control the nutritional state during the study of other physiological phenomena. The development of chemically defined nutrient preparations in which cultures of hydra or hydra cells could be grown aseptically would give the investigator complete biochemical control over the organisms.

Our ultimate goal was the propagation of hydra cells in a chemically defined medium. With this sytem, we should be able to determine the role of each tissue layer in processes such as regeneration and sexual differentiation. However, we chose to begin our experimentation with whole animals for two reasons: in general, the requirements for cell propagation are much more critical than those for growth of the intact organism. In the intact animal, specific trace nutrients may be supplied by specialized cells. There is also a more rapid loss of essential nutrilites to the external solution from the isolated cell. We hoped to discover approximate requirements before proceeding to precise studies at the cellular level. Secondly, techniques for quantitative study had already been developed for whole hydra but not for dissociated cells. Thus the nutritional value of an experimental diet could be determined by its effect on an observable physiological process such as asexual growth.

Our stock *Hydra* clone was obtained from a locally-isolated strain of *Hydra littoralis,* and was grown according to the methods of Ham and Eakin (1). When fed daily with an excess of freshly-hatched *Artemia* larvae, the *Hydra* grows at a maximum logarithmic rate. Presumably the animal receives an excess of all exogenous requirements, and the limitation of growth rate is due to necessary metabolic conversions within the cells. If the exogenous supply of a growth factor is reduced below the maximum utilizable by the animal, a reduction in the observed rate of growth should result.

In the search for a non-living diet, it was found that heat-killed *Artemia* would support asexual growth of *Hydra* for at least six months, but at a rate significantly below maximum. Although the killed *Artemia* contained adequate amounts of reduced glutathione to stimulate the feeding reaction, the solution had to be stirred gently to bring them into contact with the *Hydra's* tentacles.

The effect of the period of heating on the subsequent growth rate is depicted in Table 1. The reduction in the growth rate is seen to be progressive with time of heating. This indicated to us that some substance was being inactivated by the heat treatment so that its availability to the *Hydra* became limiting to the growth process.

TABLE 1
Relation of growth rate of *Hydra littoralis*, Ham strain, to period of heating of *Artemia* (70°)

Heating time (min.)	Growth Rate	
	Doubling time (days)	Growth Rate Constant (k)*
0	1.9	.36
3	3.3	.21
7	3.5	.20
15	4.5	.15
30	5.2	.13

$*k = \frac{\ln 2}{T}$

On the assumption that replacement of the growth-limiting factors to a nutritionally deficient diet would increase the rate of budding, we assayed numerous biochemical and biological substances for their capacities to stimulate budding when added as supplements to a diet of heated shrimp. *Artemia* heated for 7 minutes at 70° were fed to *Hydra* cultures for at least a week before the *Hydra* were used for bioassays. This period served to deplete the animals of any reserve of the growth factor.

The heated *Artemia* diet was first supplemented with defined and complex substances dissolved in the salt solution, bathing the *Hydra*. Natural extracts, vitamins, amino acids, and other possible growth factors, alone and in various combinations, were tested in this system. No stimulatory effect on the growth rate was observed in any expriment.

Since the lack of growth response to external supplements could have been due to relative impermeability of the ectodermal cells to dissolved materials, it was necessary to devise a technique for introducing the test materials directly into the coelenteron where normal absorption could take place. A diagrammatic picture of the apparatus which was designed to inject a measured volume into the individual organism is shown in Figure 1. The apparatus features a micrometer-driven micro-liter syringe for delivering quantities in the micro-liter range.

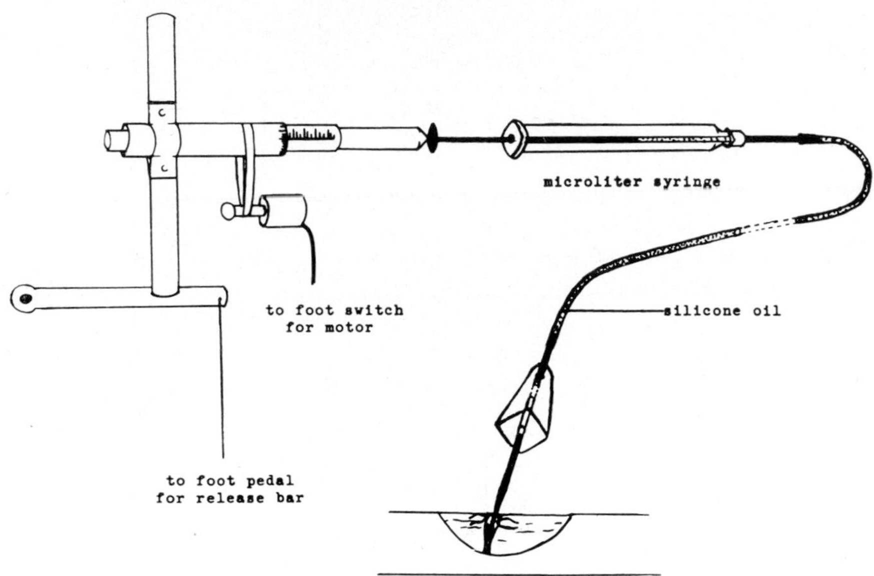

Fig. 1. Micro-injector for feeding *Hydra*.

In our standard injection test, adult *Hydra* without buds were selected from the cultures maintained on heated *Artemia*. The animals were placed in 9-depression spot plates in large Petri dishes, and each one was force-fed 0.2 μl from a glass capillary containing semi-solid agar in which the experimental diet was dissolved or suspended. Twenty-four hours after injection, the animals were examined under a dissecting microscope, and the number of new buds in each dish of nine *Hydra* was recorded and compared with that of the unfed control dish.

The relation of growth response to the quantity of material injected is shown in Figure 2. The response was proportional to the

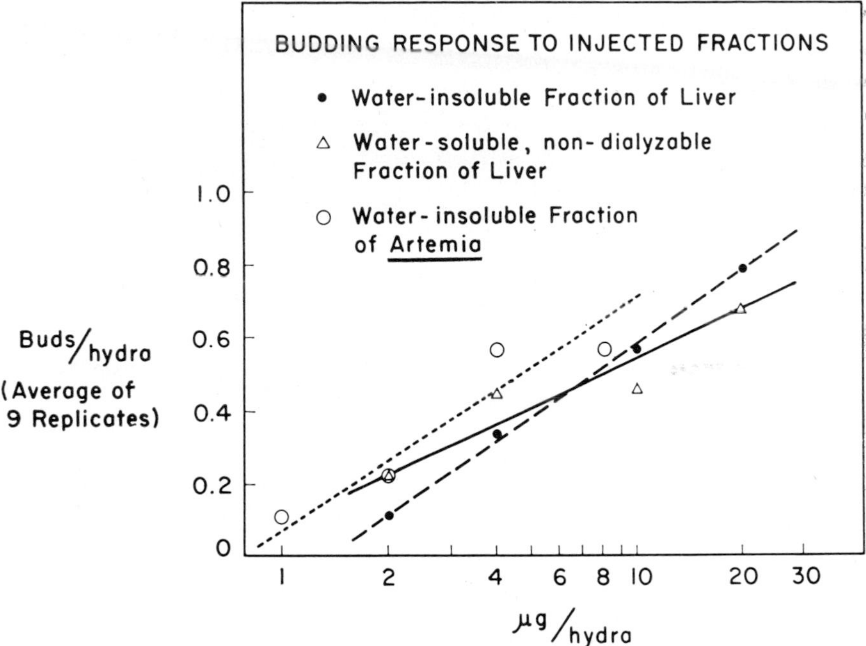

Fig. 2. Budding response to injected fractions.

logarithm of the dosage in some cases, while in the other experiments log responses were not observed.

The relative potencies of some natural materials showing activity in this system are listed in Table 2. The potencies on a dry

TABLE 2
Relative activities of natural supplements for promoting budding in *Hydra*

Material	Potency (dry weight)
Bovine liver acetone powder*	10
Mouse liver	10
Mouse kidney	8
Mouse heart	10
Chick embryo extract	10
Escherichia coli	6
Dried yeast	10
Chlorella ellipsoidea	4
Bovine liver extract, non-dialyzable fraction	10

*Used as standard and assigned arbitrary value of 10.

weight basis are expressed relative to an arbitrary standard, bovine liver acetone powder. Activity was found in micro-organisms as well as in crude mammalian tissues. Substances with no demonstrable activity when fed internally included vitamins, amino acids, protein digests, nucleic acids, carbohydrates, and microbiological media.

An active *soluble* preparation, bovine liver extract, was subjected to a number of physical and chemical tests in an effort to characterize the active constituents. The results of such tests are shown now in Table 3. The activity was found to be non-dialyzable,

TABLE 3
Potencies of modified non-dialyzable soluble extract

Treatment	Fraction of Total Solids	Potency
Unmodified non-dialyzable extract	1.00	10
Ashing	0.02	0
Heating (2 hours, 70°)		
Soluble fraction	0.20	0
Precipitate	0.80	12
Trypsin digestion	1.00	1-2

and was destroyed by ashing, characteristic of an organic macromolecule. Heating in solution precipitated but did not destroy the active material. Incubation of the extract with trypsin or chymotrypsin resulted in the disappearance of nearly all biological activity. The ultra-violet absorption spectrum of the soluble extract

TABLE 4
Potencies of ammonium sulfate fractions of non-dialyzable soluble extract

Ammonium Sulfate* Fraction	Fraction of Total Solids	Potency
0	1.00	10
0-33%	0.28	10
33-66%	0.50	10
66-100%	0.13	1
Soluble at 100%	0.09	0

*Fraction precipitated between the indicated points of saturation.

showed a peak absorption near 280 mμ, and the optical density per milligram of extract indicated a high percentage of protein. All evidence, then, indicated that the active species were included in the protein fraction.

Fractionation of the active extract with ammonium sulfate (Table 4) revealed that all activity was salted out, but was distributed

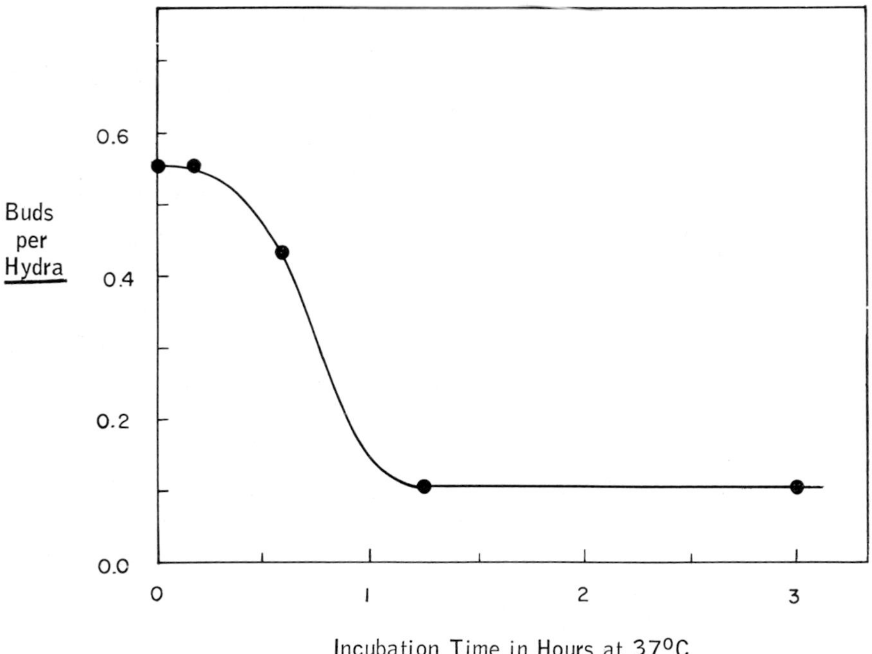

Fig. 3. Effect of period of incubation with chymotrypsin on growth promoting activity of non-dialyzable soluble extract.

among several fractions. While supporting the conclusion that the active components were proteins, this data showed that the activity was apparently common to several classes of protein.

The rate of inactivation of the extract by chymotrypsin is shown in Figure 3. From this curve it would appear that intact protein molecules, or relatively large fragments of them, are essential to activity in this extract.

It is interesting to note that all purified proteins which have been assayed were inactive in this system. These include casein, bovine albumin, insulin, hemoglobin, and six bovine plasma fractions. The wide distribution of activity in crude protein fractions, contrasted with the absence of detectable activity in highly purified proteins, suggests that the growth-stimulating factors could be small molecules bound firmly to crude protein, but removable by repeated purification. The evidence at hand has not enabled us to identify the *Hydra* growth-promoting principle with any specific previously recognized growth factors for other organisms.

While the micro-injection technique has been a very useful method in the initial investigation of nutrition, it is still a tedious procedure because of the individual attention required for each *Hydra*. The mass culture of intact animals on a defined diet would obviously require different methods. It appears from consideration of other tissues cultured *in vitro* that the absolute biochemical requirements can be determined only by study at the cellular level. With the current progress toward maintaining coelenterate cells *in vitro*, the time may be near when hydra cells may be used in nutritional research.

I think the significance of our own experiments lies not in the determination of specific nutrient requirements, but in the demonstration that *Hydra* can live and grow on a non-living diet, and that nutrition of *Hydra* can be studied quantitatively by its effects on a measurable physiological process – namely the asexual growth process. Although we have only made a start toward understanding the nutrition of *Hydra*, we are encouraged to believe that it is a step toward developing the full potential of hydra as an experimental system.

REFERENCES

1. Ham, R. G., and R. E. Eakin. 1958. Time sequence of certain physiological events during regeneration in hydra. *J. Exp. Zool. 139:* 33-54.
2. Loomis, W. F. 1954. Environmental factors controlling growth in hydra. *J. Exp. Zool. 126:* 223-234.
3. Loomis, W. F. 1955. Glutathione control of the specific feeding reactions of hydra. *Ann. N.Y. Acad. Sci. 62:* 209-228.

DISCUSSION

STREHLER: Do you need to include any particles along with these soluble protein fractions that were capable of supporting growth?

CLAYBROOK: Well, our solutions were centrifuged for six hours at 33,000 g, which means that any surviving particles must have been rather small.

LENHOFF: I think what Dr. Strehler is getting at is that perhaps the protein is being coagulated in the gut and is being engulfed as particles. We have some evidence that *H. littoralis* gastrodermis takes up mostly particles and leaves free amino acids behind in the gut (Lenhoff, H. 1961. *Exptl. Cell Research, 23:* 335-353). Thus, maybe the proteolytic enzymes destroy the growth-promoting properties of the heat-labile protein by reducing it to a non-particulate solution of free amino acids that cannot be taken up by the gastrodermis.

CLAYBROOK: We don't know what happens after it gets inside the gut.

GOREAU: What is *Hydra's* digestive juice made out of?

CLAYBROOK: I have no information on this. Do others?

LENHOFF: We have fed about a million *H. littoralis* with shrimp, until we knew, by other measurements, that the food was mostly taken up by the gastroderm. Then we forced the *Hydra* to regurgitate, took the extract, and precipitated it with 80% ammonium sulfate. We found that there was proteolytic activity at pH 2.5 and 7. These proteolytic enzymes probably aid in degrading the cells into particles. But I doubt that the extracellular enzymes degrade the particles all the way to free amino acids, because the particles, when small enough, are rapidly phagocytized by the gastroderm.

GOREAU: The reason I ask is that Claybrook's very lovely method allows one to withdraw things as well as introduce them, and I was wondering if one could do microchemical analyses on contents of the gut of the animal during various stages of digestion?

CLAYBROOK: I haven't tried this at all. I don't know.

KLINE: When you maintain the *Hydra* on heat killed *Artemia,* does the growth rate remain constant, even if reduced?

CLAYBROOK: Fairly constant. It varies slightly with the various lots of shrimp.

KLINE: Then you didn't totally destroy something that is needed. Perhaps you reduced its concentration. How did you interpret the results?

CLAYBROOK: The growth factor is not completely destroyed, but becomes limiting to growth.

KLINE: In one experiment you had heat precipitated material on which the *Hydra* were able to grow quite well.

CLAYBROOK: Right. This is the liver extract. We have not fractionated shrimp because the relative supply of liver and shrimp are not the same.

LENHOFF: Is it possible that the more you heat the shrimp, the more the shrimp's cellular integrity is destroyed? And when you put these damaged shrimp in water, essential factors leak out?

A few years ago Dr. Loomis and I were able to grow *Hydra* on frozen shrimp, but had no success with boiled shrimp. We thought then that boiling either destroyed a heat labile factor or allowed essential heat-stable factors to leak out.

CLAYBROOK: It is possible, but in a few experiments we found no activity in the supernatant that the shrimp were boiled in. I wouldn't say this was conclusive.

LENHOFF: Was this supernatant solution either ninhydrin or protein-positive?

CLAYBROOK: We didn't check at this stage but I'm sure that there were ninhydrin-positive components there.

GOREAU: What I am speculating on now assumes a nervous system! Living *Artemia* may be required because the struggle with the prey could set up a reflex which causes hydra to secrete enzymes or produce preabsorptive changes in the gastroderm, which would allow digestion to proceed in a much more complete manner. The point is this. Perhaps the animal needs to struggle with its prey? This is, of course, a complete speculation but we may be dealing here with a phenomenon on the physiological rather than biochemical level.

CLAYBROOK: I haven't tried any experiment which would answer your question.

LENHOFF: Didn't *Hydra* grow well on frozen shrimp?

CLAYBROOK: They grow at a reduced rate.

LENHOFF: At a very reduced rate?

CLAYBROOK: Not very reduced. But below that found with live shrimp. The answer to this may also be leakage from the shrimp.

LENHOFF: But they do grow on frozen shrimp. I would think that this would answer Dr. Goreau's speculation by showing that the struggling of live prey is not required.

LOOMIS: It is interesting that apparently no carbohydrate is necessary. In other words, pure protein is enough.

CLAYBROOK: Let's say carbohydrate is not limiting at this state.

LOOMIS: But you feed them solely on the 0-66% ammonium sulfate fraction of liver protein?

CLAYBROOK: This alone will not support continued growth. This is only a specific assay for the heat labile factor.

EAKIN: I think that some of you were not able to hear Dr. Claybrook clearly when he described his method for demonstrating the requirements of *Hydra* for the heat-labile factor. The *Hydra* which he used as test organisms had been cultured at a sub-optimal level of nutrition by feeding them on heated brine shrimp. The response we studied was that of boosting them from this bare maintenance level to that which we get when they are fed live brine shrimp.

LOOMIS: It is a specific assay for the heat-labile factor?

EAKIN: That's right. Even the poorly growing controls are getting a highly complicated diet in the heated *Artemia.*

LOOMIS: I have often tried to get micro-pipettes into the mouths of *H. littoralis* and out again without having them then regurgitate what I put in their stomachs. Perhaps you open their mouths with glutathione?

CLAYBROOK: No, I force it open.

LOOMIS: Maybe that's the secret!

CLAYBROOK: Yes. Then I wait until he closes his mouth on the pipette before injecting the material.

LOOMIS: And then it is water-tight as you pull out?

CLAYBROOK: The semi-solid consistency of the medium is essential here. You can't use a liquid.

LOOMIS: How much agar do you use?

CLAYBROOK: I use 0.4%, which is relatively thick. The *Hydra* closes its mouth when the pipette is withdrawn and the viscous solution remains in the gut.

LOOMIS: Will it flow down a microcapillary?

CLAYBROOK: Yes, if under pressure.

Isolation and Maintenance in Tissue Culture of Coelenterate Cell Lines

John H. Phillips
Department of Bacteriology, University of California, Berkeley, California

The *in vitro* cultivation of coelenterate tissues has been reported before (1, 2). However, attempts at the maintenance of such cultures for prolonged periods of time and serial transfer of cultured material have not apparently met with success. In addition, the evidence in support of true multiplication of cells has not been entirely convincing. The methods that will be discussed have led to the establishment of cell cultures from the anemone *Anthopleura elegantissima*. These cultures have been transferred twenty to thirty times and have been under *in vitro* cultivation for more than a year. In addition, eight of the cell lines have been through one single cell cloning. The resulting clones of eight to thirty-two cells have given rise to cultures containing 10^6 to 10^7 cells.

First will be described the procedures which have been used in isolation, cultivation and cloning of the cells, and this methodology will be followed by a description of the cells and some of their properties.

A somewhat more detailed account of methods will soon be published (5). All glassware and rubber stoppers were cleaned by autoclaving in 0.1% Na_2CO_3 (4). Glassware was wrapped in aluminum foil and sterilized by dry heat. Rubber stoppers were autoclaved in large Petri dishes. All nutrient solutions were sterilized by filtration, using Millipore filters. The nutrient medium that has been found to be most useful consists of 0.7% Edamine[1],

[1]Sheffield Chemical Company, Inc., Norwich, N. Y.

an enzymatic digest of lactalbumin, in 90% artificial sea water (3) containing 500 units of penicillin and 0.5 mg. streptomycin per ml. Growth can be obtained over a range of Edamine concentrations from 0.4 to 1.5% and artificial sea water concentrations of 40% to 100%. Yeasts and molds which are not inhibited by the antibiotic mixture have at times presented difficulties. Mycostatin has been used at a cencentration of 50 units/ml. to free cultures of these contaminants. This antibiotic has not been included routinely because it appears to be somewhat toxic to the anemone cells.

The cell suspension used for the initial isolations is prepared by mincing the animal in a beaker with a pair of scissors. In some cases, lysozyme (1.5 mg./ml. of animal) was added to degrade the mucus that is secreted. Approximately five volumes of artificial sea water is added per volume of minced tissue, and the mixture is stirred briefly. It is allowed to stand in an ice bath for approximately five minutes and filtered through two layers of cheese cloth. The filtered suspension is freed of large tissue fragments by centrifugation at 5° for 30 seconds at approximately 1000 g. The cell suspension containing very few tissue fragments is then centrifuged as above for 10 minutes. The cells are resuspended in sterile artificial sea water and the differential centrifugation is repeated. The cells are finally washed three more times with sterile artificial sea water. The last washing employs artificial sea water to which has been added antibiotics at the above-mentioned concentration. The cell suspension is diluted to a concentration of close to 3×10^7 cells/ml. This corresponds to 0.100 O.D. at 660 mμ in the Beckman Spectrophotometer Model DU and is about equal to 100 μg. of cell protein/ml. or 5×10^{-4} ml. of packed cells/ml. One-tenth ml. of such a suspension is used as the culture inoculum. Figure 1 shows the appearance of such a suspension. There is great heterogeneity of cell type, and the outstanding contaminant appears to be fragments of fibrous material from the mesoglea. The two comet-shaped objects in the center of Figure 1 are this material. The cells show a size range from 8–2 μ.

The inoculum is placed in either a 60 mm Petri dish or into a test tube of 15×130 mm. containing a piece of coverslip 10×20 mm. Five ml. of nutrient solution is added and mixed with the inoculum. The test tubes are slanted to allow the cells to settle

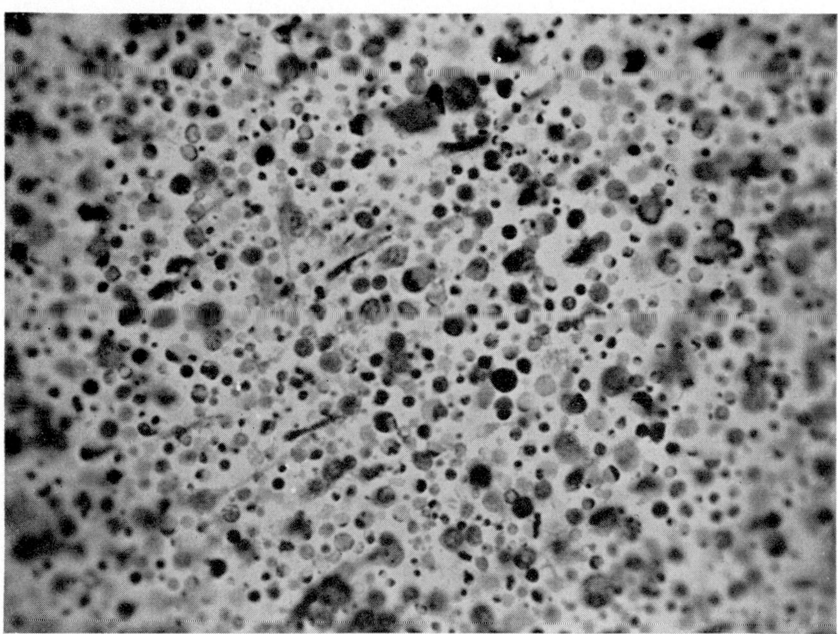

Fig. 1. Suspension of cells obtained from *A. elegantissima*. Stained with periodic acid Schiff's. Magnification 900x.

on the piece of coverslip. Either kind of preparation is incubated at 15°. The cultures are examined microscopically at a magnification of 100x. Figure 2 shows well-developed clones growing on the side of a tube culture. The piece of coverslip may be removed from such cultures and used for more detailed examination. Growing cultures can be maintained in tubes for prolonged periods of time, provided that fresh nutrient solution is added at weekly intervals. A suspension of cells can be obtained for transfer to new cultures by simply scraping some of the growth from the glass surface with a sterile spatula or through the use of lysozyme 1.5 mg./ml. in 0.3 *M* ethylene diamine tetracetic acid adjusted to pH 8.3 with NaOH. In either case, the final dispersal of the clumps of cells requires agitation. Generally, the suspension is drawn back and forth through a pipette. Cell suspensions may be standardized as indicated above; however, complete dispersal is generally not attained. The isolation of clones developing from

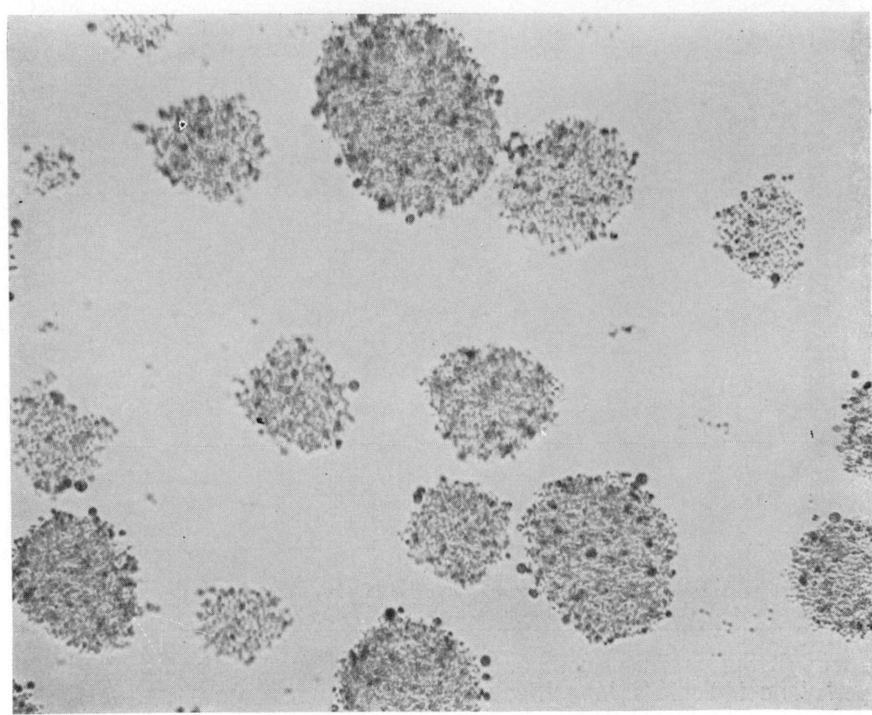

Fig. 2. Clones of *A. elegantissima* growing on the side of a test tube. Magnification 129x.

single cells is generally made difficult by the slight movement of cells over the surface of the glass. Therefore, cloning procedure of Puck (7) is generally used. Cells are mixed with 10 ml. of nutrient medium containing 0.2% agar, and the mixture is placed in a Petri dish containing a layer of 1% agar in artificial sea water. Developing clones are observed as clusters of cells that are generally separated from one another by a distance equal to the cell diameter. Development from a four through a thirty-two cell stage can be observed. The generation time is somewhat in excess of twenty-four hours. The clone can be removed with a capillary pipette and transferred to fresh nutrient solution. Because of the distinctive appearance of a developing clone, there is no difficulty in avoiding clumps of cells which were present in the inoculum.

The appearance of the cells growing *in vitro* shows certain

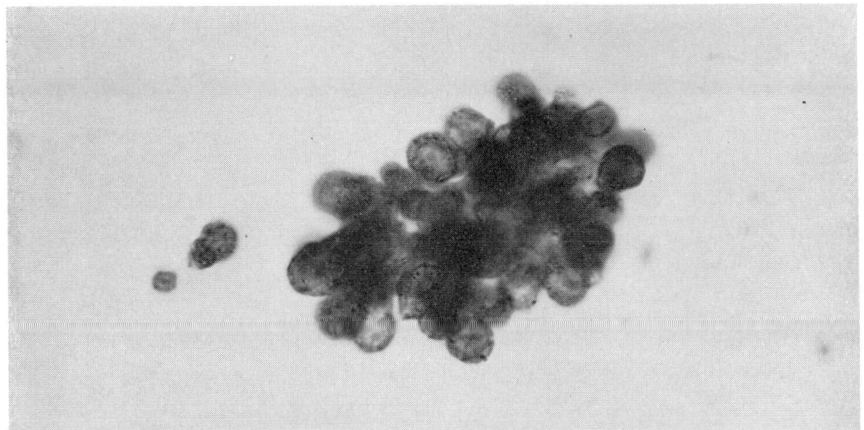

Fig. 3. Twelve-day-old clone of cells from A. *elegantissima*. Stained with periodic acid Schiff's. Magnification 900x.

peculiarities, some of which it is hoped may be corrected through the use of a better nutrient medium. Suspensions of single cells obtained either directly from animals or from cultures do not show reaggregation. On the contrary, a developing clone generally shows outgrowth and separation of cells from the growing center. The separated cells occasionally move a short distance before becoming new centers of growth.

Figure 3 shows a twelve-day-old clone developing on a cover-slip. The preparation was fixed in methanol and stained with periodic acid Schiff's stain (5). The cells are filled with a granular material that makes observation of the nucleus very difficult. These granules, when observed in living cells by phase contrast microscopy appear as barred objects resembling mitochondria. Similar intracellular structures can be observed in suspensions of cells obtained directly from the animal, but such cells do not show as high a concentration of these objects. When these cultured cells are removed to artificial sea water containing ethylenediamine tetraacetic acid (EDTA), they rapidly change their appearance to that shown in Figure 4. The addition of sodium acetate to 0.1% Edamine medium appears to produce a similar effect which is under investigation at the time of this writing. Until the concentra-

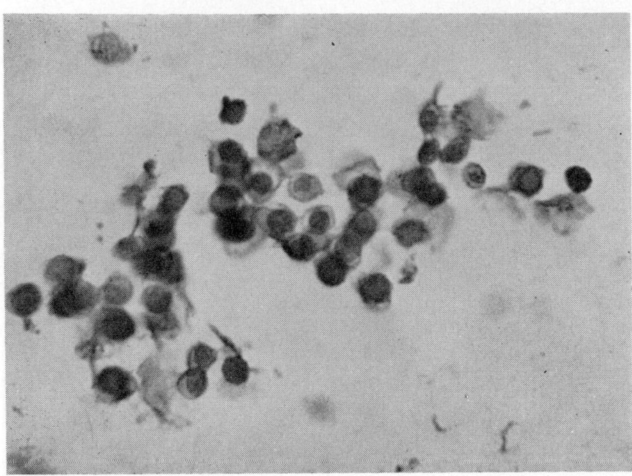

Fig. 4. Cultured cells washed with artificial sea water. Stained with periodic acid Schiff's. Magnification 900x.

tion of these particles can be controlled, observation of mitosis in developing clones is impossible.

The cells, particularly those toward the center of the clone in Figure 3, are surrounded by a red staining, carbohydrate-containing material which apparently acts as an intercellular cement. It can be weakened by both lysozyme and EDTA, but these agents even in combination do not result in complete separation of the cells. Since lysozyme functions as a $\beta(1 \rightarrow 4)$ N-acetyl hexosaminidase (8), the presence of this carbohydrate derivative in the material appears likely. The material is not susceptible to the chitinase of *Helix pomatia*, hyaluronidase, nor trypsin. The action of EDTA suggests either the presence of bridges formed by divalent ions or possibly the activation of the lysozyme-like enzyme that has been detected in the secretions of these animals (6). Pollak's trichrome stain (9) has also been used in studies of this material. It is again stained red. This staining reaction is given by elastic fibers. Mucus assumes a green coloration by this staining procedure. It appears likely that the material in question is other than mucus. Until the nature of this material is better understood, the methods for its degradation are available, quantitative work—for example, the accurate determination of generation time and cloning efficiency—is made difficult.

The ease with which cell lines from this anemone can be established and maintained in the laboratory is encouraging. It will be of interest to determine if the cells of other coelenterates behave in a similar manner.

These studies were supported by grants from the National Science Foundation and the United States Public Health Service.

REFERENCES

1. CARY, L. R. 1931. Report on invertebrate tissue culture. *Carnegie Inst. Wash. Yr. Bk. 30:* 379-381.
2. LEWIS, M. R. 1915-1916. Sea water as a medium for tissue cultures. *Anat. Rec. 10:* 287-299.
3. MACLEOD, R. A., E. ONOFREY and M. E. NORRIS. 1954. Nutrition and metabolism of marine bacteria. I. Survey of nutritional requirements. *J. Bact. 68:* 680-686.
4. MADIN, S. H., P. C. ANDRIESE and N. B. DARBY. 1957. The *in vitro* cultivation of tissues of domestic and laboratory animals. *Amer. J. of Vet. Res. 69:* 932-941.
5. PHILLIPS, J. H. *In vitro* maintenance and cultivation of cells from marine invertebrates. *Methods in Medical Research* (in press).
6. PHILLIPS, J. H. Immune mechanisms in the Phylum Coelenterata, Second Annual Symposium on Comparative Biology. *The Lower Metazoa: Comparative Biology and Phylogeny.* To be published by Academic Press, N. Y.
7. PUCK, T. T., P. I. MARCUS and S. J. CIECIURA. 1956. Clonal growth of mammalian cells *in vitro. J. Exp. Med. 103:* 273-284.
8. SALTON, M. J. R. and J. M. GHUYSEN. 1959. The structure of di and tetra saccharides released from cell walls by lysozyme and streptomyces F_1 enzyme and the $\beta(1 \rightarrow 4)$ N-acetyl hexosaminidase activity of these enzymes. *Biochim. et Biophys. Acta 36:* 552-554.
9. SANO, M. E. 1949. Trichrome stain for tissue section, culture, or smear. *Amer. J. Clin. Path. 19:* 898.

DISCUSSION

MUSCATINE: Was the animal kept in artificial sea water?

PHILLIPS: Our artificial sea water preparation is capable of maintaining the intact animal for a long period of time, but they are normally kept in real sea water.

MUSCATINE: Is there any particular criterion that you use for the well-being of the animal?

PHILLIPS: No. It just continues to look healthy.

GOREAU: That is a beautiful piece of work. Do you know what cell types your cultures actually come from? Have you tried adding zooxanthellae?

PHILLIPS: I haven't tried adding zooxanthellae. Some people at Stanford are interested in this problem. I am planning to give them my cultures to do this. With respect to the cell that I have growing in culture, this becomes an extremely difficult question to answer. For one thing, the appearance of the cells growing in culture may be markedly different from the cells that one sees in the intact animal as all the cells tend to round up on being freed from the tissue mass. This makes it impossible, on the basis of cell shape, to decide whether it is endoderm, mesoglea, or ectoderm.

GOREAU: Perhaps you could start your cultures with scrapings from specific areas rather than the whole animal.

PHILLIPS: This is something we want to try. I have not devoted a great deal of work to these culture lines although I've had them in the laboratory for sometime.

GOREAU: A very important matter to anyone who has ever tried to dissect living coelenterates is the horrible problem of being flooded with mucus. Are you actually cutting this down with lysozyme?

PHILLIPS: Definitely. There is one trick to that. The lysozyme should not be added to sea water. High electrolyte concentration is quite inhibitory to the action of lysozyme. It decreases its activity by almost 50%. That's the reason I add it directly to the animal before mincing the tissue.

There is another thing I should mention, namely, the use of fluorescent antibody techniques for identification of materials within tissue. I have carried out work of this sort with these cells using rabbit anti-anemone serum and fluorescently labeled dog anti-rabbit globulin serum. This leads to a nice fluorescent uptake by the cells growing in culture, and it also results in an uptake of fluorescence by whole cell suspensions. But, I would not care to put this forth as anything but supporting evidence for these cells being from the anemone. I think this proof must come from repeated isolations, such as we carried out, and from a comparative study of the morphology of the cells. Also a consideration of the cloning efficiency assists in discarding the possibility that the cultured cell is some parasite present in small numbers within the animal.

WAINWRIGHT: Have you tried collagenase on the intercellular material?

PHILLIPS: No. Those are the only enzymes I have tried so far. It is resistant to trypsin and hyaluronidase but degraded by lysozyme.

WOOD: I was not quite clear about your statements concerning the mitochondria. Have you tried a specific mitochondrial staining technique or do you have other criteria for identification?

PHILLIPS: No. I simply said that they resembled mitochondria in that they were markedly bar shaped. That's all.

STREHLER: Is there only one morphological type of cell?

PHILLIPS: One sees a variety of cell types in developing cultures. For example, the ratio between nuclear and cytoplasmic size varies as well as the distribution of the granules within the cells. At the same time clone cultures derived from a single cell also shows this variation.

SLAUTTERBACK: If the anemone is anything like hydra, you can determine whether or not they are gastroderm cells by exposing the animal to a thorotrast solution for a short time. Thorium dioxide serves as an excellent tag because only gastroderm cells pinocytize it.

WOOD: Could you be certain that free cells derived from ectoderm would not pinocytize or phagocytize some thorotrast?

PHILLIPS: These cells do show a rapid uptake of such materials as bovine and human serum albumin. If one labels such proteins with azo dyes within 15 minutes you get cells with brightly stained inclusions and the cells remain colored for long periods of time. In fact, it was in connection with immunological studies that I first became interested in cultivating these cells.

SLAUTTERBACK: In response to Dr. Wood's comment, my suggestion was that the animal be exposed to the colloidal thorium dioxide before it was cut up. In that case there would be no thorium in the ectoderm cells.

PHILLIPS: True, if the label remains.

PASSANO: What is the chromosomal integrity in your clones over a period of time?

PHILLIPS: I don't know. Until I can get rid of these granules and control their formation I do not want to even attempt to observe mitotic figures.

STREHLER: Does colchicine block their mitosis?

PHILLIPS: I have not tried it yet.

Symbiosis in Marine and Fresh Water Coelenterates

LEONARD MUSCATINE
Laboratories of Biochemistry, Howard Hughes Medical Institute, Miami, Florida

In studying the significance of symbiotic algae for the nutrition and growth of their invertebrate hosts, we have been guided by two objectives: a) to establish the existence of a nutritional relationship between algae and host, and b) to characterize the chemical basis of this relationship.

Direct evidence for the contribution of carbon compounds from symbiotic algae to the tissues of the host has been demonstrated in a sea anemone (9), a coral (3), and in green hydra (5).

In this paper, we demonstrate a direct relationship between algal symbionts and changes in mass or growth of a marine and a fresh-water coelenterate. Our data show that retarded weight loss, enhanced growth, and prolonged survival of the animals studied could be attributed to the presence of symbiotic algae.

STUDIES ON SEA ANEMONES[1, 2]

Experiments demonstrating retardation of weight loss were conducted on *Anthopleura elegantissima* (Brandt, 1835), an intertidal anemone which contains zooxanthellae within its gastrodermal cells (Fig. 1). Specimens without algae, found beneath fish canneries

[1]Part of a thesis submitted in partial fulfillment of the requirements for the degree of doctor of Philosophy, Department of Zoology, University of California, Berkeley.

[2]This investigation was supported by a fellowship (EF-9653) from the National Institutes of Allergy and Infectious Diseases, Public Health Service.

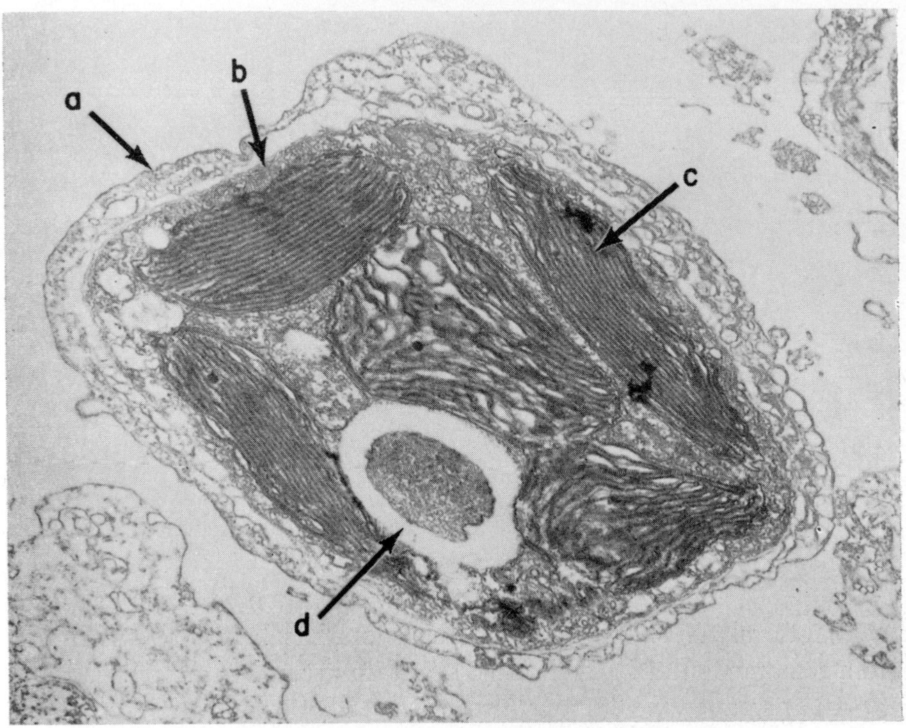

Fig. 1. Electron micrograph of a transverse section through a musculo-epithelial cell of an anemone showing the intracellular location of an algal cell. a) animal cell. b) algal cell. c) chromatophore. d) pyrenoid. (Prepared with the assistance of Miss Jane Westfall)

at Pacific Grove, California, served as controls and are referred to as albinos.

In order to evaluate quantitatively the effect of the algae on the nutrition of the host, we measured changes in weight of normal and albino anemones starved in light and darkness for 11 weeks. Reduced weight, i.e., weight under water, was used to measure weight changes. This method eliminates error from surplus fluid and, in contrast to dry weight, allows repeated measurements on living individuals.[3]

[3]There were no major changes in the specific gravity of the animals themselves during the course of the experiment, showing that all of the observed changes were true weight changes.

Fig. 2. Arrangement of apparatus for rapid measurement of the reduced weight of a sea anemone in sea water of known temperature and density. The animal is suspended by a thin constantan wire hooked into its actinopharynx.

Two groups of five normal anemones were placed into aerated containers of twice-filtered sea water at 14.0° ± 1.5°. One group was continually illuminated by 200 ft. c. of fluorescent illumination (Champion–Warm White) while the other was kept continually in darkness. Both groups were allowed to starve.[4] The reduced weight of each individual was measured (Fig. 2) at intervals of four days or more and the sea water in all containers was renewed weekly. Individuals in darkness were weighed in dim light. As additional controls, two groups of five albino anemones were treated in a manner identical to the normal symbiotized anemones. Details

[4]Fed anemones were unsatisfactory experimental animals. Erratic behavior (e.g. premature egestion, failure to feed) interfered with attempts to control feeding.

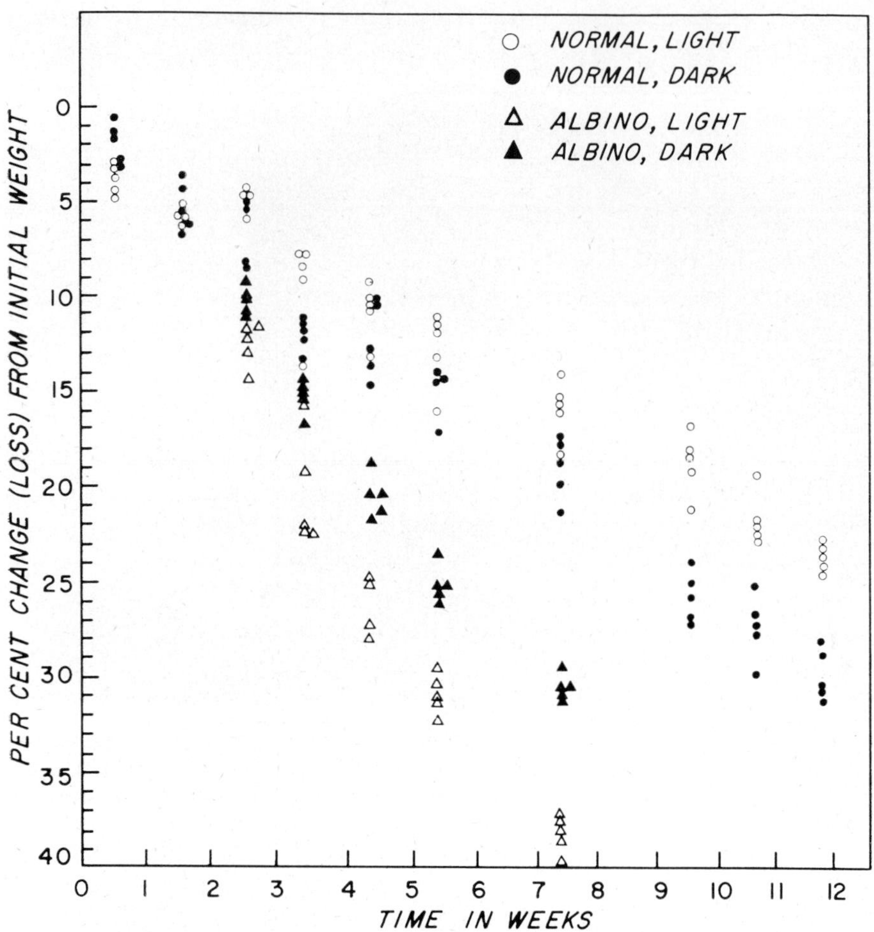

Fig. 3. Change in reduced weight of normal and albino anemones starved in light and darkness. The ordinate is the percent change from initial weight and denotes weight loss.

of other methods in these experiments are given elsewhere (8). Reduced weight changes of symbiotized and albino anemones starved in light and darkness are depicted in Figure 3, and expressed as percent change from initial weight vs. time in weeks. The results show that during starvation all anemones lost weight at a near constant rate, and that symbiotized anemones lost weight at about half the rate of albinos. The possibility that light could have directly affected weight loss was tentatively ruled out since albinos in light and darkness lost weight at the same rate. We therefore conclude that the lower rate of weight loss by symbiotized anemones is related to the presence of algae.

These observations, along with evidence from tracer studies (9), suggest that during starvation carbon contributed by the algae, together with host excretory nitrogen, is used for the synthesis of organic compounds necessary for maintenance of weight. This view emphasizes the possible secondary role of the algae in reclaiming waste nitrogen.

STUDIES ON HYDRA

With the introduction of techniques for the mass culture of *Hydra* (7) an opportunity presented itself for quantitative studies on plant-animal symbiosis in the laboratory. *Chlorohydra viridissima,*[5] a hydra containing zoochlorellae within its gastrodermal cells (14), may now be grown under controlled environmental conditions and in a fluid of known ionic constitution. Growth may be measured in terms of protein or logarithmic increase in number of hydranths (6). In addition, problems encountered with sea anemones, such as removal of algae and erratic feeding behavior, are easily resolved.

C. viridissima was routinely grown in our laboratory in the following culture medium ("M" solution): $10^{-3}M$ Tris (hydroxy) methylaminomethane buffer, pH 7.6, $10^{-3}M$ $CaCl_2$, $10^{-3}M$ $NaHCO_3$, $10^{-4}M$ KCl, and $10^{-4}M$ $MgCl_2$, in de-ionized water.

Algae-free *C. viridissima* were obtained by growing green individuals in M solution plus 0.5% glycerin (v/v) for 7-10 days, following the original technique of Whitney (13). These albinos then grew normally in M solution and did not regain an algal flora.

Growth studies. All growth experiments were conducted at 21°-23° using the method of Loomis (7). Ten hydranths (five uniform hydra, see ref. 4) from mass cultures were put in 30 ml. of M solution in shallow Petri dishes placed four inches from a single 40-watt fluorescent light (Sylvania-Cool White). Daily, the

[5]Tentative identification.

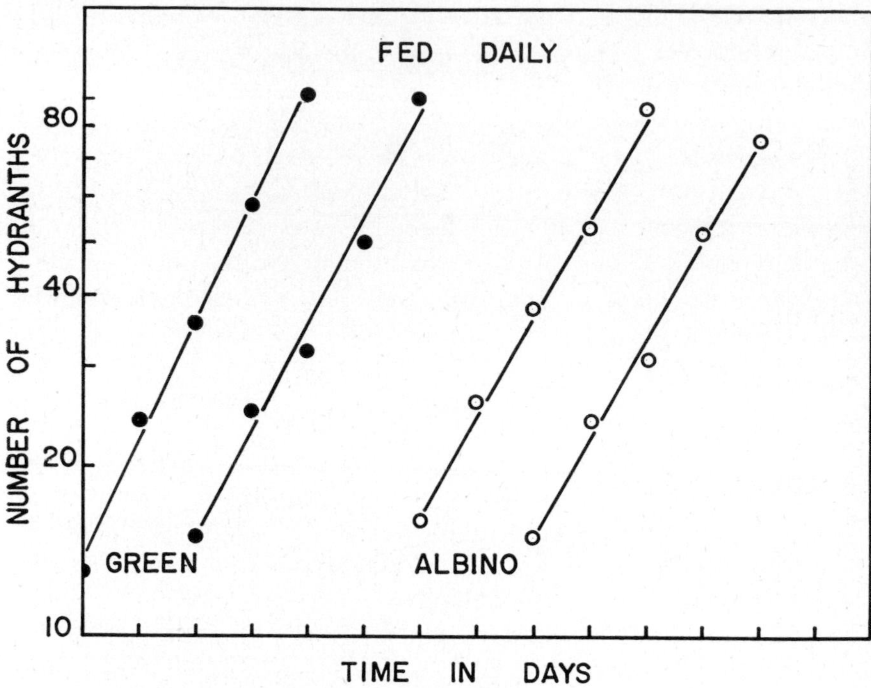

Fig. 4. Semi-log plot of growth rates of duplicate cultures of green and albino *C. viridissima* fed daily in the light.

number of hydranths was counted and then each hydranth was fed on a dense suspension of *Artemia* nauplii. One hour after feeding and again, six hours later, the culture medium was renewed. This routine was followed for 5-7 days.

Figure 4 shows that green and albino *C. viridissima,* when fed daily, have nearly identical logarithmic growth rates. These results imply that the algae do not contribute anything to the host that cannot be acquired from an exogenous food supply. Under optimal conditions, nutritional benefit would not be expected to manifest itself in terms of growth of the host because the maximum growth rate (k_{max}), a property intrinsic to the species, cannot be exceeded, regardless of the magnitude of the algal contribution. Therefore, we conducted growth experiments in which the amount of food was limited, reasoning that this would then allow benefit from the algae to express itself. Figure 5 demonstrates that, when fed every second

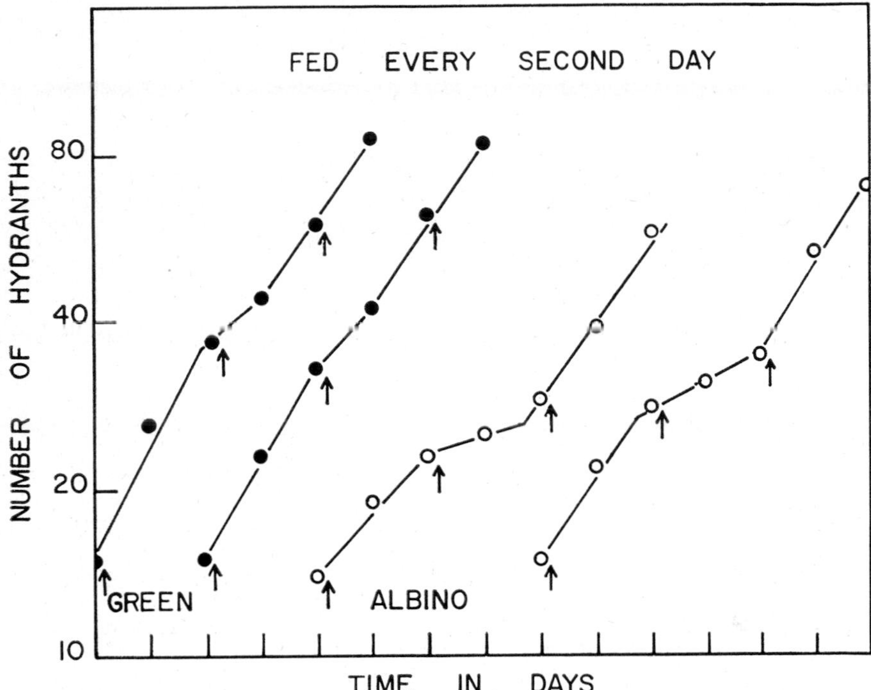

Fig. 5. Same as Figure 4 but fed every second day. Arrow denotes time of feeding.

day, green hydra deviated only slightly from normal logarithmic growth. But under the same conditions, albino hydra showed not only a more pronounced deviation, but also required more time to regain normal growth after feeding was resumed. More striking differences appeared when these two groups were fed every third day. Figure 6 illustrates the sharp decline in rate of budding by both groups during the interval without food. But after feeding, green hydra immediately resumed a normal maximum growth rate. In contrast, growth of albinos lagged and did not return to normal.

The effect of complete elimination of food is shown in Figure 7. Ten hydranths of each kind were removed from mass cultures and starved in the light in 30 ml. of M solution in Petri dishes (4″ diam.). The culture medium was renewed once daily. Under these conditions, green hydra continued to produce buds for 7-9 days and

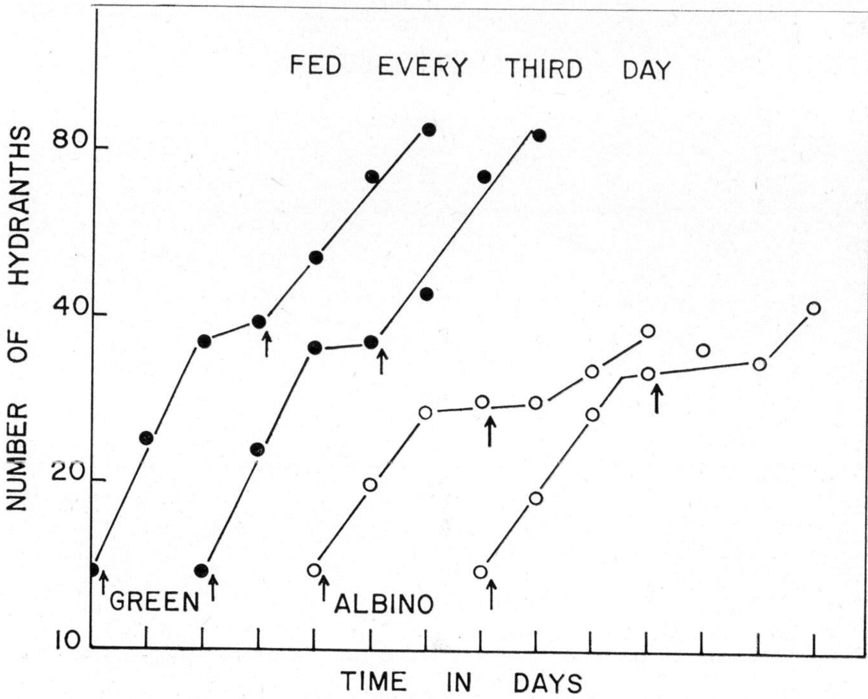

Fig. 6. Same as Figure 5 but fed every third day.

survived an additional 7-10 days until gradual diminution in size resulted in death. In contrast, albino *C. viridissima,* under these conditions, stopped budding after 1-3 days; within the next six days, all had disintegrated. These results show that the algae are essential for prolonged survival under starvation conditions.

Early disintegration and death of albinos was unusual since a characteristic of most species of hydra, including green *C. viridissima,* is to gradually "waste away" when starved (1). One explanation of this death gives us a clue to a possible nutritional role of the algae. Dixon (2) has stated that tissue death results from inability to synthesize coenzymes. By removing algae from *C. viridissima* we may have removed a source of coenzymes, or coenzyme precursors, normally available from algae during starvation or from food during normal feeding conditions. This idea fits well with results of limited food experiments, where green hydra show maximum growth imme-

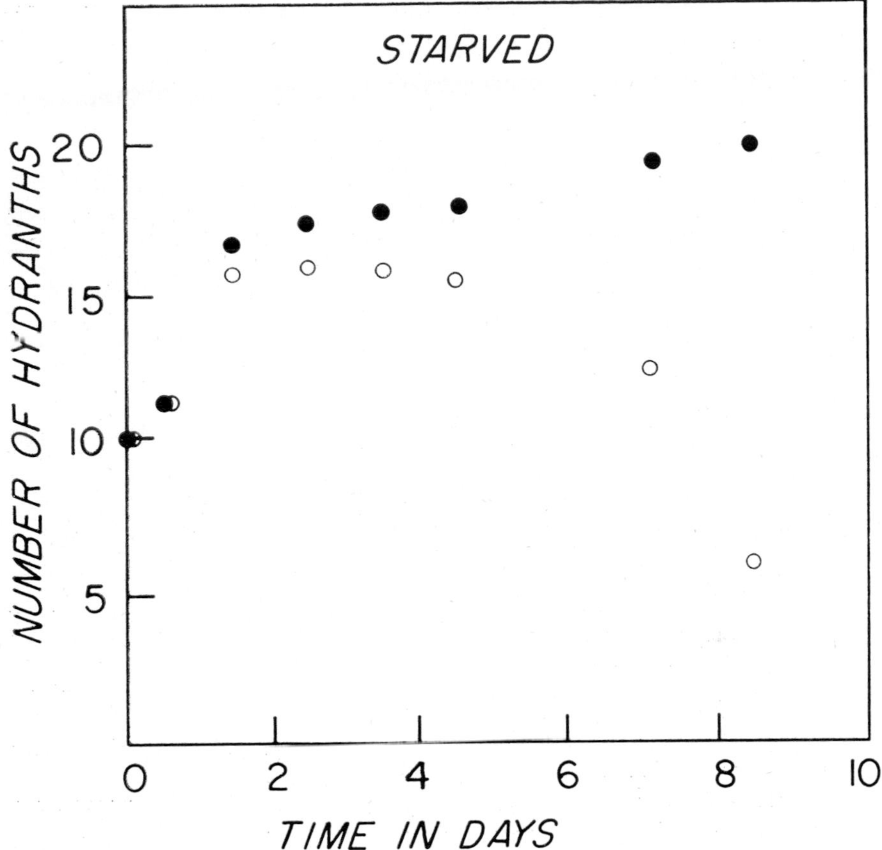

Fig. 7. Bud production and survival of green (closed circles) and albino (open circles) *C. viridissima* starved in light. Each point represents the mean number of hydranths in duplicate culture vessels.

diately after feeding (Figs. 5, 6) suggesting that they are primed with cofactors necessary for the efficient conversion of crustacean protein into coelenterate protein. In contrast, albinos showed a lag after feeding. This lag may represent the time during which a cofactor from food is mobilized.

These data take on special interest when compared to the results of field studies on the nutrition of corals. Corals containing zooxanthellae grow optimally in spite of a low exogenous food supply (10, 11, 12). Our results with *C. viridissima* suggest that symbiotic algae can account for this by promoting efficient utilization of available food.

ACKNOWLEDGEMENTS

It is a pleasure to acknowledge the counsel of Drs. C. Hand and R. I. Smith at the University of California, Berkeley. Studies on hydra were initiated under the guidance of Dr. H. M. Lenhoff, to whom I am indebted for help in all phases of this investigation.

REFERENCES

1. Brien, P. 1961. The fresh-water hydra. *Amer. Sci. 48:* 461-475.
2. Dixon, M. 1941. *Multi-enzyme systems.* Cambridge, 100 pp.
3. Goreau, T. F. and N. I. Goreau. 1960. Distribution of labeled carbon in reef-building corals with and without zooxanthellae. *Science 131:* 668-669.
4. Lenhoff, H. M. and J. Bovaird. 1961. A quantitative chemical approach to problems of nematocyst distribution and replacement in *Hydra. Develop. Biol. 3:* 227-240.
5. Lenhoff, H. M. and K. F. Zimmerman. 1959. Biochemical studies of symbiosis in *Chlorohydra viridissima. Anat. Rec. 134:* 559.
6. Loomis, W. F. 1954. Environmental factors controlling growth in hydra. *J. Exp. Zool. 126:* 223-234.
7. Loomis, W. F. and H. M. Lenhoff. 1956. Growth and sexual differentiation of hydra in mass culture. *J. Exp. Zool. 132:* 555-574.
8. Muscatine, L. 1961. Some aspects of the relationship between a sea anemone and its symbiotic algae. Ph.D. Thesis, University of California, Berkeley, 100 pp.
9. Muscatine, L. and C. Hand. 1958. Direct evidence for transfer of materials from symbiotic algae to the tissues of a coelenterate. *Proc. Nat. Acad. Sci. 44:* 1259-1263.
10. Odum, H. T. and E. P. Odum. 1955. Trophic structure and productivity of a windward coral reef community on Eniwetok atoll. *Ecol. Monogr. 25:* 291-320.
11. Sargent, M. and T. S. Austin. 1949. Organic productivity of an atoll. *Trans. Amer. Geophys. Union 30:* 245-249.
12. Sargent, M. and T. S. Austin. 1954. Biologic economy of coral reefs. U. S. Geol. Survey Prof. Pap. 260E, pp. 299-300.
13. Whitney, D. D. 1907. Artificial removal of the green bodies of *Hydra viridis. Biol. Bull. 13:* 291-299.
14. Wood, R. L. 1959. Intercellular attachment in the epithelium of *Hydra* as revealed by electron microscopy. *J. Biophysic. Biochem. Cytol. 6:* 343-352. See also p. 55, this volume.

DISCUSSION

WAINWRIGHT: Is the number of hydranths proportional to the total amount of protein?

MUSCATINE: Yes, the relationship is linear up to about 75 hydranths.

WAINWRIGHT: Is this so in the starved experiment?

MUSCATINE: Preliminary experiments show that after 5 days of starvation albinos consist of less protein per hydranth than the greens.

EAKIN: Are you carrying along the colorless algae as a parasite in your albino organism?

MUSCATINE: Microscopic examination after treatment with glycerin indicates that algae are no longer present. We use only those albinos which do not regain an algal flora when placed back in the glycerin-free culture solution.

EAKIN: I will be reporting on an organism we developed by culturing *Chlorohydra* in the dark, one which we call "brown *Chlorohydra,*" and which undoubtedly corresponds to your "albino." We have not been able to detect the presence of any colorless algae in them.

BURNETT: One of my students, Peter Wernik, finds that albinos take in more glycogen and protein reserve droplets than do green hydra.

MUSCATINE: Do you feel that the green hydra use food more efficiently than the albinos?

BURNETT: I don't know. Possibly the greens aren't requiring as much; a hydra always takes in just about what he needs. Did I understand you to say that your animals budded during 8 days of starvation?

MUSCATINE: Yes, budding by green hydra persists for a week. They double their number in this time.

GOREAU: What is the ratio of plant to animal biomass in *Chlorohydra?*

MUSCATINE: I have no information on the algae in *Chlorohydra* yet. But I have good data for *Anthopleura elegantissima* where one can determine the biomass of the alga flora by using quantative pigment techniques.

GOREAU: You mean chlorophyll?

MUSCATINE: Yes, and the various carotenoids. Using the method of Richards with Thompson, and using cell counts and dry weight data from pure suspensions of zooxanthellae, we find that in *Anthopleura*, the ratio of animal to algae on a dry weight basis is about 332 to 1.

GOREAU: Such data is very important in relation to turnover studies.

CLAYBROOK: How critical is the magnesium requirement for *Chlorohydra*? Is this essential or does it merely increase the growth rate?

MUSCATINE: The maximum doubling time of green or albino hydra is about 1.2 days. Without magnesium it is only 1.9 to 2.8 days.

LENHOFF: I think it's important to add that they *require* magnesium in order to grow. When we first received our *Chlorohydra*, we could not grow them on any of our other culture solutions. The last cation that we tried was magnesium. Then they doubled nearly every day.

CLAYBROOK: In our experiments with *Chlorohydra,* we don't add any magnesium to the solution.

MUSCATINE: Well, there is a possibility that they get enough in their food, or perhaps you have a different strain of animals?

CLAYBROOK: It could be.

EAKIN: Although we have maintained our *Chlorohydra* in synthetic solutions to which we have added no magnesium (solutions which give optimal maintenance conditions for *Hydra littoralis*), we find that the addition of Mg^{++} decreases the doubling time and on occasions has caused clones showing signs of depression to return to normal.

LOOMIS: We grow them happily in 5% artificial seawater. We make up an MBL artificial seawater with deionized water, not distilled. That's the main thing, no copper. In fact, we have nearly a dozen hydroids growing in artificial seawater. *Cordylophora* grows nicely in 10% MBL water while *Chlorohydra* grows in 5% MBL. Of course, that has magnesium in it.

I would like to make another point. Some day, somebody ought to study how glycerine makes the endothelial cells spit out their contained *Chlorella.* It would be interesting to study this incredible reaction, as well as to try and reinfect albino green hydra with free *Chlorella.* I don't think this has ever been done with green hydra, or lichens either. In other words, you can separate; but no one has yet recombined the two symbiotic forms that I know of.

SLAUTTERBACK: Regarding reinfection, I have taken eggs, which as you know are white, from *Chlorohydra* and hatched them separately. If the resulting albinos are returned to a culture of green hydra, they remain white for about 2 weeks.

FULTON: I think some German workers have succeeded in reinfecting white *Chlorohydra,* but not other species of hydra. Incidentally, we found that the antibiotic chloramphenical cures green hydra of the algae in a couple of days, much faster than glycerine.

MUSCATINE: What concentration was used?

FULTON: I'm not certain, but I think it was 200 μg. per ml.

MUSCATINE: I tried various algicides with the anemones, and neither the commercial product Algaedyne, which is a colloidal silver solution, nor a high concentration of Streptomycin, nor starvation in darkness succeeded in totally ridding the animal of its algae. When starved in darkness the animal becomes very small but still retains algal cells which can be shown to increase in pigment content. This might be regarded as evidence for heterotrophic activity in these zooxanthellae.

FULTON: Did you try chloroamphenicol?

MUSCATINE: No.

BURNETT: Have you ever noticed differences in the distribution of the algae along the column?

MUSCATINE: Yes, very often one sees regional differences. However, I am not sure of the significance of this.

BURNETT: I mention this because I had a chance to observe a very interesting green hydra in Brien's laboratory. This animal (*H. viridis*) underwent what seems to be a somatic mutation. The peduncle on this form resembles a stolon and is several times larger than the gastric region. The whole animal may be one and a half inches long, surprising dimensions for a green hydra. The peduncle, unlike that of normal *H. viridis,* contains more algal bodies per cell than the gastric region. Also food materials pass into this region in greater amounts than into a normal peduncle. What is most interesting is that this mutant form not only reproduces asexually by budding but also by pinching off the distal portion of its peduncle. This detached portion then regenerates into a complete organism. It is marvelous!

EAKIN: Did you try increasing the oxygen tension while growing the albino hydras?

MUSCATINE: Well, we're just getting into gas analysis. We have conducted preliminary experiments growing green and albino hydra in air plus 0.4% CO_2, but the results were not definitive. Eventually we will control pCO_2 and pO_2.

EAKIN: It will be interesting to see if the high oxygen tension can reverse some of the effects observed in the absence of the algal chlorophyll.

MUSCATINE: Yes, that's a good way to attack this, going through the algae. I would also like to see if green hydra show an action spectrum for growth rates which can be related to the absorption spectrum of chlorophyll.

On the Relation of Calcification to Primary Productivity in Reef Building Organisms

T. F. Goreau

Physiology Department, University College of the West Indies, Mona, Jamaica, W. I., and Department of Marine Biochemistry and Ecology, New York Zoological Society.

Coral reefs are tropical shallow water communities built up by calcareous organisms attached to the sea bottom. Such ecosystems may be regarded as biochemical factories which catalyse a large scale transfer of dissolved calcium and carbonate ions from sea water into the sediments as insoluble calcium carbonate. The resulting reef limestones are deposited in typical formations which may in time become several thousand feet thick, as for example in some of the Pacific atolls (9).

A unique characteristic of coral reefs, found in no other depositional system in the biosphere, is that maximum biological accretion of calcareous matter takes place only in the turbulent surface waters where the forces of mechanical and chemical erosion are also at a maximum. Corals and algae which build reefs do so by secreting hard calcareous masses that become aggregated into an organised coherent structure adapted for maximum attenuation of mechanical stresses set up by the constant battering of the seas, yet so shaped as to expose a maximum surface area for efficient matter-energy exchange with the environment. The papers of Tracey *et al.* (16) and Emery *et al.* (1) should be consulted for further aspects of this problem.

In the West Indies, the interlocking reef framework is built up by the larger Scleractinia and Milleporidae, their separate colonies becoming cemented into a single unit by lithothamnioid algae. The finer, more voluminous, lagoon and forward slope sediments are produced chiefly by calcareous green algae, with Scleractinia, Gorgonia, Foraminifera, sponges, mollusks, arthropods and echinoderms contributing in various proportions depending on local factors. Owing to its stability and exposure to the seas, the framework is probably the site where most of the calcium carbonate production of the reef occurs. Only a fraction of this is ultimately deposited *in situ* since the greater part of the calcareous material produced here is washed out by waves and redeposited in the calmer water of the lagoon or the seaward slope.

A large proportion of the total biomass of coral reefs is due to algae which grow in great abundance in all zones, ranging from the shallowest parts of the rampart to depths exceeding two hundred feet on the forward slope. The algal population of reefs can be divided into two categories: the free-living fleshy, filamentous, and calcareous algae; and the symbiotic unicellular zooxanthellae living in coelenterates.

All reef-building Scleractinian corals without exception contain zooxanthellae. So do most Hydrocorals, Actinaria, Zoanthidea, Alcyonaria and Gorgonia living in reefs. According to the existing nomenclature, those calcareous coelenterates which have zooxanthellae are said to be hermatypic, or reef-building; whereas those species lacking zooxanthellae are said to be ahermatypic or non-reef building. The former are limited in their vertical distribution to the upper parts of the euphotic zone and never grow in dark places. The ahermatypes are usually found in deep water below the euphotic zone although some species occur in shallow water where they tend to favour dark crevices. The basic difference between hermatypic and ahermatypic coelenterates is that the former grow much faster to much larger sizes than the latter. Nevertheless, some ahermatypic corals are known under certain conditions to form deep-sea banks which bear a superficial resemblance to shallow water reefs (14).

Although there is an absolute correlation between the presence of zooxanthellae in calcareous coelenterates and their ability to build reefs, the relationship of the algae to their hosts and to the bio-economy of the reef as a whole is not yet clearly understood. The so-called "zooxanthella problem" has been the subject of much controversy because some investigators have failed to recognise the multiplicity of host-symbiont relationships in the different groups of coelenterates: ranging from total nutritional dependence on zooxanthellae in some xeniid Alcyonacea (2) to nutritional independence in the Scleractinia which are specialised carnivores (21). There can be little doubt that zooxanthella-coelenterate symbioses have evolved independently in many unrelated groups at different times, thus accounting for the haphazard variety of the association in the various classes and orders of the phylum. For further details and references regarding the zooxanthella problem, the papers of Yonge (19, 20), Vaughan and Wells (17), Odum and Odum (10), and Goreau (4) should be consulted.

CALCIUM DEPOSITION AND PHOTOSYNTHESIS IN REEF CORALS

Growth in corals is achieved by an increase in mass of the calcareous skeleton and a concommittant proliferation of the overlying tissues. Our recent underwater studies on reef corals suggest that even within any given species there may be no constant relationship between these two kinds of growth and that colony shape is to a certain extent controlled by variations in the ratio of new skeleton to new tissue. To study the factors which regulate calcification in corals and other calcareous organisms, we have developed new methods for the fast quantitative assay of growth by the use of radioactive tracers. Calcification is determined from the rate with which Ca^{45} ions added to the sea water medium is deposited into the skeleton as Ca^{45} CO_3 under various conditions, e.g. light and dark. The procedure, which has been described elsewhere (3, 6), requires only a few hours; the experimental runs can be carried out in the field, and growth gradients are determined by sampling different parts of experimental colonies.

Our observations demonstrate that calcification in reef-building corals is dependent on the ambient light intensity to the extent that growth in fourteen species tested is on the average ten times faster in sunlight than in darkness (6). Calcification is reduced by approximately fifty per cent on a cloudy day under otherwise similar conditions. By contrast, the calcification rates of some shallow water ahermatypic corals lacking zooxanthellae do not respond significantly to changes in light intensity. The stimulant effect of light on reef coral calcification disappears when the zooxanthellae are removed by culturing corals in darkness for about three months.

Inherent species specific factors, independent of the zooxanthellae, also exert an important influence on calcium deposition. One example of this is the growth gradient of ramose corals such as *Acropora cervicornis* where the large pale apical polyps that contain relatively few zooxanthellae calcify several times faster than the much smaller adjacent lateral corallities the tissues of which are packed with large masses of zooxanthellae. The enzyme carbonic anhydrase also appears to play an important role in coral calcification. We have found carbonic anhydrase activity in representative species of all major groups of Coelenterata. The occurrence of the enzyme has no relationship to the calcareous habit, or to the presence of zooxanthellae, which themselves do not contain significant amounts of carbonic anhydrase. The treatment of reef corals with a specific carbonic anhydrase inhibitor (Diamox, Lederle) results in an average fifty per cent reduction of the calcification rate in the light, and a seventy five per cent reduction in darkness. The effect of carbonic anhydrase inhibition on the calcification rate is partially reversed in the light when the zooxanthellae are photosynthesizing. It therefore appears that carbonic anhydrase and the zooxanthellae act in synergy to potentiate calcium deposition in corals (3).

The mechanisms responsible for the stimulation of skeletogenesis in corals by photosynthesis of zooxanthellae are not clearly understood. If the two reactions are linked through some common pathway, the coupling must be of a facultative type since calcification can proceed in the absence of photosynthesis, although at a much reduced rate. We have observed that calcification is speeded up very quickly following the exposure of the corals to adequate light intensities. The short time constant of the potentiation makes it unlikely that the stimulation is due to production of nutrients by the zooxanthellae, but rather to prompt changes in concentration of some substrate common to photosynthesis and calcification. In previous papers (3, 4) we advanced the working hypothesis that acceleration of $CaCO_3$ deposition would occur if algal photosynthesis were to remove CO_2 from the system and cause the equilibrium reaction

$$Ca(HCO_3)_2 \rightleftharpoons CaCO_3\downarrow + H_2CO_3\uparrow$$

to go to the right. Although the evidence for this is fairly pursuasive, other mechanisms may also be involved. Some of these will be discussed below.

In principle, the rate of $CaCO_3$ production could be stimulated in at least two ways: directly through control of the steady state bicarbonate concentration in the tissues as shown above, or indirectly by augmenting the supply of free energy available for active calcium transport through an increase in the rate and efficiency of cellular metabolism. In the discussion below, we will consider some of the possible indirect mechanisms. The onset of photosynthesis by the zooxanthellae immediately produces a rise in the intracellular oxygen concentration which may result in some increase in the rate and efficiency of metabolism in the coral. Thiel (15) and Yonge (19), among others, have already emphasized the probable importance of *in situ* production to the coral, but no specific mechanisms were proposed. There is at present no information on the relation between the pO_2 of the medium and the rate of coral growth. Nearly all hermatypic corals are net oxygen producers during the day, and the water circulating in the growing parts of the reef is as a rule supersaturated with oxygen (8, 10, 11, 12, 13) so that the dependence of calcification on oxygen would be difficult to measure in these organisms. In two ahermatypic corals lacking zooxanthellae (*Tubastrea* and *Astrangia*) we observed no significant changes in calcium deposition rates under conditions where the oxygen saturation of the medium varied between fifty and one hundred and twenty two per cent, suggesting that calcification rates in these corals are relatively independent of oxygen concentration within the limits tested.

Given an adequate supply of oxygen in the medium, far reaching effects on the rate and efficiency of metabolic reactions can be brought about by increasing the rate with which soluble waste products are removed from the coral cells (20). This is a far more potent metabolic stimulant than increasing the oxygen concentration. It has long been known that velocities of metabolic reactions are strictly limited by the rates with which the end products are removed from the immediate environment. In higher animals, this is accomplished by specialised circulatory and excretory systems which are lacking in the coelenterates. In the absence of zooxanthellae, or in darkness, corals are forced to rely on diffusion alone to get rid of the soluble inorganic waste products of cell metabolism. This is a slow process, especially when the surface area for exchange is reduced by retraction of the polyps into the calyces. This situation is radically altered in the presence of zooxanthellae which require for photosynthesis and primary production those very substances that the coral host must get rid of, e.g. CO_2, phosphates, nitrates, sulphates, ammonia, etc. Yonge and Nicholls (21) showed for some corals that zooxanthellae are capable of sufficiently high rates of photosynthesis to utilise not only all the soluble inorganic phosphate produced by coral colonies, but that additional phosphate is absorbed from the surrounding sea water.

Under conditions of adequate illumination, the zooxanthellae are to be regarded as combined intracellular lungs and kidneys. The observed speeding up of calcification in reef corals exposed to bright light may in part be due to an increase of the rate and efficiency with which metabolism can supply free energy to the carrier mechanism concerned with active calcium transport. The question whether the calcification rate is indeed related to the metabolic rate, and whether this is in turn influenced by the level of algal photosynthesis in the manner indicated above is now under investigation in our laboratory.

CARBONATE DEPOSITION, GROWTH AND PRODUCTIVITY

Elsewhere, we advocated the view that Ca^{++} and HCO^{-}_{3} ions dissolved in the ambient medium are the source of the mineral deposited in the skeleton as $CaCO_3$, and that these are brought to the calcification site by separate pathways (3). In order to test this directly we developed a technique in which the uptakes of Ca^{45} and C^{14} carbonate were measured simultaneously in a variety of calcareous coelenterates and algae, under natural conditions in the reef. As before, light and dark runs were carried out simultaneously, the experiments lasting between five and six hours. After washing and drying the specimens, activities due to Ca^{45} and C^{14} deposited in the skeleton were quantitatively isolated, and separated from the C^{14} activity fixed in the coenosarc as organic matter by photosynthesis of the zooxanthellae. A detailed description of this technique will be published later.

The data in Table I summarises results of field experiments carried out for the purpose of measuring simultaneously calcium and carbonate transfer rates from the medium into the test organisms. The plants and animals used in these investigations, and listed in Table I, belong to three different ecological categories: Group 1 consists of shallow water ahermatypic coelenterates which contribute only insignificant amounts of calcareous matter to the reef; Group 2 contains three hermatypic coelenterates which are chiefly reef framework builders; Group 3 has three hermatypic algae, the remains of which form the bulk of the fine calcareous lagoon and slope sediments. All these species are found in the actively growing part of the reef rampart at Maiden Cay, Jamaica, where these experiments were carried out.

The first two columns of Table I give the transfer rates of Ca^{45++} and $HC^{14}O^{-}_{3}$ into the mineral skeleton, the third column gives the rate of photosynthetic fixation of C^{14} into organic matter, e.g. the primary productivity. In the ahermatypic coelenterates lacking zooxanthellae, there are no significant light-dark differences in the calcium deposition rates, but in the hermatypic coelenterates containing zooxanthellae and in the hermatypic algae, these differences are extremely pronounced. An exception was the red alga *Amphiroa* where the calcification rate in darkness was much higher than in light. Not unexpectedly, the organic carbon fixation values observed in ahermatypic species were extremely low, and were probably due to heterotrophic exchange, or photosynthesis of boring algae in the skeleton.

The primary carbon fixation observed in hermatypic coelenterates was due to photosynthesis by zooxanthellae. The boring algae were present in only very small amounts in our samples and it is assumed that their contribution to the total productivity was also very small. Owing to uncertainty of the proportion of the plant biomass in corals, the data are given in terms of total nitrogen, e. g. animal plus plant. The highest calcification and productivity rates were observed in the hermatypic algae. The two species of *Halimeda* behaved like the hermatypic corals in that calcification was much faster in light than in darkness, but in *Amphiroa* there was a negative correlation between photosynthesis and skeletogensis. We believe that light inhibition of calcification in this species is produced by a shortage of available carbonate due to competition for CO_2 as a common substrate by extremely high levels of photosynthesis. This problem is now being investigated in our laboratory.

There is a positive correlation between the calcium deposition rate and the photosynthetic rate as measured by the specific primary productivity, e. g. the amount of organic matter produced in

TABLE 1

Specific calcification and productivity rates of hermatypic and ahermatypic organisms.

Category	Species	Light or Dark	μg.Ca/mg.N/hr	μg.carbonate–C/mg.N/hr.	μg.organic–C/mg.N/hr.
Ahermatypic Coelenterata without Zooxanthellae	*S. roseus*	light	12.0	3.30	1.250
		dark	13.2	2.46	0.489
	A. solitaria	light	8.7	1.33	0.547
		dark	8.6	0.77	0.400
	T. tenuilamellosa	light	5.5	0.56	0.217
		dark	5.6	0.85	0.161
Hermatypic Coelenterata with Zooxanthellae	*A. cervicornis* (*apical cm.*)	light	126.3	17.93	12.090
		dark	35.1	4.09	0.861
	M. complanata	light	59.6	10.19	19.680
		dark	25.0	6.44	1.640
	P. furcata	light	26.7	8.14	13.800
		dark	5.6	0.63	0.532
Hermatypic Algae	*H. tuna*	light	178.0	23.21	26.390
		dark	77.9	9.36	0.905
	H. opuntia	light	256.1	38.46	50.520
		dark	72.6	11.82	0.899
	A. fragilissima	light	68.3	43.33	56.320
		dark	792.6	87.24	2.180

μg carbon fixed per milligram nitrogen per hour. The highest calcification and productivity values are observed in the calcareous algae. In the light, the calcification rates in the two *Halimedas* are about 1.5 to 10 times faster than in the hermatypic corals, and about 20 to 40 times faster than in the ahermatypes. The carbon fixation rates in the *Halimedas* are only from 2.5 to 4 times greater than those in the hermatypic corals, the productivity values for the ahermatypes being neglected as they have no zooxanthellae.

The approximate diurnal calcification and carbon fixation rates of the various species tested are shown in Table II. The daily calcium deposition was calculated on the simplifying assumption of twelve hours darkness and twelve hours sunshine equal in intensity to the average isolation between 10 a.m. and 4 p.m. during a late winter day in Jamaica. The daily productivity values were calculated on a twelve hourly basis since no photosynthesis occurs at night. These figures are uncorrected for respiration. Tables I and II show that the differences in the calcification rates between groups are far greater than the corresponding differences in the carbon fixation rates, but more data are needed to establish whether a quantitative correlation exists here. Obviously such comparisons can have meaning only on a broad ecological level since we do not yet know if the physiological mechanisms of calcification in the various groups of organisms used for these experiments are equivalent. Nevertheless, the overall correlation is probably not due to chance; it emphasizes the fundamental role

TABLE 2

Daily calcification and carbon fixation rates of hermatypic and ahermatypic organisms.

Category	Species	Calcium deposition in μg./mg.N/day	Carbon fixation in μg/mg.N/day
Ahermatypic Coelenterata without zooxanthellae	*S. roseus*	292.4	
	A. solitaria	207.6	
	T. tenuilamellosa	133.2	
Hermatypic Coelenterata with zooxanthellae	*A. cervicornis* (*apical cm.*)	1936.8	145.08
	M. complanata	1015.2	236.16
	P. furcata	387.6	165.60
Hermatypic algae	*H. tuna*	3070.8	316.70
	H. opuntia	3944.4	606.24
	A. fragilissima	10330.8	675.84

played by photosynthesis in facilitating the deposition of calcareous matter in a wide variety of hermatypic organisms, irrespective of the possibility that the mechanisms concerned may be very different.

Comparison of the results summarised in the first two columns of Table I shows that skeletogenesis rates calculated from Ca^{45} uptake are much higher than those calculated from the simultaneous C^{14} carbonate uptake. In $CaCO_3$ the stoichiometric mass ratio of calcium to carbon is 40/12 or about 3.335. This ratio should apply to the mineral constituent of the coelenterate and algal skeletons which is mostly $CaCO_3$, though some of the algae may contain traces of dolomite in addition to calcite and aragonite (18). However, the ratios calculated from our data are nearly all higher than the theoretical value, and they vary over a wide range. This either indicates that the organisms are secreting a skeletal mineral greatly enriched in calcium, or that the specific activities of the C^{14} and Ca^{45} labelled percursors change with respect to the external medium, and to each other, during the process of deposition. As there is no experimental evidence for calcium enrichment we are inclined to explain the apparent carbonate deficit shown in our data on the basis of the second alternative.

The transfer rates given in Table I were calculated on the assumption that during $CaCO_3$ deposition the specific activities of the Ca^{45} and C^{14} labelled percursors do not change with respect to the sea water or to each other, a condition that would occur only if the system were in isotopic equilibrium. However, this was not the case in our experiments which were run over sufficiently short periods of time that it was impossible for the test colonies to achieve isotopic equilibrium. Therefore it is to be expected that the specific activities in the newly formed skeletal $CaCO_3$ would be less than in the dissolved Ca^{++} and HCO_3^- of the medium if the labelled exogenous atoms were to exchange with intracellular stores of unlabelled atoms to final deposition into the skeleton.

Given that the molar fluxes of calcium and carbonate are equal and linked by some common pathway, and using the specific activities of the precursors dissolved in the sea water as a reference base, the calculated deposition rates will be the higher for that component which has suffered the least isotopic dilution, e. g. calcium, and the lower for that constituent which was diluted the most during its passage through the cells, e. g. carbonate. This suggests that the reservoir of intracellular carbonate available for exchange with absorbed exogenous carbonate is much greater than the internal pool of freely exchangeable calcium, and that the tissue calcium turnover rates must therefore be much higher than those of carbonate. In previous experiments, we have demonstrated that the exchangeable calcium in corals is indeed maintained at a low level in corals (5, 7). The simultaneous introduction of isotopically labelled calcium and carbon makes it possible to assess the relative sizes of the pools of exchangeable endogenous calcium and carbon by the principle of dilution volumes in a situation where no isotopic equilibration has occurred. Under these conditions, our calculated transfer rates indicate that the internal pool of carbon available for exchange with exogenous carbonate being deposited into the skeleton is about two to fifteen times greater than the amount of exchangeable calcium.

SUMMARY AND CONCLUSIONS

1. Coral reefs are tropical shallow water communities where intensive biological calcification occurs, resulting in net accumulation of limestone into the sediments. Photosynthesis appears to be in some way essential to reef formation. The most important reef-building organisms are calcareous algae and coelenterates, corals included. All reef-building coelenterates without exception contain symbiotic zooxanthellae. Corals without zooxanthellae grow slowly and never play a significant role in the building of reefs.

2. The zooxanthellae do not themselves calcify, but their presence results in a very powerful enhancement of calcification in the coral host as soon as photosynthesis begins. We have shown that stimulation of growth by light requires zooxanthellae since this effect does not occur in reef corals from which zooxanthellae are removed, nor does it occur in ahermatypic corals which never have algal symbionts. Of three calcareous algae tested, two calcified much faster in light than in darkness, and in one the effect was reversed.

3. There is a rough correlation between calcification rate and specific photosynthetic rate as measured by the organic productivity. The highest calcification and productivity rates were noted in the calcareous algae, but in one of these we observed a very strong reduction of $CaCO_3$ deposition in the light in the presence of a very high rate of photosynthesis. Calcification and primary productivity rates in three hermatypic coelenterates with zooxanthellae are on the average about sixty per cent lower than in the calcareous algae. Their slowest calcification rates were observed in the ahermatypic corals that have no zooxanthellae.

4. Under the conditions of our experiments, it was found that labelled calcium was deposited up to seventeen times faster than labelled carbonate. This discrepancy may be the result of very large differences in the amount of exchangeable endogenous carbon in relation to the amount of calcium available for exchange, the former being very much larger than the latter so that intracellular dilution of the absorbed C^{14} was much greater than that of Ca^{45}.

5. Several mechanisms linking photosynthesis and calcification are discussed. $CaCO_3$ production may be enhanced: (1) through removal of CO_2 from the calcification site by photosynthesis and/or carbonic anhydrase; (2) from stimulation of coral metabolism by photosynthesis of the zooxanthellae, which in turn increases the amount of energy available for active calcium and carbonate transport through the tissues into the skeleton. There is no evidence that metabolic efficiency in reef corals is increased by augmenting the oxygen supply over and above that already available from the environment. The zooxanthellae probably exert their effect by speeding up the rate with which metabolic waste products are removed from the vicinity of the host's cells since the algae require as raw material for photosynthesis those very inorganic substances that the coral must get rid of. Rapid removal of these from the host cells must set up strong local concentration gradients resulting in a large increase of metabolic efficiency, thus making more free energy available for a $CaCO_3$ secretion.

6. Photosynthesis plays a double role *vis à vis* the reef: it increases the free energy of the community through primary production and it produces in corals and algae the optimum physiological conditions necessary for rapid and efficient secretion of calcium car-

bonate. In corals, the coupling of the calcification reaction to photosynthesis, though facultative, is almost certainly due to a direct link via a common metabolic pathway, rather than to synthesis and diffusion of nutrients from the zooxanthellae to the host. There can be no question that the great increase in rate and efficiency of limestone secretion associated with photosynthesis must, on a community level, be of decisive importance to the formation, growth and maintenance of tropical coral reef ecosystems.

REFERENCES

1. EMERY, K. O., J. I. TRACEY and H. S. LADD. 1954. Geology of Bikini and nearby atolls. *U. S. Geol. Survey Prof. Pap. 260-A* 265pp.
2. GOHAR, H. A. F. 1940. Studies on the Xeniidae of the Red Sea. *Mar. Biol. Sta. Ghardaqa, Egypt, Pub. 2:* 25-118.
3. GOREAU, T. F. 1959. The physiology of skeleton formation in corals. I. A method for measuring the rate of calcium deposition by corals under different conditions. *Biol. Bull. 116:* 59-75.
4. GOREAU, T. F. 1961. Problems of growth and calcium deposition in reef corals. *Endeavour 20:* 32-39.
5. GOREAU, T. F. and V. T. BOWEN. 1955. Calcium uptake by a coral. *Science 122:* 1188-1189.
6. GOREAU, T. F. and N. I. GOREAU. 1959. The physiology of skeleton formation in corals. II. Calcium deposition by hermatypic corals under various conditions in the reef. *Biol. Bull. 117:* 239-250.
7. GOREAU, T. F. and N. I. GOREAU. 1960. The physiology of skeleton formation in corals. IV. On isotopic equilibrium exchange of calcium between corallum and environment in living and dead reef-building corals. *Biol. Bull. 119:* 416-427.
8. KOHN, A. J. and P. HELFRICH. 1957. Primary organic productivity of a Hawaiian coral reef. *Limn. and Oceanogr. 2:* 241-251.
9. LADD, H. S., E. INGERSON, R. C. TOWNSEND, R. C. RUSSELL and H. K. STEPHENSON. 1953. Drilling on Eniwetok Atoll, Marshall Islands. *Am. Assoc. Petr. Geol. Bull. 37:* 2257.
10. ODUM, H. T. and E. P. ODUM. 1955. Trophic structure and productivity of a windward coral reef community on Eniwetok Atoll. *Ecol. Monogr. 25:* 291-320.
11. ODUM, H. T., P. R. BURKHOLDER, and J. A. RIVERO. 1959. Measurements of productivity of turtle grass flats, reefs, and the Bahia Fosforescente of Southern Puerto Rico. *Inst. Mar. Sci. (Texas).* Publ. *6:* 159.
12. SARGENT, M. C. and T. S. AUSTIN. 1949. Organic productivity of an atoll. *Amer. Geophys. Union Trans. 30:* 245-249.
13. SARGENT, M. C. and T. S. AUSTIN. 1954. Biologic economy of coral reefs. *U. S. Geol. Surv. Prof. Pap. 260-E:* 293-300.

14. Teichert, C. 1958. Cold and deep water coral banks. *Am. Assoc. Petr. Geol. Bull. 42:* 1064.

15. Thiel, M. E. 1929. Zur Frage der Ernährung der Steinkorallen und der Bredeutung Ihrer Zooxanthellen. *Zool. Anz. 81:* 295.

16. Tracey, J. I., H. S. Ladd and J. E. Hoffmeister. 1948. Reefs of Bikini, Marshall Islands. *Geol. Soc Am. Bull. 59:* 861-878.

17. Vaughan, T. W. and J. W. Wells. 1943. Revision of the suborders, families and genera of the Scleractinia. *Geol. Soc. Amer. Spec. Pap. 44:* 363 pp.

18. Vinogradov, A. P. 1953. The elementary chemical composition of marine organisms. *Sears Found. Mar. Res. Mem. II:* 647 pp.

19. Yonge, C. M. 1940. The biology of reef building corals. *Gt. Barrier Reef Exped. Sci. Rep. I*(13): 353-391.

20. Yonge, C. M. 1957. Symbiosis. *Geol. Soc. Amer. Mem.* 67(I): 429-442.

21. Yonge, C. M. and A. G. Nicholls. 1931. Studies on the Physiology of corals. V. The effect of starvation in light and darkness on the relationship between corals and zooxanthellae. *Gt. Barrier Reef Exped. Sci. Rep. I*(7): 177-211.

DISCUSSION

WAINWRIGHT: First I'd like to wave a small flag because you who have trays of hydra in your laboratory and even you oceanographers with laboratories in a ship don't have any idea under what difficulties Dr. Goreau is working and what he has done in taking his laboratory down onto the reef. Think of diving to 100 feet with 200 pounds of machinery on your back and then doing a critical experiment using glassware, radioisotopes, and living animals.

Now I want to ask a question. Do you know what the limiting factors in calcification are?

GOREAU: No, not yet, if we exclude light for the moment. Contrary to what I said earlier, it may be possible to culture some species of corals *in vitro*. We must never assume, however, that the growth or accretion rates we measure under those conditions are equal to those occurring on the reef. Nevertheless, laboratory studies are useful because we can rigidly control the environment, the concentration of such substances as HCO_3^- and Ca^{++} and the additions of inhibitors or stimulants, etc. We are planning such studies, but haven't gotten around to them yet, so I cannot really answer your question.

MUSCATINE: Do you feel that calcification in corals is augmented by removal of CO_2 by zooxanthellae?

GOREAU: Yes. If we assume the hypothetical scheme of calcification which I published some years ago, then the removal of CO_2 from the system would tend to drive the equilibrium to the right and increase the rate of $CaCO_3$ formation.

MUSCATINE: This differs from the scheme of Wilbur and Jodrey who found that calcification in their oyster mantle preparations was increased about five fold if a source of CO_2 such as oxaloacetate was added to the external medium.

GOREAU: Oxaloacetate is an intermediate in the Krebs cycle. Any increase in the rate of this cycle may have rather non-specific effects, and changes in calcification rates would tell us little. Nevertheless, it's a very interesting possibility and we are planning work along similar lines. Unfortunately, as Wainwright mentioned, there are certain small difficulties in running such experiments.

MARTIN: In mammals, the accretion of bone substance is not a one-way affair, but as accretion goes on, elimination and dissolution of bone material also goes on. I wonder if these views contribute any insight into the problem.

GOREAU: Yes. This is a very important point. Bone and coral differ in at least one fundamental way. Bone is mesodermal and remains at all times part of the internal medium of the body. At least 20% of the bone mineral is exchangeable with calcium and phosphate dissolved in the body fluids. In addition, mammalian bone is vascularized and full of cells. The corallum, on the other hand, is an ectodermal mineral deposit which lies outside the body of the coral polyp. We have evidence that once the $CaCO_3$ is deposited there, it undergoes little or no further exchange with the environment or with the coral; that is, it seems to be essentially isolated as long as it is covered by a layer of living tissue.

LOOMIS: Dr. Goreau has shown that the rate of calcification at the end of a coral branch is something like tenfold what it is at a shoulder. I find this position effect fascinating since the two environments appear identical at first glance.

Another point is that CO_2 plays a double role: (a) it is part of the calcium carbonate which is part of the corallum, and (b) it exerts a pH effect. Now when the light is shining on the algae, free CO_2 is rapidly photosynthesized and the pH goes up to maybe 11 or 12.

GOREAU: Corals have alkaline phosphatases with optima at about pH 11.0 (Goreau, 1953, *P.N.A.S. 39:* 1291). We thought at first that these enzymes were concerned with calcification, but results of our histochemical studies (Goreau, 1956. *Nature 177:* 1029) make this appear unlikely.

LOOMIS: Under illuminated conditions you get precipitation of calcium carbonate through increase of pH. Therefore, CO_2 has two roles in calcification: one as the carbonate ion, and one as free CO_2.

GOREAU: I am not sure that I agree with you. I wish we could measure CO_2 and pH in living calcifying corals. Let me comment on the first part of your question regarding differential growth at tips and sides of branches in *Acropora cervicornis.* Actually conditions are almost certainly not identical at the tips and sides of branches. This species has an inborn factor which controls the rate and pattern of calcification in the colony – and thus determines colony shape. It is a function inherent in the coral not the zooxanthellae, and within some limits seems to have little relationship to photosynthetic carbon fixation as I mentioned in my talk.

PHILLIPS: How long a period of photosynthesis do you allow in these experiments?

GOREAU: Approximately 6 hours.

PHILLIPS: Bean and Hassid (Assimilation of $C^{14}O_2$ by a Photosynthesizing Red Alga, *Iridophycus flaccidum.* Bean, R. C. and W. Z. Hassid. 1955. *J. Biol. Chem. 212:*411-425) found in their studies an assimilation of $C^{14}O_2$ in *Iridophycus flaccidum,* a marine red algae, that 90 odd percent of the C^{14} was in an alcohol-soluble phase. Alcohol extraction might be a possible way of getting around your wet ashing. What is the method you use?

GOREAU: It is a modification of a technic published by Folch and Van Slyke. Instead of using a mixture of concentrated sulphuric and phosphoric acids as the primary ashing agent, we use mixtures of 70% perchloric and concentrated nitric acids with a bit of potassium iodate added. We cannot use sulphate in any form because we wish to avoid converting the calcium to the sulfate and phosphate salts.

PHILLIPS: The 80% ethanol might be worth trying since it would avoid the use of this rather explosive reaction mixture.

GOREAU: We have had no trouble with it because we are using only 300 mg. samples in which there is less than 20 mgs. of organic matter present.

HAND: Would you comment on the number of algae in the growing tip as compared with the number farther away.

GOREAU: Histological sections show fewer zooxanthellae in the growing tip of *A. cervicornis.* The mg. N/mg. chlorophyll *a* ratio is also much higher in the axial polyps than in the lateral polyps—indicating a lower specific photosynthetic rate in the growing tip.

HAND: This suggests that where there is less algae, there is more calcification.

GOREAU: Yes, at least in *A. palmata* and *A. cervicornis.*

The Development of *Cordylophora*[1]

CHANDLER FULTON
Department of Biology, Brandeis University, Waltham 54, Massachusetts

One of the challenging problems of development is the manner in which a multi-cellular organism acquires and regulates its shape, pattern, or proportion. Colonial hydroids offer especially favorable material for study of this problem because their colonies are composed of a repeating pattern of hydranths arranged on tubular stems and stolons (Fig. 1). Hydroid colonies grow asexually by the elaboration of stolons attached to a substratum; at regular intervals the stolons send up uprights which bear hydranths, grow, and branch. The primary concern of this paper is the manner in which colonies develop this regular, repeating pattern.

I chose to work with the brackish-water hydroid, *Cordylophora lacustris,* because it is exceptionally hardy and has a simple colony pattern. For study of the development of colonies, it is advantageous to have a refined and reproducible method of laboratory cultivation similar to that developed by Loomis for *Hydra littoralis.* One can grow *Cordylophora* colonies on glass microscope slides slanted in beakers of culture solution, with no flow of water or other special treatment (1). The defined culture solution contains ionic sodium, potassium, calcium, magnesium, chloride, and bicarbonate. All of these ions, with the exception of bicarbonate, are essential for growth at a maximum rate, and the proportion of the ions is critical. The cultures are fed *Artemia* larvae once daily, and the culture solution changed after feeding and again later in the day. Between feedings, the beakers are kept in the dark at 22°, though

[1]A much abridged form of the paper presented at the meeting. Relevant literature citations and supporting data will be presented in papers to be published elsewhere, and may be found in reference (2).

neither light nor slight variations in temperature are critical. These standard conditions (1) have been used for all the experiments discussed here, since variation of the conditions leads to alterations in colony pattern.

The number of hydranths in a *Cordylophora* colony increases exponentially with time in the beaker-slide cultures, as do the hydranths of *Hydra* in Loomis cultures. It is thus possible to compute the growth rate of this colonial organism, using standard equations for exponential growth. This growth rate has been used to evaluate the growth conditions described above. *Cordylophora* colonies double about every three days, or more slowly than *Hydra littoralis*, which doubles in less than two days. The fact that *Cordylophora* colonies grow exponentially even though they are colonial is of interest and we shall return to it later.

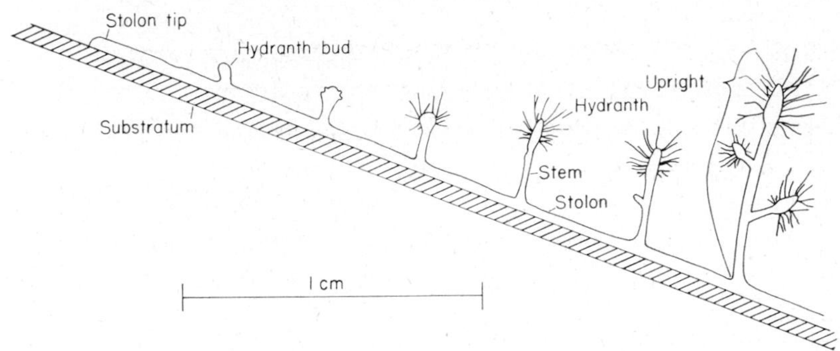

Figure 1. Diagram illustrating the basic pattern and macroscopic features of a *Cordylophora* colony. Sketched from a photograph of a laboratory colony.

This culture method provided uniform *Cordylophora* colonies with which I could begin to study colony formation. Time-lapse movies taken to study the growth of colonies revealed a markedly organized system of peristaltic waves, which probably act to circulate nutrients through the colonies.[2] These waves are proximally oriented, beginning at the tip of each hydranth and passing down

[2]A movie demonstrating the features of peristalsis in *Cordylophora* was shown at the meeting. The apparent synchrony of peristalsis is still being studied.

through the tissue of the colony to the tips of the stolons. The waves are rhythmic, though very slow, occurring about two or three times an hour in a resting colony. The rate of peristalsis jumps threefold on feeding, to a frequency of about eight times an hour, and then declines back to the resting rate.

The most striking feature of this peristalsis is that it is sychronized throughout a colony, in that the waves begin at the tip of each hydranth simultaneously. Further, if one ties a ligature on any of the uprights in a colony, the hydranth at the apex of that upright will, in time, begin to beat out of synchrony with the rest of the colony. In other words, disrupting the integrity of the colony (both tissue and coelenteron fluid) eliminates the synchrony. Even if one accepts the conclusion that *Cordylophora* has nerve cells (Mackie, this symposium), I find it difficult to envision how a stimulus is transferred through a colony in such a manner that each hydranth begins a perstaltic wave at the same time. I would suggest, however, that the synchrony indicates an order of integration in these colonial organisms which we have not hitherto suspected. I suspect also that understanding of colony development will involve further consideration of the orientation, rhythmicity and synchronization of the peristalisis.

On superficial examination, a *Cordylophora* colony looks like a forest of little trees. I have attempted to distinguish the component events which produce this forest, and in so doing have found it possible to describe in simple, quantitative terms how the forest develops. Careful observation of colonies reveals that they are entirely composed of a series of interconnected pipes, each consisting of a cylinder of tissue surrounded by a tubular perisarc.[3] These tubes are of essentially uniform diameter. Thus one can conceive of a *Cordylophora* colony as a plumbing system with 0.2 mm. pipelines; the description of a colony can be reduced to a description of the kinds of tubes which comprise it, the relative positions of these tubes with respect to one another, and the way in which they are formed and grow.

Stolon tubes, as they grow along the substratum, can give rise

---

[3]This approach to the colonies excludes the hydranths from consideration. Interesting observations on factors influencing the shape of hydranths, as well as entire colonies, have been presented by Kinne (3).

to two types of tubes: secondary stolons and uprights. Secondary stolons leave their parent stolons at right angles along the substratum, while uprights leave at right angles away from the substratum. Uprights, in contrast to stolons, are hydranth-bearing tubes, and give rise to one additional hydranth-bearing tube, the side branch. Side branches leave upright tubes at about 45 degree angles away from the substratum. Thus one can classify three types of tubes: stolon, upright, and side branch.

Other differences further distinguish these tubes. Hydranth-bearing tubes develop only directly behind growing tips; they never develop in any other part of the colony. They are spaced at regular intervals along their tube of origin; upright tubes in particular occur at about three mm. distances along the stolon. In contrast, stolon tubes never develop at growing tips, but always come out of some old part of the colony, as at the base of a well-developed upright. Further, stolon tubes are not spaced regularly; rather secondary stolons develop erratically with respect to any other part of the colony.

How do these tubes grow? Since they are of uniform diameter, one can determine the growth rate of individual tubes by measuring increase in length with time. This has been done by photographing a colony over the course of a few days or a week in a growth chamber in front of a time-lapse camera. The movie is then used to plot the extension of the tube as a function of time. Such plots, for both stolons and uprights (side branch growth has not been measured), demonstrate that these tubes increase in length linearly with time. Stolons grow at a rate of about 0.1 mm. per hour, and uprights at a rate of 0.05 mm. per hour.

You will recall that a colony as a whole grows exponentially in terms of hydranth number. The colony also grows exponentially in terms of dry weight, so that hydranth number is a measure of the mass of a colony. The observation of linear growth of tubes poses a dilemma: if the tubes which comprise a colony grow at a constant rate how does the colony as a whole grow exponentially? This question was first examined by model-building. One can diagram a colony in the form of a geometric progression, such that linear growth of tubes with regular branching at constant intervals gives rise to exponential growth of the whole. Such a model does not look like a *Cordylophora* colony in that 1) there is more branching than in an actual colony, and 2) the uprights are too tall relative to their parent stolons.

The geometric progression model was redrawn in terms of the appearance of colonies growing under standard conditions, as shown in Figure 2. The growth during any unit of time is indicated by a pattern: black, stippled, etc. The stolon is visualized as grow-

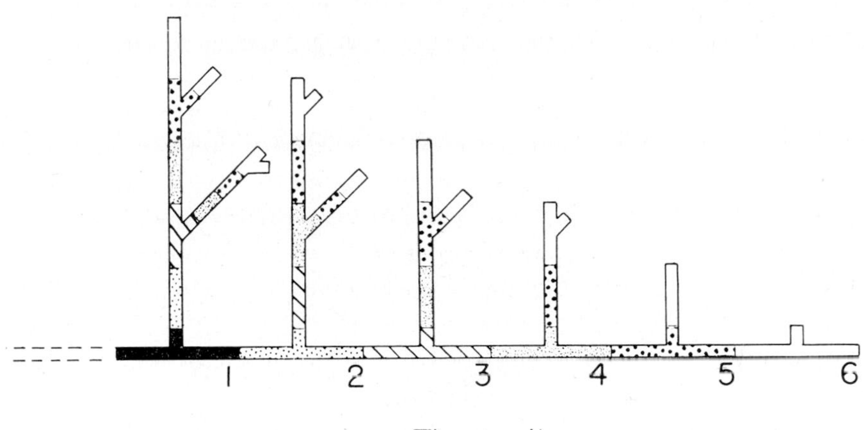

Figure 2. A model illustrating the growth of a hypothetical colony over a period of six time units. See text for explanation.

ing one unit per unit time (i.e., linearly), and producing uprights at a rate of one per unit time. During the same time unit, an upright grows only one-half unit, and a side branch only one-quarter unit. However, uprights and side branches continue to produce new tubes at the same distances as uprights are produced by stolons (i.e., one unit), and thus produce new tubes at rates of 0.5 and 0.25 tubes per unit time respectively.

Such a model takes into account the linear growth of tubes and normal branching pattern, and gives rise to a two-dimensional colony which bears a striking resemblance to laboratory colonies (cf. Figs. 1 and 2). If one computes the increase in hydranth number of such a hypothetical colony with time, however, one finds that it continually falls away from exponential. This is in contrast to actual colonies, which do approach exponential increase in hydranth number. One can escape this new dilemma by doing what the colonies do, namely by introducing secondary stolons at intervals. If one adds such secondary stolons at appropriate times, one can make the growth of the model colony closely approach exponential. I do not know as yet whether or not this is the way colonies maintain exponential growth.

Laboratory colonies appear to develop in accord with the model. This has been determined by measuring every relevent variable of the pattern of individual colonies, a task much facilitated by the use of a marking technique. If colonies are dipped into trypan blue, the perisarc is stained a deep blue while the tissue is unstained and unaffected. When such a colony is grown in the absence of trypan blue, all new growth is colorless while that part of the colony present as perisarc at the time of marking remains blue. Thus new growth can be precisely measured as separate from old. The measurements support the picture of colony formation just described, except that branch tubes appear to grow more slowly, or at about one-eighth the rate of stolon tubes. But upright tubes grow at almost exactly one-half the rate of stolon tubes.

In conclusion, it has been possible to reduce the development of a *Cordylophora* colony to the growth and branching of a series of tubes: stolons, uprights, and side branches. The parameters of colony shape may be summarized in tabular form:

				Relative growth rate	
Tube	*Source*	*Angle and position*	*Spacing*	*Colonies*	*Model*
Stolon	Stolon	90°, along substratum	erratic	1	1
Upright*	Stolon	90°, away from subst.	~3 mm.	½	½
Branch*	Upright	45°, away from subst.	~3 mm.	¼	~⅛

*These tubes also differ from stolons in that they bear hydranths and only develop at growing tips.

A model has been developed integrating many of these aspects of asexual colony development, and the development of individual colonies studied in relation to the model.

From my point of view, the major result of this study is that, by reducing the development of a colony to a series of constituent events, it becomes possible to analyze the individual events which give rise to the shape of a colony. Many questions immediately pose themselves. For example, why do upright tubes grow at half the rate of stolon tubes? Why do hydranth-bearing tubes develop only behind growing tips, while stolon tubes develop away from these tips? What produces the regular spacing of upright tubes? What determines the angle at which each tube leaves its parent tube? As yet, none of these questions has even a preliminary answer, but I hope that at least I have provided you with a more dynamic picture of these hydranth-bearing pipelines.

REFERENCES

1. FULTON, C. 1960. Culture of a colonial hydroid under controlled conditions. *Science 132:* 473-474.
2. FULTON, C. 1960. The Biology of a Colonial Hydroid. Ph.D. Thesis, The Rockefeller Institute, New York.
3. KINNE, O. 1958. Adaptation to salinity variations: some facts and problems. In *Physiological Adaptation* (C. L. Prosser, ed.). Washington, American Physiological Society. pp. 92-106.

DISCUSSION

MACKIE: Before the discussion turns to the main topics of Dr. Fulton's paper I'd like to comment on the colonial rhythm shown by *Cordylophora*—the synchronized waves of peristalsis in the hydranths. We have also seen this in Dr. Strehler's film of *Pennaria.* This sort of activity demands a specialized conduction system. Recently, R. K. Josephson has recorded action potentials from the stems of *Cordylophora* and *Tubularia.* I cannot give the full details but in *Tubularia* there are two rhythmically occurring patterns of activity and one of these patterns has distinct motor effects.

I'd also like to reiterate that neurons have been identified histologically throughout stems and hydranths in *Cordylophora,* so there's no need for scepticism about the existence of a nervous system in these colonial forms.

CROWELL: This frequency (of three times an hour or so for hydranth movement) surprises me, because, in the stolon anyway, if one watches the movement back and forth of the fluid, one gets a periodicity in the order of 3 to 5 minutes in all the hydroids I've looked at.

FULTON: Have you looked at *Cordylophora*?

CROWELL: Yes.

FULTON: In the *Cordylophora* stolons I've followed, there are a pair of filling and emptying cycles about every twenty minutes, which corresponds to the frequency at the hydranths.

CROWELL: I don't doubt that. What you see in the hydranths, I think, is different from the typical back and forth flow in the stolons.

FULTON: I don't think so, but we're still in the process of finding out.

CHAPMAN: I wonder if you have any information about the relationship between culture conditions, such as tonicity, temperature, and pH, on the spacing of these uprights?

FULTON: I have voluminous information. Actually not much affects interupright spacing, but many things affect the general pattern of colonies. Kinne has made a thorough study of the effects of different dilutions of seawater and of different temperatures on colony pattern. I think that all it would be wise to say right now is that the pattern which I get is the pattern one gets in standard culture solutions at 22° with one feeding a day and all the ritual. One can get almost any colony shape one wants simply by varying one parameter or another. So this is quite a labile system.

LOOMIS: What strikes me in your nice growth records is a sort of feeling that the stolon is trying to escape from itself. In other words, it is trapped in its own one dimensional line and starts growing a shoot upwards. Then growth has to escape from this shoot and does so first to the right and then to the left. New growth largely takes place in a new axis at right angles to old growth, which is another way of saying that growth can take place only at an open and advancing tip. This growth inhibition along an established stolon may be related to the fact that *Cordylophora,* unlike hydra, will not grow on the bottom of a Petri dish but needs to be suspended on a microscope slide in a beaker of water. The reason for this "Fulton effect" as I call it, seems to be the greater sensitivity of *Cordylophora* to pCO_2, for we have found that a pCO_2 as low as 1.5% atm. inhibits its growth while *Hydra* can stand up to 10% atm. Thus, *Cordylophora* on the bottom of a Petri dish sits in its own "halo zone" of high pCO_2 and inhibits itself, whereas *Cordylophora* on a slide is continually bathed by the thermal currents that exist within a beaker and can easily be shown with methylene blue. Perhaps this apical inhibition of stolon growth by pCO_2 may partially explain the growth pattern of *Cordylophora.*

Developmental Problems in *Campanularia*[1]

Sears Crowell[2]
Department of Zoology, Indiana University, Bloomington, Indiana

This report reviews a limited number of experimental studies on the thecate or calyptoblastic colonial hydroid *Campanularia flexuosa* (Hincks). The selection of topics has been biased by the fact that most studies of developmental problems in hydroids have employed either hydra or athecate (gymnoblastic) species (e.g. *Cordylophora, Corymorpha, Hydractinia, Tubularia*). This report I think, can be most useful if emphasis is placed upon the peculiar features of thecate forms and on differences between the two groups. No attempt has been made to cover comprehensively the morphogenesis of thecate hydroids or related work of other investigators. I have tried to point out a few of the interesting unsolved problems

The principal topics are:

1. Patterns of colonial growth
2. Alterations of the pattern of growth
3. Aging
4. Regression and replacement of hydranths
5. Reconstitution studies
6. Hydranth differentition

[1]The research has been supported by a research grant (H-1948) from the National Heart Institute, U.S.P.H.S., and by a grant-in-aid from the American Cancer Society.

[2]Department of Zoology, Indiana University, Bloomington, Indiana and the Marine Biological Laboratory, Woods Hole, Mass. Contribution No. 707 from the Department of Zoology, Indiana University.

PATTERNS OF COLONIAL GROWTH

This brief report cannot cover the extensive literature on patterns of growth. By 1914 Kühn (10) had provided a comprehensive review and his figures have been used and recopied ever since. Recently Berrill has clarified many points concerning hydroid morphogenesis, and his recent book (2) provides us with both an excellent survey and a bibliography.

The pattern of colonial growth of a typical athecate hydroid is shown in Figure 1 A. The oldest hydranth, terminal in position, is designated as *1,* the next oldest, *2,* etc. There is a zone of growth just proximal to each hydranth. Each such zone contributes to further increase in the size of the colony in two ways: it lengthens the pedicel or stem in which it lies, and it gives off laterally at regular intervals a new hydranth bud with its own distinct growth zone. A newly produced hydranth initially has few tentacles and is small. Tentacles are gradually added as the hydranth grows in size. It is easy to determine the relative ages of the hydranths of a colony with this growth pattern, on the basis of both the position and

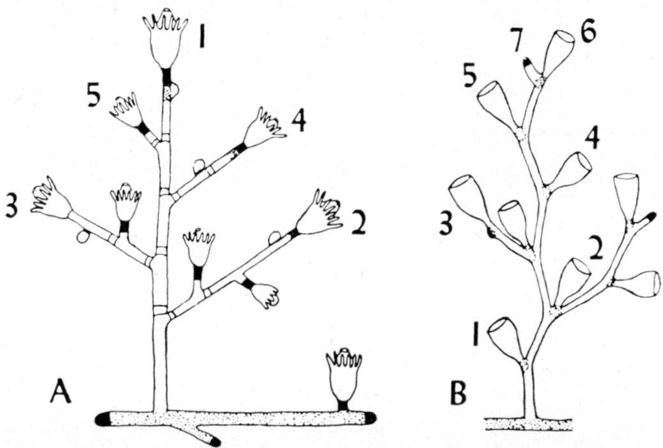

Fig. 1. Diagrams to show the growth pattern of colonial hydroids. A. The pattern typical of most colonial athecate species. B. The pattern of many thecate species, e.g. *Campanularia, Obelia.* The black regions are zones of growth. The numbers show relative age of hydranths. From Kühn (10).

the size of hydranths. This is clearly illustrated in the photographs of *Cordylophora* (Fig. 2) and *Pennaria* (Fig. 3); and both correspond almost perfectly with the idealized pattern of Figure 1 A.

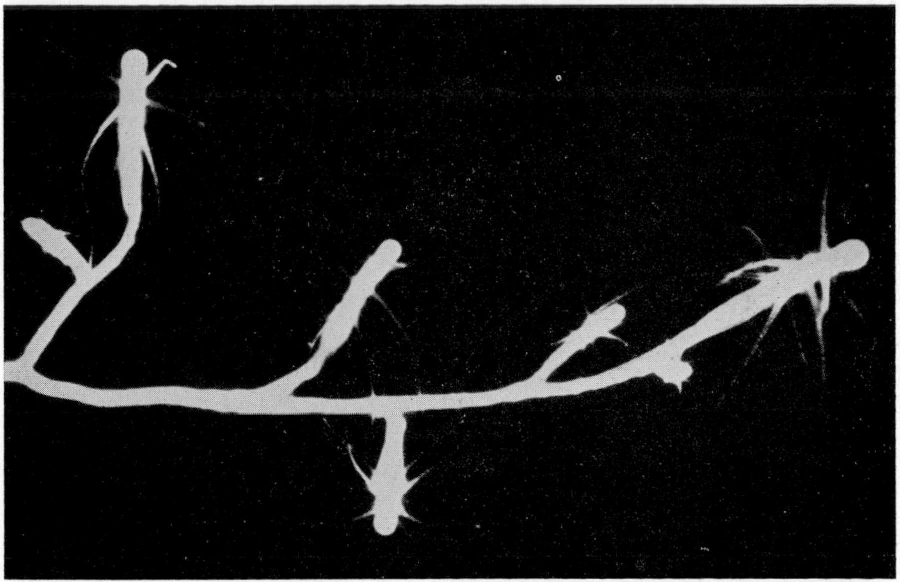

Fig. 2. Pattern of a small colony of *Cordylophora*. From a color photograph by Charles Wyttenbach.

Figure 1 B illustrates the typical growth pattern found in many thecate species. Growth zones give rise to the stems (pedicels) of new hydranths but do not add to the length of the stem itself. Hence the order of the age of the hydranths (in a young colony) is from the base upward, *1, 2,* etc., in Fig. 1 B. The youngest hydranth is terminal—the opposite of the pattern in athecate species.

In thecate species the pedicel of a new hydranth is completely formed before the hydranth itself is produced. After the pedicel attains its full length it enlarges at its tip to make a hydranth bud, which then quickly differentiates into a hydranth. By the time the hydranth emerges from its enclosing hydrotheca, it is fully functional, and has its full set of tentacles and its full size. It grows no more. The photograph of *Campanularia* (Fig. 4) shows that all hydranths are of the same size. The bud of the hydranth which will be produced next is at the top, and proximal to this is the beginning of the outgrowth of the next pedicel.

Some species of both thecate and athecate hydroids are solitary, and there are other species in which all hydranths arise only from the attaching stolon (e.g. *Hydractinia*). Yet another pattern of colonial growth, in which the growth zones are apical, is seen in sertularians and plumularians—presumably the most advanced of the thecate hydroids. These too provide challenging problems for experimental morphologists but cannot be considered here.

Fig. 3. Pattern of a small portion of a colony of *Pennaria*. From a color photograph by Charles Wyttenbach.

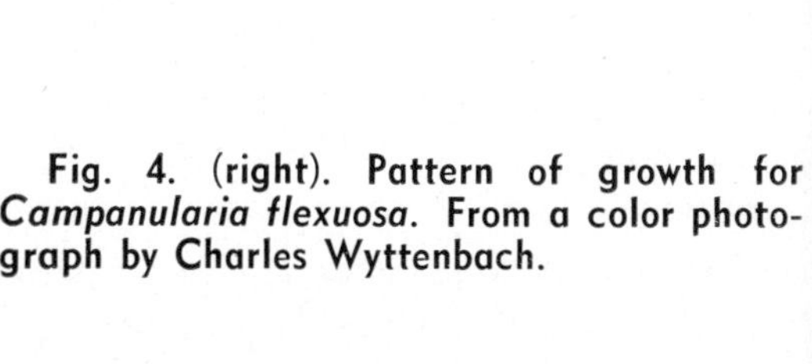

Fig. 4. (right). Pattern of growth for *Campanularia flexuosa*. From a color photograph by Charles Wyttenbach.

The precise patterns of growth in hydroids tempt one to construct mathematical models such as those which Fulton has developed and presented so well in this symposium. I am confident that similar models could be constructed for *Campanularia*. The preciseness of patterns also invites us to attempt to alter them.

ALTERATIONS OF THE PATTERN OF GROWTH

The basis for our first studies on *Campanularia* was the belief that procedures which would alter the pattern of growth would give some insight into the underlying controlling conditions. Young colonies grown at different temperatures gave colonies or similar form, but their growth schedule was strikingly altered. At higher temperatures the apical growth of each new pedicel and hydranth was accelerated, but at cooler temperatures the *initiation* of the growth of each new pedicel occurred so much sooner that these colonies as a whole grew just as rapidly (7).

This experiment showed that the factors which control the initiation of new growth are different from those which control rate of growth in an already established growing region.

In a more elaborate experiment all growth zones and prospective growth zones were compared in colonies kept at different nutritional levels. Figure 5 C shows diagramatically all of these zones. It could be predicted that with sub-optimal feeding there must be either a general uniform slowing down of all activities or a favoring of some at the expense of others. The latter proved to be the case. In general, lowered nutrition did not greatly affect the rate of growth in an already established part, but it did delay or stop the initiation of new growth. For example, the main stolon grew almost as well in nearly starved specimens as in well fed ones, and it produced new uprights. However, the initiation of subterminal growth by the uprights was delayed. As a consequence of these two effects the whole pattern of partly starved colonies was strikingly different from that of well fed ones. The two were about equally extensive along the substrate, but the height was conspicuously different.

It is easy to conjecture that this difference is adaptive in nature: It is better for a colony at an unsatisfactory feeding site to move along than to add more feeding units where it is.

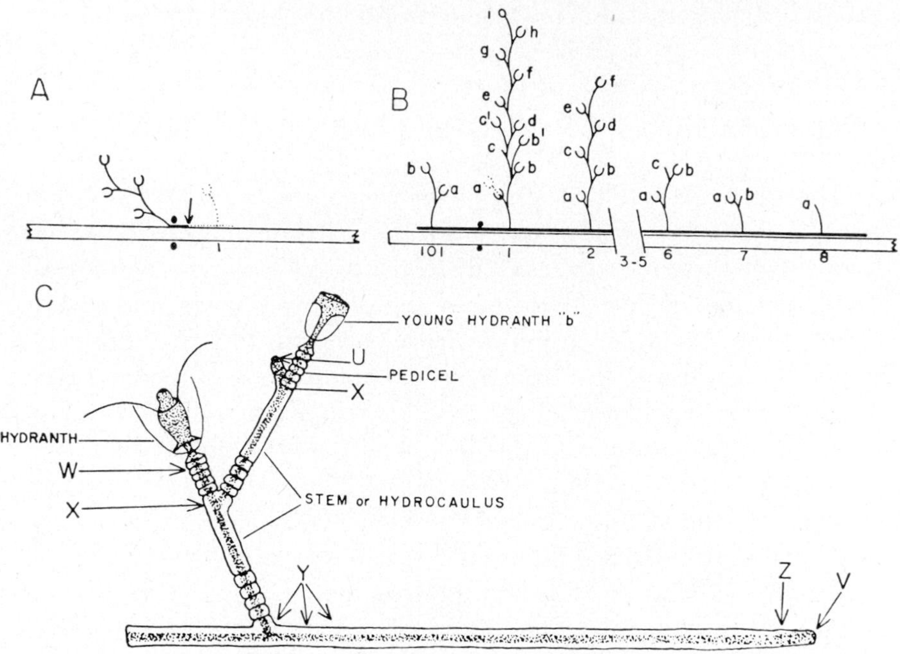

Fig. 5. ***Campanularia.*** **A. Technique of subculturing by placing an upright beneath a thread which has been tied around a slide. The new growth is suggested by the dotted line. B. Pattern of a colony of the age used in the nutrition experiment discussed in the text. The numbers designating age of the upright correspond with those in Fig. 6. C. The zones of growth and prospective growth in** ***Campanularia*** **are indicated: W. to Z. (With permission; Fig. 1 of ref. 4).**

AGING

The most striking observation, by serendipity, in the experiment just discussed was that the increase in height of the older uprights (stems with their hydranths) was much more adversely affected by reduced nutrition than the comparable growth of younger uprights in the same colony. The growth in length of the uprights depends on recurrent initiation of each new node—it is intermittent, not continuous. Figure 6 summarizes the experimental results. The groups are arranged in the order of decreasing food supply, and in each group the oldest upright is No. 1 at the left. In the well fed groups, *glut* and 4/2, old and young uprights had grown at the same rate. In all the others the younger grew faster (4).

The effect of age of stem in slowing or limiting terminal growth was studied further (8). In one test the more basal levels of an upright were removed every few days so that it consisted of only the 4 to 8 youngest hydranths. The terminal growth, in these cases, did not stop; the total length of stem produced was more than three

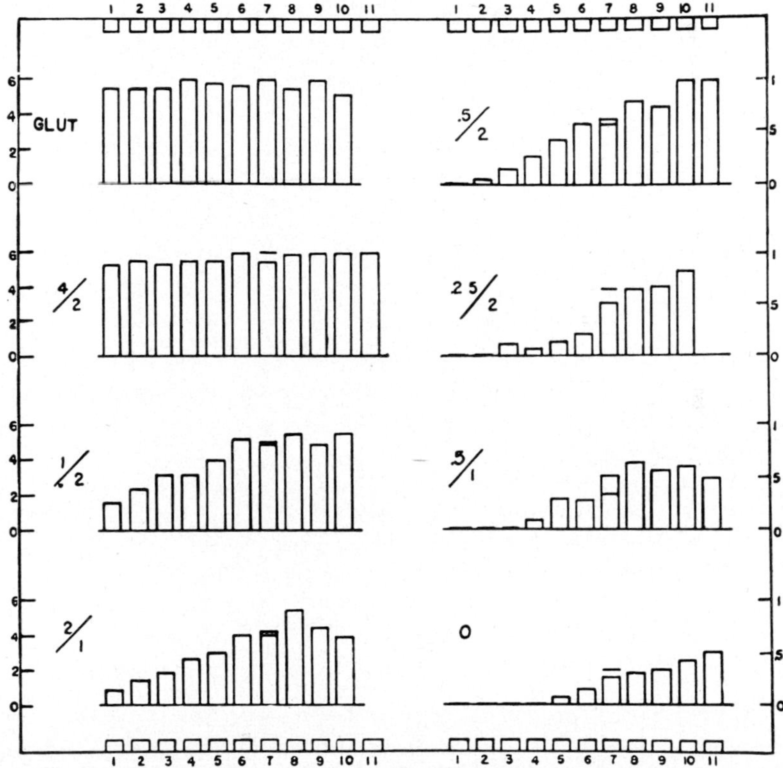

Fig. 6. Terminal growth related to nutritive level and to age (height) of upright. The subfigures are arranged in decreasing order of nutritive level; within each the oldest upright is at the left. (With permission; Fig. 3 of ref. 4).

times greater than that observed in normal specimens or than that reported as the maximum height for this species in nature. Other experiments, but not all, showed evidence of an aging factor inhibitory to growth. These studies are being continued.

REGRESSION AND REPLACEMENT OF HYDRANTHS

In all thecate hydroids which have been examined hydranths are short-lived; they regress and are resorbed after about one week (3). In Figure 4, for example, it may be noticed that there is only a pedicel at the location, lowest left, where the oldest hydranth "ought" to be; it had regressed. In this symposium, Dr. Strehler is presenting much of our information (12) concerning this regression-replacement cycle and its implications for the understanding of aging.

When regression occurs, the materials of the hydranth go back into the colony and are available as nutrition for further growth, a point which has been proved by Berrill (1) and Nathanson (11). [See comment by Crowell in the discussion of the paper by Strehler in this symposium (p. 396).]

In contrast with thecate species athecate hydroids do not regress, so far as we know, except under adverse conditions. We have, for example, records of *Cordylophora* hydranths which lived for more than three months even when food was limited and growth was almost at a standstill (not previously reported).

RECONSTITUTION EXPERIMENTS

Hydroid tissues can be dissociated mechanically giving tiny clumps of cells, which can be pushed together into a loose mass. In both thecate and athecate species these clusters reorganize themselves into a double-layered hollow sphere with epidermal cells on the outside, endodermal cells inside. Up to this point thecate and athecate tissues are similar in behavior. The subsequent events differ strikingly and emphasize in a different way the contrast between the two groups in the manner in which a hydranth develops.

In a day or two in *Cordylophora* and other athecate forms a small bud (sometimes several) appears on the upper side of the cellular ball and quickly develops four or so tentacles. If fed, it will grow. In *Campanularia,* a growth zone appears on the ball and produces either a stolon or a pedicel. This grows out for several days using the materials in the ball. Finally, after about a week, in exactly the same sequence as in ordinary hydranth development, a new small but complete hydranth is produced. Figure 7 shows sketches of this for *Campanularia.*

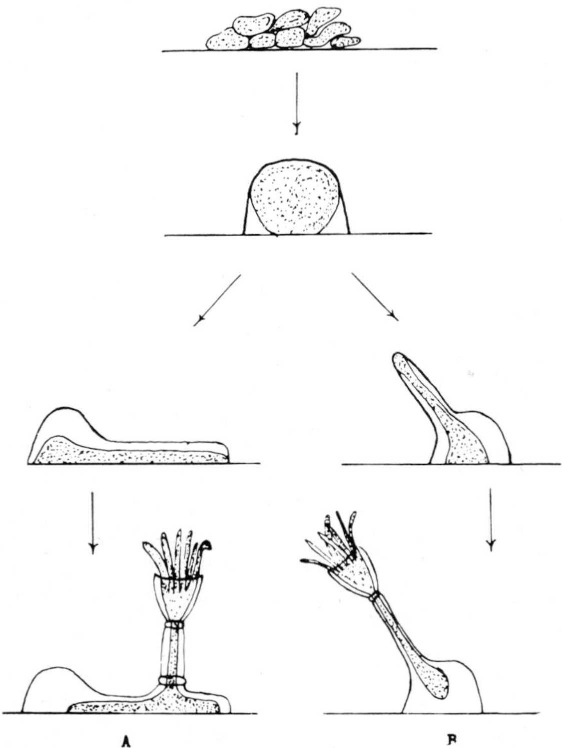

Fig. 7. Sketches of the production of hydranths from dissociated tissues of *Campanularia.* At the top are clumps of cells which have been pushed together. Within a few hours these rearrange themselves into a hollow ball. This ball may produce a hydranth in either of two ways: at the left, by the production of a stolon from which a pedicel and then a hydranth develops; at the right, by the production of a pedicel at the top of which a hydranth develops (From Hartman, ref. 9).

Here again we must raise the question: What is it that is being moved from the old part to make the new? Are cells moving? Are old cells breaking down to give substances that are moved and reutilized? We do not yet know the answers.

At Indiana, Mr. Hartman (9) undertook to find differences among the tissues taken from different parts of a colony in respect to their capacities when dissociated. No differences were found among tissues from stem, stolon, or early hydranth buds of *Campanularia.* Tissue taken from adult hydranths, however, did not reconstitute. This led, naturally, to tests of different stages of hydranth development. When a late stage of hydranth development was used, but one in which there was not yet any visible differentiation, Hartman found that the tissues reaggregated and within a few hours produced differentiated hydranth parts with an irregular organization. Two examples showing patches of tentacles, and in one case a hypostome, are illustrated in Figure 8. Evidently

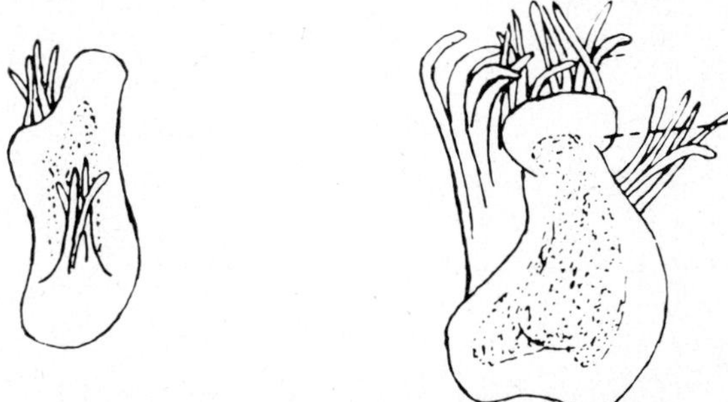

Fig. 8. Two examples of the irregular structures which differentiated when tissues from a late hydranth bud were dissociated and allowed to reaggregate. There are patches of well developed tentacles, and in the example at the right there is a hypostome (From Hartman, ref. 9).

each region of the scrambled tissues was already set in the course of its differentiation. A further test of the distal tissues of buds at this age showed that they were like the whole in making irregular structures at once. But the tissues taken from the proximal halves of such buds reconstituted according to the same pattern as stem, stolon, or early bud tissue.

HYDRANTH DIFFERENTIATION[3]

The manner of development of thecate hydranths, their failure to grow, and the fact that they regress after only about a week suggest that they have little regenerative or regulative ability. We have cut tentacles from young hydranths and find that they do not regenerate appreciably. If the hypostome is cut off regression ensues within a few hours. To carry this matter further back into stages of hydranth development we undertook several types of simple operations on hydranth buds.

Athecate hydranths which have had parts removed replace them. The three sketches of Figure 9, for example, illustrate the

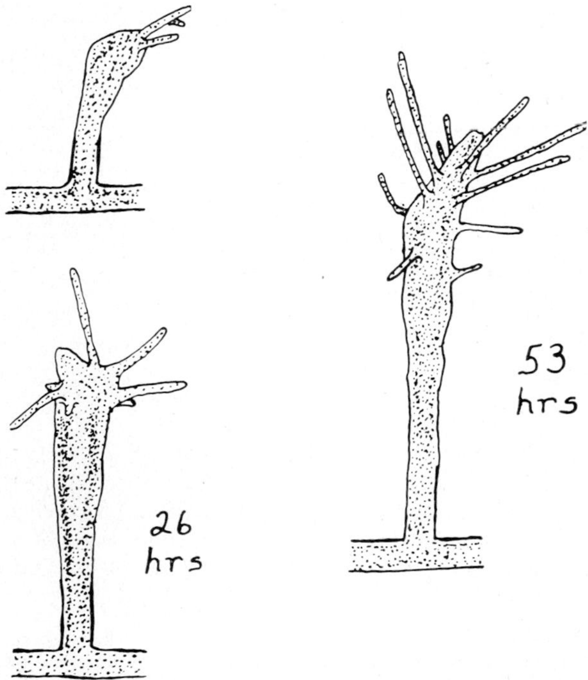

Fig. 9. Rapid restoration of tentacles and hypostome in *Cordylophora* following the removal of the hypostome and most of the tentacles.

[3]The experiments described in this section have not been presented elsewhere except in abstracts (5, 6).

quick regeneration which followed removal of the hypostome and most of the tentacles in a small young hydranth of *Cordylophora.* An analagous operation, illustrated in Figure 10, was performed several times on hydranth buds of *Campanularia.* Both the excised piece and the part which remained proceeded to differentiate just as they would have if no operation had been made. The isolated little pieces consisted of little more than tentacles and a hypostome. Such little creatures captured *Artemia* larvae and passed them into the hypostome. They lived unchanged for about four days—a normal life span for an unnourished hydranth. Similarly the "half hydranths" still on the colony showed normal activity but no restitution of the missing tentacles.

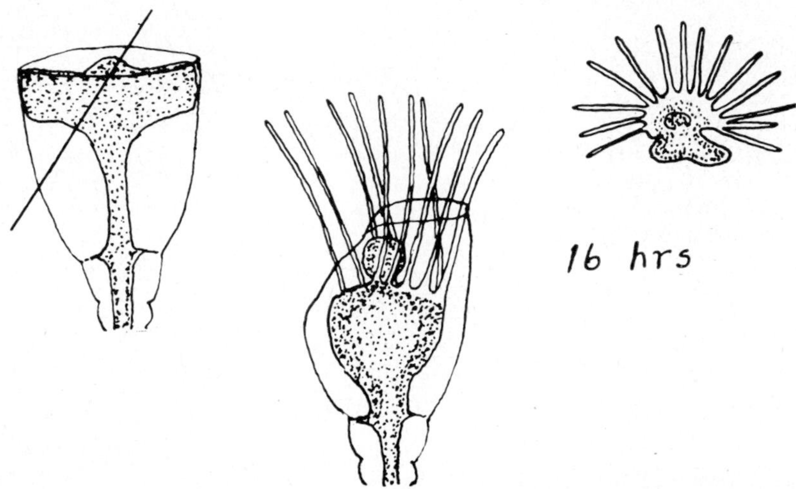

Fig. 10. The left half of the upper portion of a late hydranth bud of *Campanularia* is cut off. Both parts differentiate just what they would have produced normally, and there is no later restoration of missing parts.

In another series of experiments we cut off and isolated very young hydranth buds of *Campanularia,* as shown in Figure 11. These were of such small mass that it would be impossible for them to develop a normal hydranth. Had these been athecate hydranth buds one would have predicted that they would produce either nothing, because of the small size, or at best a tiny hydranth. These isolated

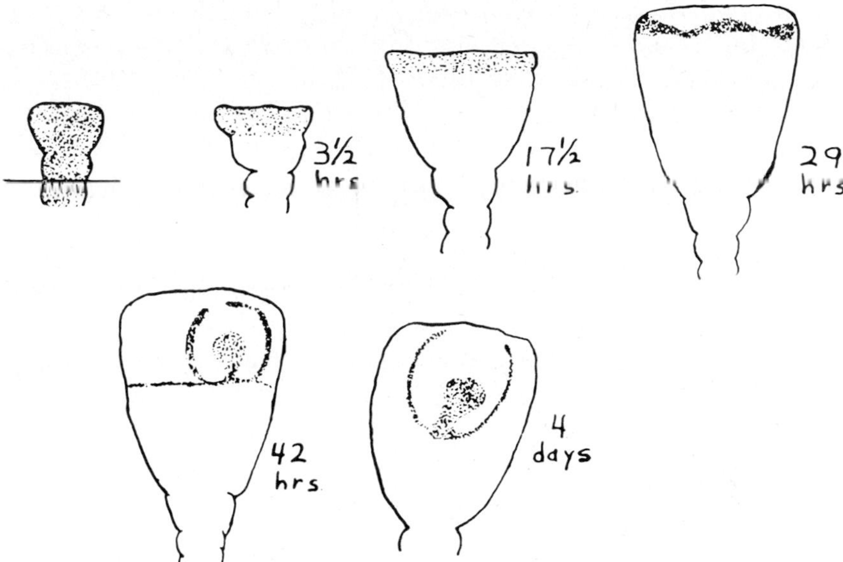

Fig. 11. Profile sketches of the morphogenesis of an isolated early hydranth bud of *Campanularia*. The finally differentiated disk consists of little more than a hypostome surrounded by a full circle of tentacles. The outer line represents the secreted perisarc; the tissue is stippled.

buds of *Campanularia,* however, showed an extraordinary ability to continue to perform the activities ordinarily performed by the distal-most tissues of a normally developing hydranth. They gradually spread themselves laterally, laying down externally the hydrothecal perisarc, and they continued to do so until a hydrotheca of ordinary size was produced. By this time the tissue itself was only a thin disk at the position where hypostome and tentacles would differentiate in a whole bud. Then the disk differentiated into just these distal-most parts.

The whole process just described proceeded much more slowly than is the case in normal development. If one were dealing only or mainly with cell migration it would be expected that the events could occur at nearly normal speed. The slowness suggests that new cells are being produced, as is believed to be the case in ordinary hydranth development, and old ones are being destroyed and utilized. Regardless of the validity of this suggestion, it is clear that distal-most tissues have held rigidly to the sequence of events characteristic of these tissues in normal development.

CONCLUSIONS

It is clear that the pattern of colonial growth can be altered in *Campanularia* by changes both in temperature and in nutritive level. The alterations are largely due to the sensitivity of zones of prospective growth.

Differences in hydranth morphogenesis are striking when one compares the processes in thecate and athecate species. In the thecate form, *Campanularia,* a hydranth of full size is produced by a series of events which are not easily altered; they show little ability to regulate. Once produced thecate hydranths do not grow, they do not regenerate parts which have been removed, and they regress and are resorbed after living for only a few days. In all these respects the reverse is true for athecate species.

We know that old parts are utilized for new growth, but we do not know in what form materials are moved: as tissues? cells? fragments? chemical substances? This needs study. More attention also should be given to the initiation of new growth by zones of prospective growth. For analysis of these particular problems thecate species, such as *Campanularia,* are probably better than athecate forms.

ACKNOWLEDGEMENTS

The author must acknowledge the assistance of Malcolm Rusk and Ruth Curtiss Telfer who were with him at the beginning of the studies of *Campanularia;* of Charles Wyttenbach who has made many contributions of ideas and time and whose photographs have been copied here; of Fred Wilt, Richard Manassa, Annelle Gibbon, Jean Lowry, Maurice Hartman, and Pat Clapp all of whom have had some part in the work summarized here.

The paper ought to be dedicated to the memory of Frederick S. Hammett who long ago proclaimed the special virtues of *Campanularia* for studies of growth.

REFERENCES

1. Berrill, N. J. 1949. The polymorphic transformations of *Obelia*. *Quart. J. Micr. Sci. 90:* 235-264.

2. Berrill, N. J. 1961. *Growth, Development, and Pattern.* W. H. Freeman and Company, San Francisco. 555 pp.

3. Crowell, S. 1953. The regression-replacement cycle of hydranths of *Obelia* and *Campanularia*. *Physiol. Zool. 26:* 319-327.

4. Crowell, S. 1957. Differential responses of growth zones to nutritive level, age, and temperature in the colonial hydroid *Campanularia*. *J. Exp. Zool. 134:* 63-90.

5. Crowell, S. 1960. Non-regulative differentiation in the thecate hydroid *Campanularia*. *Anat. Rec. 138:* 341-342.

6. Crowell, S., and M. Hartman. 1960. Reorganization capacities of dissociated tissues of *Campanularia flexuosa*. *Anat. Rec. 138:* 342.

7. Crowell, S., and M. Rusk. 1950. Growth of *Campanularia* colonies. *Biol. Bull. 99:* 357.

8. Crowell, S., and C. Wyttenbach. 1957. Factors affecting terminal growth in the hydroid *Campanularia*. *Biol. Bull. 113:* 233-244.

9. Hartman, M. E. 1960. A study of the reorganization capacities of dissociated tissues of *Campanularia flexuosa*. M.A. Thesis, Indiana University.

10. Kühn, A. 1914. Entwicklungsgeschichte und Verwandtschaftsbeziehungen der Hydrozoen. I Teil: Die Hydroiden. *Ergeb. Forschr. Zool. 4:* 1-284.

11. Nathanson, D. L. 1955. The relationship of regenerative ability to the regression of hydranths of *Campanularia*. *Biol. Bull. 109:* 350.

12. Strehler, B. L., and S. Crowell. 1961. Studies on comparative physiology of aging. I. Function vs. age of *Campanularia flexuosa*. *Gerontologia 5:* 1-8.

DISCUSSION

FULTON: I am much impressed with the similarity of the growth pattern of *Campanularia* and *Cordylophora*. For example, if you starve *Cordylophora*, the stolon is the least affected part.

CROWELL: We didn't say anything about longevity. *Cordylophora* hydranths don't die after a week or so as do calyptoblast hydranths.

FULTON: As far as I know *Cordylophora* hydranths never die.

STREHLER: I would like to speak on that point. We have studied *Bouganvillia* hydranths for as long as 25 days and haven't seen a single individual die. They continued to increase in size as they got older. On the other hand the oldest *Campanularia* that we've ever found is eleven days of age. That's at about 17°. You can find older ones if you lower the temperature. *Clytia,* by contrast to *Campanularia* adjusts in size to the amount of food that is available. In *Campanularia* you get essentially the same size hydranths regardless of how well or poorly one feeds the colony. If it starts to make a hydranth it makes one of the standard size. Although *Clytia* hydranths do vary in size they don't grow after they're fully formed. You can get very tiny hydranths if the colony is starved and some hydranths as large as *Campanularia* if they are well fed. If *Clytia* is growing on *Artemia* and for some reason they don't catch their food on a regular basis, they very soon get to a size where they can't ingest *Artemia* because none of the hydranths are large enough.

CROWELL: There is some variation in *Campanularia.* If one uses tissue masses of different sizes, one finds that there is a lower limit where one gets no hydranths. Above that, one gets specimens somewhat smaller than normal and with a smaller tentacle number. Then if one uses still larger masses one gets correspondingly larger hydranths. It's not very striking though.

STREHLER: There is one implication in a word that you used. You said that there was a zone of "proliferation" down near the developing bud and I just wonder how you would explain certain experiments we did last summer which consisted of giving a colony 100,000 r of X-rays, enough so that the slides on which they were growing became deep amber in color. Still, after ten days, a few new hydranths were formed in the radiated colony. Just a few, it's true.

CROWELL: Subterminal hydranths?

STREHLER: These were replacements, I believe, i.e. subterminal. The point is, that it's hard for me to see how cell division could occur after that amount of radiation. I would propose alternatively, that there are cells which have already divided and which probably lie in the stolon. At the proper signal these cells migrate into the region of what one might call growth, but which I think may better be considered as regions of differentiation and morphogenetic movement where no cell division is taking place.

CROWELL: I think what you suggest is perfectly possible. The evidence for mitosis in these growing tips is most unsatisfactory. Berrill says mitosis occurs in growing hydranths but he never presents any illustration of this mitotic activity. This is one reason why Mr. Lunger is now trying to look at these growth zones using the electron microscope. We hope to understand these processes at the cellular level. We certainly cannot right now.

STREHLER: At the end of this afternoon's session I hope to show some time-lapse movies of an irradiated colony. I call this movie "On the Beach."

FULTON: Can I interject something? I have been trying very hard to find out where cell division occurs in *Cordylophora.* I don't know whether it's me or the animal, but I cannot see any chromosomes. If anybody knows how to see mitosis in adult hydroids I would be very happy to hear of it.

CROWELL: Send me a copy of the letter.

LYTLE: The only place we have been able to find mitotic figures in *Cordylophora* is in early embryos.

FULTON: This is easy.

LYTLE: Not as easy as one might expect. We had to look at a lot of sections to find any mitotic figures.

FULTON: Adult tissues must divide for they grow about one-tenth of a millimeter an hour. There must be cell division somewhere.

SLAUTTERBACK: In reference to the transected bud, I was quite interested in your "rob Peter to pay Paul" expression. I take this to mean that any one cell possesses not just a single pattern of differentiation, but all the possible patterns necessary for the production of a whole hydranth. And in this case, a cell may carry out each of these patterns sequentially until it has gone through all the steps normally carried out by many different cells. Do I understand correctly, or is there some mitosis going on and it is the daughter cells which make tentacles where the parent cell has made perisarc or stem or something else?

CROWELL: I don't think we know.

SLAUTTERBACK: This intrigues me very much because we've come upon dedifferentiation and redifferentiation in the pedal disc. If one amputates the pedal disc, the secretory cells are soon replaced but not from the undifferentiated interstitial cell as might be expected, but by partial dedifferentiation of cnidoblasts followed by differentiation into secretory cells. This observation is possible because the nematocysts persists in these cells throughout the process. In fact, the mature secretory cells often contain a partly disintegrated nematocyst. Furthermore, even the organelle development characteristic of the cnidoblast persists for a time after the secretory cell, with its very different organelles, has begun to function. I think this is one of the rarer demonstrations of a partial dedifferentiation and then redifferentiation of the same cell into an entirely different cell line. I wonder if that is what is going on in your situation, or whether you have mitosis intervening, or what?

CROWELL: If one starts with a little colony consisting of a stolon and a few hydranths, and does not feed it, one often finds that there is new growth of the stolon and then production of new hydranths from the new stolon. I have seen this in *Campanularia* and *Cordylophora*; Berrill has described it. Of course, as new stolon and hydranths are growing at one end, old hydranths and stolon are regressing at the other end. One does get regression of hydranths of *Cordylophora* in this situation; however, there is no regression in well fed colonies. Of course, such a system gradually gets smaller—as long as it lasts it produces new parts at the expenses of the old.

SLAUTTERBACK: I wonder whether there is a degradation of cells followed by reuse of the degraded material to make new cells, or whether there is a dedifferentiation, migration and redifferentiation of the original cells from the old hydranths.

CROWELL: That is just the point that is not understood.

SLAUTTERBACK: In the pedal disk it is the old cells that are reused, i.e. redifferentiated.

FULTON: This must also be the case in *Cordylophora* because the stolons of a starving colony will keep extending over the slide for months; the hydranths and stolon tissue behind the advancing tips being resorbed and regenerating continuously. Since there is no other source of nutrients, old cells must be reused. In line with this, I wanted to emphasize that there is normally no regression of hydranths in *Cordylophora.* Kinne (1956, *Zool. Jahrb., Abt. Physiol. 66:* 565) followed individual hydranths for about 140 days, and I have observed them for several months with no indications of regression.

STREHLER: Does the hydranth continue to get larger during all that time?

FULTON: They may grow very very slowly. They reach adult size I'd say in about a week of growth.

CROWELL: You haven't said whether new cells are being produced by using substances derived from old cells, or whether the same cells are producing the new parts by migrating.

FULTON: I don't know. All I'm saying is that they can't be using up too much because they will go on for months.

CROWELL: It will go on a long time.

LYTLE: Or it's a very efficient system for recycling materials.

STREHLER: It would be very interesting to know whether the same cells stay in the fully formed hydranth if it's not growing. That is, is there a cycle of cell replacement? One should be able to find out by seeing the effect of large doses of X-radiation on the longevity of *Cordylophora.* Will it kill them in the same doses which double the longevity of *Campanularia*?

SLAUTTERBACK: Every attempt we have made to demonstrate an increased mitotic rate following amputation of hydra heads has been unsuccessful. The formation of a new head with its tentacles appears to be strictly a matter of migration of cells from the column. There is no change in the level of differentiation of these cells nor is there any visible increase in mitotic activity.

CROWELL: How successful are you in finding mitosis down in the lower region?

SLAUTTERBACK: We can see them fairly commonly in the interstitial cells with the electron microscope but not with the light microscope.

LENHOFF: We measure changes in the number of nematocysts in *H. littoralis* using a specific test for hydroxyproline, the imino acid that makes up much of the nematocyst capsule. We find that decapitated *Hydra* which regenerate complete sets of tentacles show no net increase in hydroxyproline although starved *Hydra* are able to synthesize this unessential imino acid. Thus, it appears that regenerating animals use the nematocysts that they already have in their body tubes, and no new increase in the number of cnidoblasts occurs by cell division.

BURNETT: We easily demonstrate mitosis in whole hydra by staining them in methylene blue at pH 7 after first digesting them with ribonuclease (1 mg. ml. for 3-5 hours). The enzyme removes all cytoplasmic RNA and makes the hydra more transparent. By simply scanning the surface of the whole animal, one can see nests of interstitial cells in synchronous division.

MACKIE: I have often seen mitosis in the cell-body part of epitheliomuscular cells. The fiber part is not affected. It's rather interesting in silver preparations because the achromatic figure is chromatic and the chromatic figures is achromatic.

WOOD: Couldn't one use radioautography to trace the formation of DNA? This might give an indication of the mitotic rate or turnover of cells.

FULTON: If you can figure out how to get labeled thymidine into the animals, I'll be happy to do it. I've tried and seen nothing.

Patterns of Budding in the Freshwater Hydroid *Craspedacusta*[1]

CHARLES F. LYTLE[2]
Department of Zoology, Indiana University, Bloomington, Indiana

Craspedacusta sowerbii Lankester is a freshwater hydrozoan observed sporadically in many lakes, ponds, quarries, and impoundments of North America. It is best known for its conspicuous medusa stage (Fig. 1), although the life cycle also includes a nearly transparent polyp stage, which is microscopic and devoid of tentacles. These polyps are attached permanently to various submerged objects and grow as single hydranths or more commonly as small colonies of two to seven simple hydranths joined at their base (Fig. 2). There is no investing perisarc on the hydranths of *C. sowerbii* though a loose case of detritus can usually be seen around the basal portion of the hydranths and the base of the colony. This detritus is held by a mucous secretion of the epidermal cells.

An individual hydranth is typically flask-shaped and measures approximately 0.3-0.5 mm. in length, while a colony composed of several hydranths may reach an overall diameter of two to three millimeters. The hydranths may be divided roughly into four regions: 1) a distal capitulum bearing several dozen nematocysts; 2) a constricted neck region; 3) expanded budding region; and

[1]This paper is contribution No. 706 from the Department of Zoology, Indiana University and is based on a portion of a thesis submitted to the faculty of Indiana University for the Ph.D. degree. This investigation was supported in part by a predoctoral fellowship CF-8674 from the National Cancer Institute, United States Public Health Service.

[2] Present address: Department of Zoology, Tulane University, New Orleans 18, Louisiana. The author wishes to express his appreciation for the guidance and support of Drs. Sears Crowell and Robert Briggs.

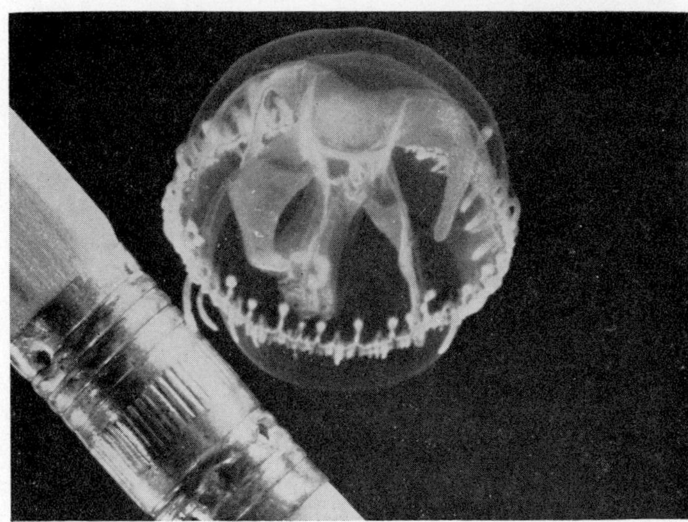

Fig. 1. High-speed photograph of a swimming medusa. Magnification approximately 3X.

4) a basal region by which it attaches to the substrate and/or to neighboring hydranths.

These hydranths carry on asexual reproduction by producing three types of buds (Fig. 3): 1) hydranth buds which remain attached to the parent to form small colonies; 2) frustule or planuloid buds which separate from the parent and creep a short distance before developing into new polyps; and 3) medusoid buds which are released as free-swimming medusae. Under optimal conditions all three types of buds are formed laterally as outgrowths of the body wall near the middle or budding region of the hydranth (*vide* ref. 21). Differential growth in the case of hydranth buds results in the subsequent basal attachment of adjacent hydranths.

Several previous workers have observed the budding processes of *Craspedacusta* polyps (3, 6-10, 12, 14-22), but only Reisinger (20, 21) and McClary (14) have studied specific factors which influence the production of buds under laboratory conditions. Reisinger (20, 21) found that a sudden elevation of temperature from 20° to 25-27° could initiate medusa budding. McClary (14) studied the growth and reproduction of polyps at

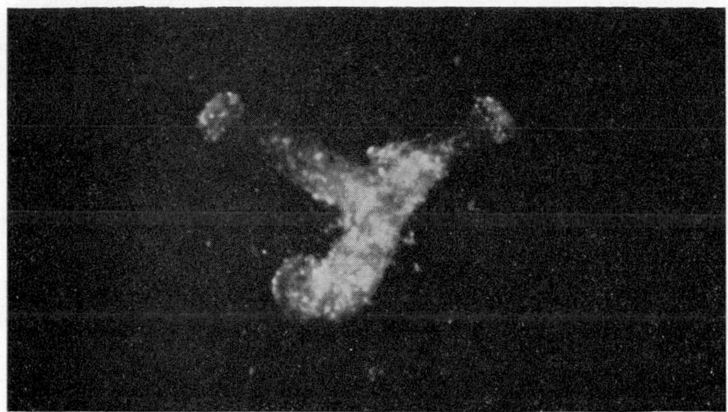

Fig. 2. Macrophotograph of a polyp colony with three hydranths. The neck and capitulum of the lower hydranth are reflexed. Magnification approximately 40X.

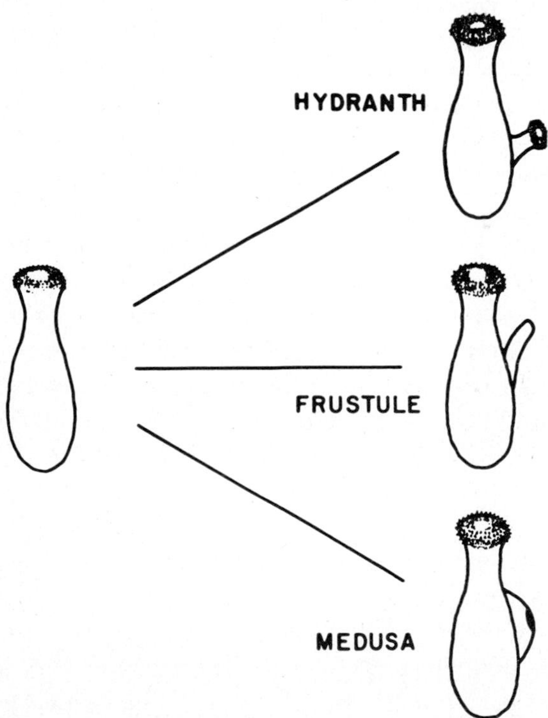

Fig. 3. Diagram illustrating the three types of buds produced by *Craspedacusta* polyps.

four different temperatures and demonstrated that a temperature shift was not necessary for the initiation of medusa budding. He also observed that the three budding processes exhibited different temperature optima. In his experiments, frustule production was maximal at 25°, hydranth budding was maximal at 12° and 20°, and medusa buds were produced only at 28°.

The work discussed in the present report is concerned with the sequence of budding in developing colonies, some effects of temperature and nutrition on the growth and reproduction of polyp colonies, and certain physiological interactions between the different budding processes.

METHODS AND MATERIALS

Polyps of *C. sowerbii* were collected on glass microscope slides submerged in a limestone quarry pool near Bloomington, Indiana, where populations of the medusae were known to occur regularly (13). Laboratory stocks were established; and for these experiments frustules were removed from stock cultures, isolated in Syracuse watch glasses, and incubated in an 18.5° (± 1.5°) constant temperature room. Approximately two days later the culture dishes were transferred to shallow glass trays through which charcoal-filtered tap water was continuously passed. In most experiments the shallow glass trays were partially immersed in constant-temperature baths. Culture water was provided from a charcoal filtration system manufactured by the Illinois Water Treatment Company, Rockford, Illinois (Model No. CC-24).

Polyps were fed counted numbers of oligochaete worms (*Aeolosoma hemprichi* Ehrenberg) by hand on alternate days or at specified intervals. The worms were cultured on rice-agar plates containing a mixture of protozoa and bacteria as described by Brandwein (2).

PATTERNS OF BUDDING

The basic pattern of development and reproduction of a polyp colony is illustrated in Figure 4. Fifteen frustules were isolated at the

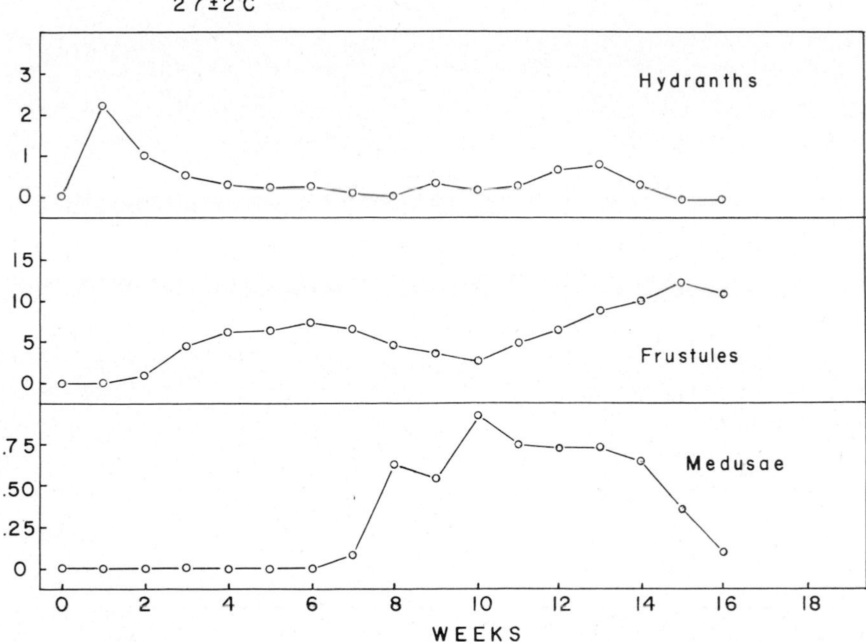

Fig. 4. Budding pattern of 15 polyps reared at 27°(±2°). Values on the abscissa represent the number of buds of each type produced per colony.

start of this experiment and cultured at 27° (± 2°). All frustules had differentiated into polyps and produced an average of two hydranths each by the end of the first week. Hydranth budding declined during subsequent weeks but increased to a second peak during the 13th week. Frustule production began during the sixth week and declined to a minimum during the tenth week before rising to a new high during the 15th week. Medusa buds appeared during the seventh week (immediately following the decline of frustule production) and were produced continuously through the 16th week.

The basic sequence of events exhibited by these colonies was an initial phase of rapid hydranth production, a phase of rapid frustule production, and a phase of medusa budding. Secondary increases in hydranth budding and frustule budding were also observed during the latter portion of the phase of medusa budding.

A similar sequence of events was also observed in colonies reared at 20° and at 19-23°. At 20° (± 1°) (Fig. 5) the frequency of all three types of budding was reduced though the same basic budding pattern was observed: an obvious initial peak of hydranth production, a phase of rapid frustule production followed by a slight decline, and a phase of medusa budding. At 19-23° (Fig. 6) all three types of budding were increased and the three phases of asexual reproduction were again clearly demonstrated.

Colonies grown at different temperatures clearly demonstrate that under the relatively constant laboratory culture conditions three expressions of morphogenesis occur in a sequence of distinct phases. These activities are not mutually exclusive, but seem to exhibit a clear separation between the different phases. The common basic pattern was observed at all temperatures, though certain specific variations were noted in the duration of each phase as well

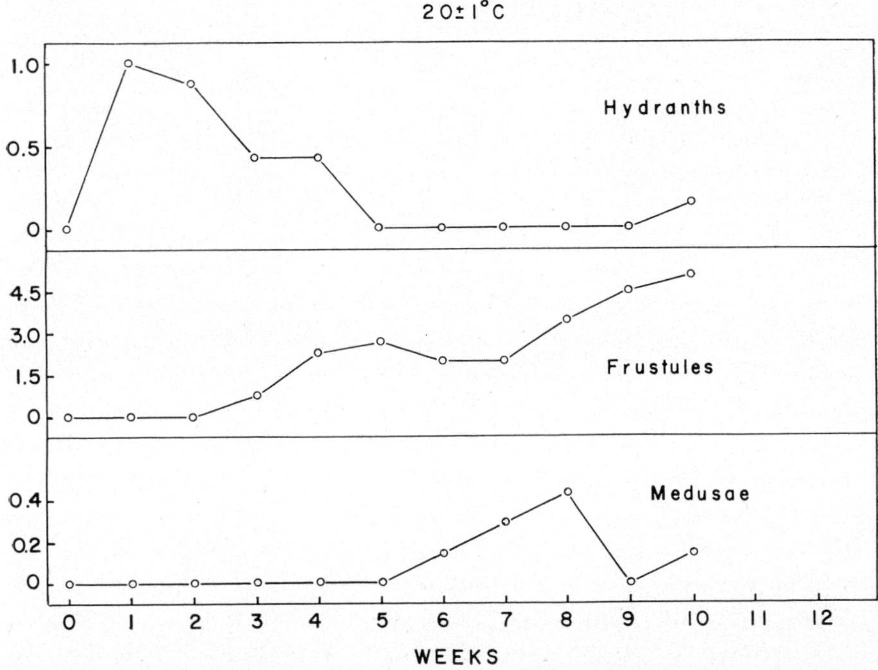

Fig. 5. Budding pattern of ten polyps reared at 20°(±1°). Values on the abscissa represent the number of buds of each type produced per colony.

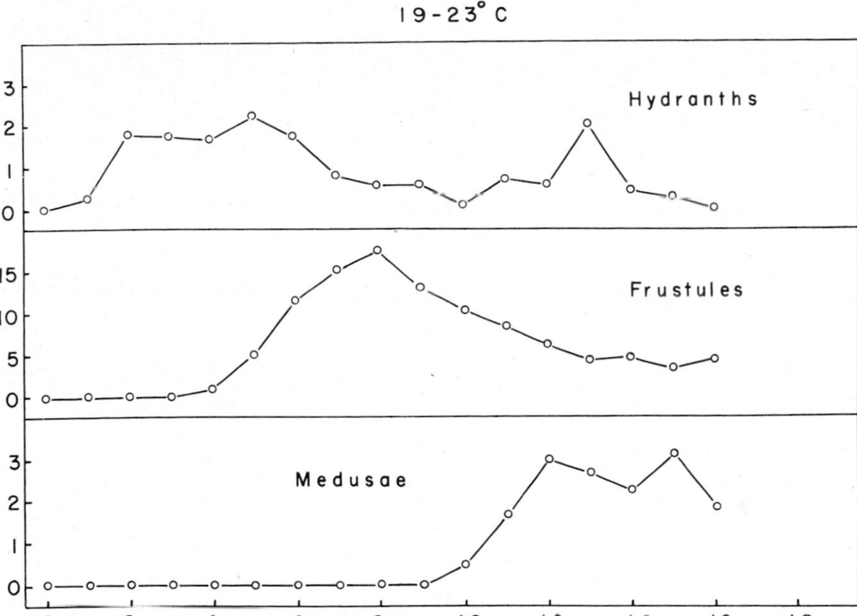

Fig. 6. Budding pattern of 13 polyps reared on a water table with the temperature rising slowly from an initial 19° to a maximum of 23° and returning to 19° at the end of 16 weeks. Values on the abscissa represent the number of buds of each type produced per colony.

as in the absolute and relative numbers of buds of each type produced at the various temperatures.

My temperature experiments also indicate the existence of certain interactions between the three budding processes. Figure 7 illustrates the relationship between hydranth budding and medusa budding. At all three temperatures there was an initial rapid rise in the number of hydranths per colony, medusa buds appearing only after the production of hydranths ceased or greatly declined. Medusa buds were produced earliest at 20° when the total number of hydranths produced was the smallest. Medusa buds were produced latest in the 19-23° colonies when the total number of hydranths was the greatest (Table 1). When subjected to statistical analysis (analysis of variance), differences in the time of appearance of the

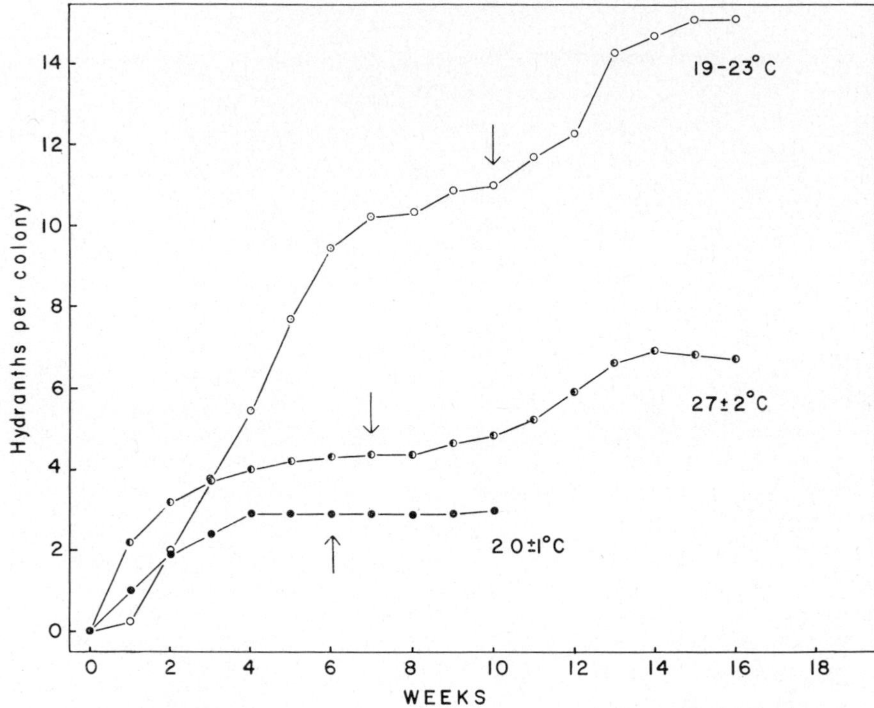

Fig. 7. Relationship of colonial growth and the initiation of medusa budding at different temperatures. Values on the abscissa represent the cumulative number of hydranths per colony. Arrows indicate the appearance of the first medusa buds.

first medusa buds were found to be significant at the 95% level.

The relationship between the production of frustules and the appearance of medusa buds is illustrated in Figure 8. Colonies at all three temperatures exhibited an early rise in the production of frustules and a later decline. In each case frustule budding began after a decline in the initial rapid production of hydranth buds, and medusa buds appeared immediately following the decline in production of frustules.

These experiments clearly suggest that hydranth budding may limit medusa budding, since medusa buds always appeared after hydranth budding had declined or stopped. Furthermore, the shortened phase of hydranth budding at 20° is associated with the earliest formation of medusa buds, while the extended period of

TABLE 1

Age of polyp colonies at the appearance of the first medusa bud at various temperatures.

	20° (±1°)	27° (±2°)	19-23°
	45 days	45 days	72 days
	47	50	72
	47	51	73
	51	56	72
	56	54	75
		55	80
		56	78
		58	67
		62	68
		65	74
		57	
		57	
		60	
		62	
Mean:	48.6 days	56.3 days	73.1 days
S.D.	2.7	2.8	1.6

hydranth budding at 19-23° is associated with a significant delay in the appearance of medusa buds. It also appears that medusa budding may in turn limit frustule production since in all cases the appearance of medusa buds is preceded by a decline in the production of frustules.

Further evidence for this interaction between medusa budding and frustule budding has been provided by McClary (14). He observed no medusa budding in colonies reared at 12°, 20°, and 25°. In each of these groups there was an irregular but progressive increase in the rate of frustule budding for 102 days. His 28° colonies exhibited a rise and subsequent decline in the production of frustules, with the decline corresponding to a maximum in medusa budding.

To study further interactions between hydranth budding, frustule budding, and medusa budding, we have investigated the effect of increased and decreased nutrition on polyp colonies in several ways. In the previous experiments described, frustules for the establishment of experimental colonies were taken from stock cultures

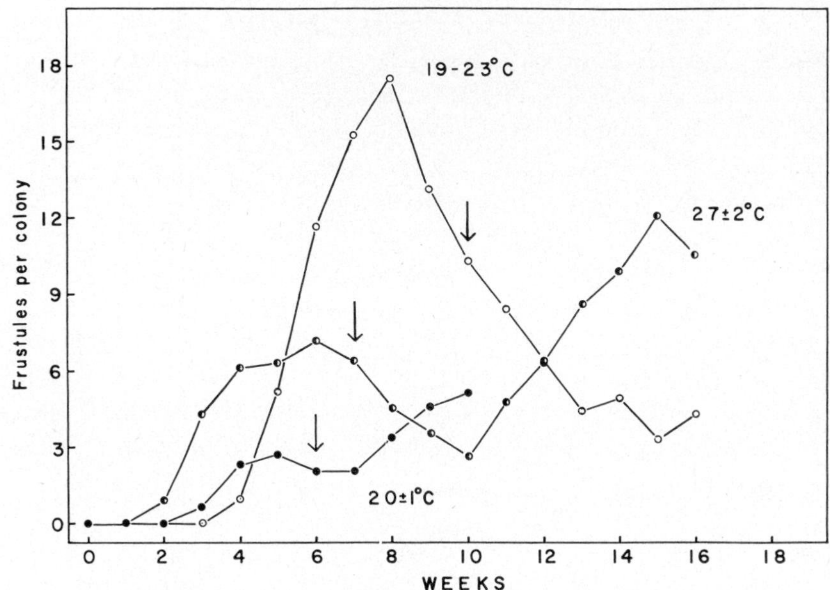

Fig. 8. Relationship of frustule budding and medusa budding at different temperatures. Values on the abscissa represent the number of frustules produced per colony per week. Arrows indicate the appearance of the first medusa buds.

maintained at 23° or below. Frustules from such cultures were generally opaque as a result of large reserves of food material contained in the gastrodermal cells (16, 17). These food reserves occurred in distinct cytoplasmic granules or droplets and appear to be similar to the "protein reserve droplets" or "sphérules de reserves" contained in the gastrodermis of *Hydra oligactis* (4), *Hydra attenuata* (23), and in the polyp stage of the African freshwater medusa *Limnocnida* (1). Histochemical tests have indicated that these granules or "reserve bodies" may contain RNA, DNA, protein, carbohydrate, and fats in varying proportions.

Frustules produced by *Craspedacusta* colonies cultured at temperatures higher than 23° are appreciably less opaque, indicating smaller amounts of reserve food materials. Colonies reared from 27° frustules demonstrate a strikingly different developmental pattern from those reared from frustules produced at low temperatures.

Figure 9 illustrates the development and budding of two groups of animals reared from 27° frustules at two different feeding rates. The animals represented by the open circles were fed on alternate days as in the previous experiments. They exhibited an initial phase of rapid hydranth production followed by the initiation and rapid increase in frustule production—but no phase of medusa budding and no decline in the rate of frustule production. Therefore, in the absence of medusa budding the available food material went preferentially into the production of frustules. The second peak of hydranth budding during the 13th week does not appear related to the absence of medusa budding in these animals, since a similar secondary peak is observed at the same time in parallel groups of animals grown at this temperature which do produce medusa buds.

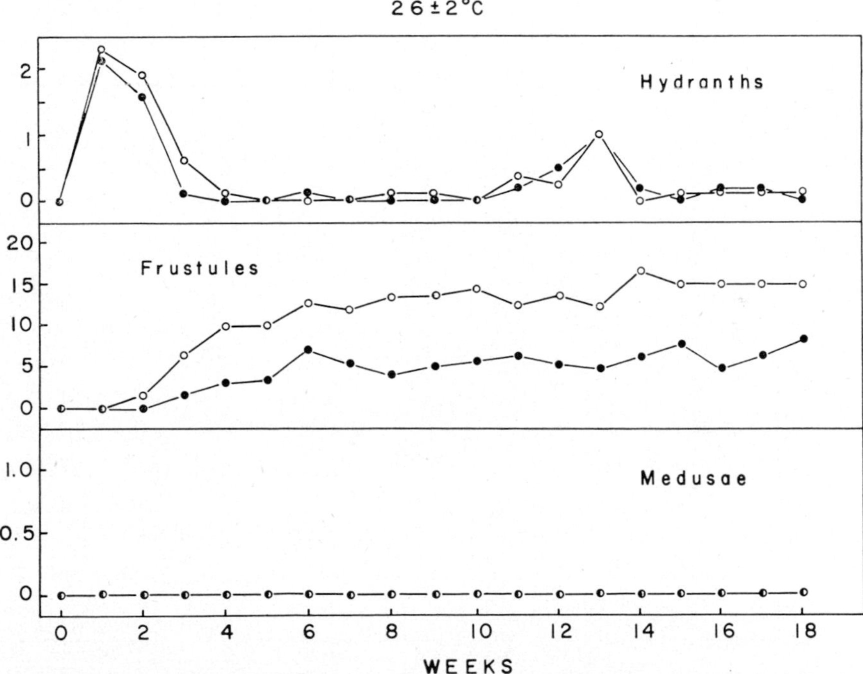

Fig. 9. Budding pattern of colonies reared from 27° frustules at two different feeding rates. Colonies represented by the open circles were fed on alternate days and those represented by the filled circles were fed every third day.

The animals represented by the filled circles were fed every third day. These animals demonstrate that the rate of hydranth budding is not significantly decreased by the lowered nutritional level but that frustule production is differentially affected. Therefore, this experiment provides direct evidence of a physiological interaction between medusa budding and frustule budding and further indicates that this interaction is at least partially nutritional.

Another experiment with different nutritional levels further illustrates the interactions between these three morphogenetic processes. Colonies were reared at 23° from frustules taken from low temperature stocks until several hydranths had been formed. These colonies were starved for approximately four weeks to deplete their nutritional reserves and were divided into three groups fed at different rates. As indicated in Figure 10, the production of hydranths showed

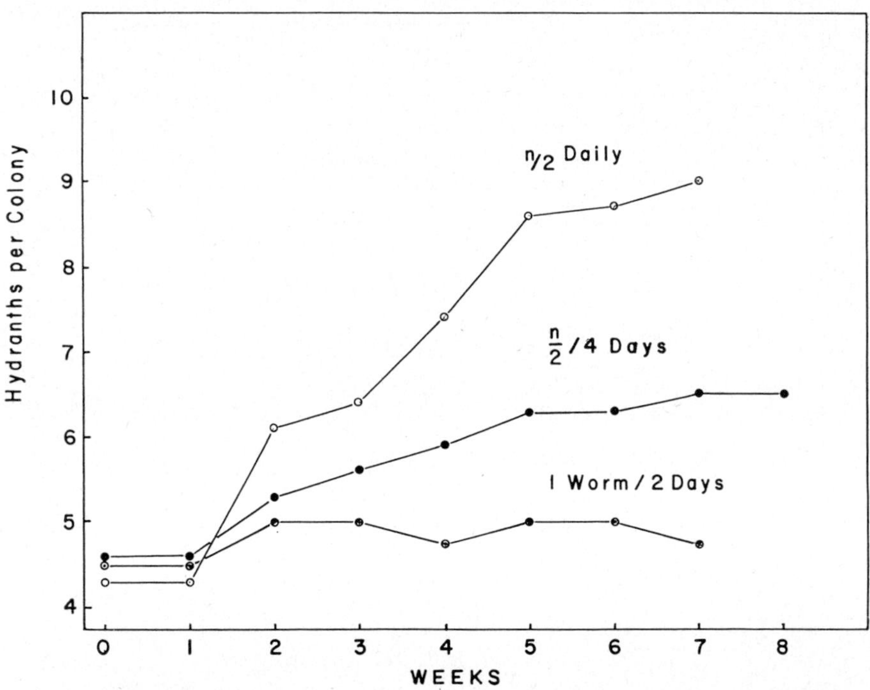

Fig. 10. Colonial growth at three different feeding rates (n=the number of hydranths per colony at the time of feeding). Cultures maintained at 23° (±1°).

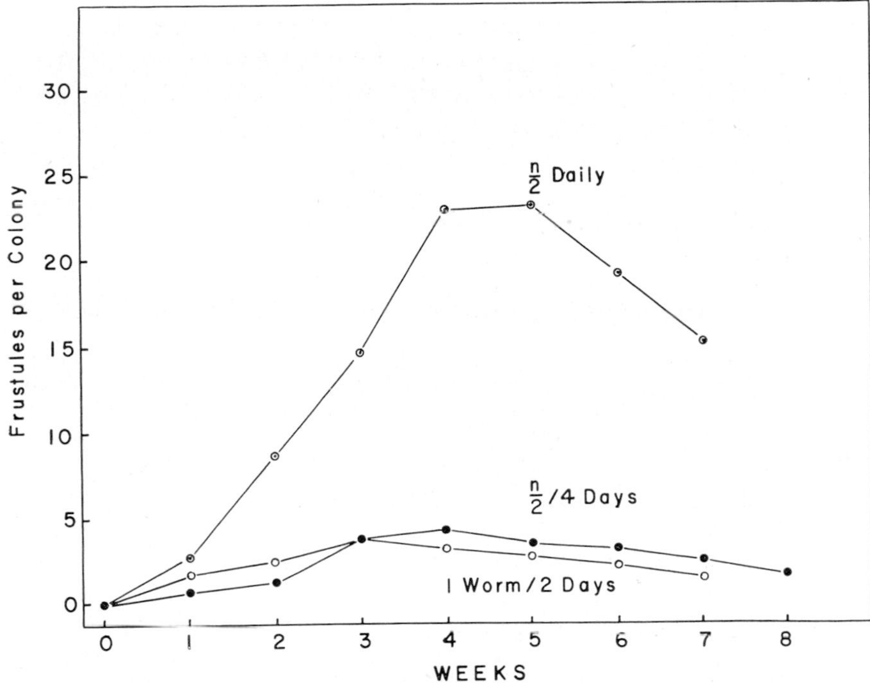

Fig. 11. Production of frustules at three different feeding rates (n=the number of hydranths per colony at the time of feeding). Cultures maintained at 23° (±1°).

a direct and proportional increase with increased rates of feeding. The production of frustules, however, was affected differentially (Fig. 11). The animals at the two lower feeding rates produced only a few frustules while the animals at the highest rate showed a large increase in the number of frustules produced. Much of the additional food went preferentially into the production of frustules.

The effect of these different feeding rates is summarized in Figure 12. At the lowest feeding rate there were few buds of each type produced. At the intermediate feeding rate there was a 240% increase in the production of hydranths over those produced at the lowest rate of feeding and a 60% increase in the production of medusa buds. Only a 5.1% increase was observed in the production of frustules. At the highest rate of feeding there was a further increase (211.8%) in the production of hydranth buds over the inter-

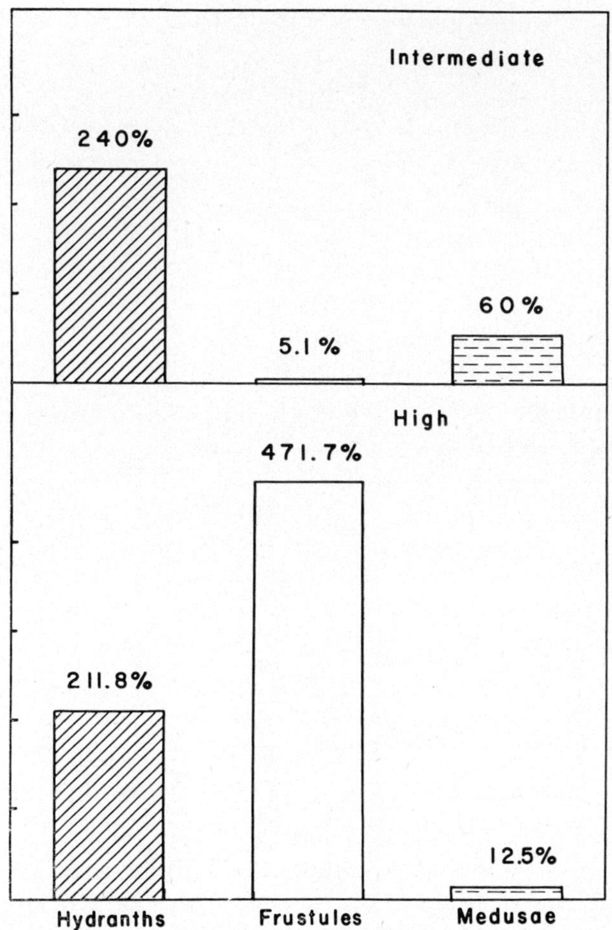

Fig. 12. Differential utilization of food materials by the three different budding processes at three different feeding rates. The number of buds at each rate is expressed as a percentage of those produced at the next lower rate.

mediate rate of feeding, but a much smaller increase in the production of medusa buds (12.5%). Frustule budding was tremendously increased (471.7%). Thus at the different nutritional levels food material was utilized differentially by the three different budding processes as observed also in the previous experiment.

Hydranth budding appears to limit medusa budding since medusa buds always appear after growth has declined or stopped, and because the abbreviated phases of growth at 20° and 27° are associated with the early formation of medusa buds. The longer growth phase at 19-23° is associated with a delay in the formation of medusa buds. Also hydranth budding is the least affected of the three types of budding by lowered nutritional level. A similar inverse relationship between growth and medusa budding was found in *Hydractinia* by Hauenschild and in *Obelia* by Grell (11). Crowell (5) also found a definite order of priority in the utilization of nutritive substances among the several growth zones of *Campanularia* when overall growth was experimentally limited. Significantly, he observed that the formation of gonangia appeared to require a high nutritive level.

Medusa budding appears to limit frustule production since in all cases the appearance of medusa buds is preceded by a decline in frustule budding. The production of frustules always reached an initial peak after the completion of the initial growth phase and declined prior to the appearance of medusa buds. This decline in frustule production was most marked in the 19-23° colonies which produced the greatest number of medusa buds, and least pronounced in the 20° colonies where the fewest medusae were produced. In cultures of high temperature frustules which produced no medusa buds, there was no subsequent decline in the rate of frustule production after the initial maximum was reached. The relationship between hydranth budding and frustule budding was less clearly demonstrated, but there were some indications of a similar interaction between these two processes also.

These experiments clearly demonstrate that temperature between 20° and 27° is not a limiting factor in the production of medusa buds by isolated colonies in culture if sufficient food is provided, contrary to the observations of Reisinger (20, 21) and McClary (14). Studies on nutrition have shown that lowering of the feeding rate within this temperature may diminish and/or greatly delay the production of medusa buds.

Experiments on the effect of various nutritional levels on the budding processes of isolated colonies demonstrate that the three budding processes are affected differentially by increased feeding rates. At very low feeding rates, medusa budding may be reduced or eliminated, few hydranths are formed, and few frustules are produced. At intermediate rates a large proportion of the food materials are utilized in hydranth budding and in medusa budding. Frustule production is still low. At high feeding rates the largest portion of the food materials is utilized in the formation of frustules and proportionally less goes into the production of new hydranths and medusa buds. Therefore these experiments provide some physiological basis for the observed interactions between these three budding processes and suggest that these three morphogenetic processes are, at least in a sense, antagonistic, involving alternate pathways for the utilization of metabolic substrates. My present hypothesis is that hydranth budding, frustule budding, and medusa budding represent alternate morphogenetic pathways, and that the control of budding in this system may depend upon physiological competition for specific metabolic substrates.

REFERENCES

1. BOUILLON, J. 1958. Etude monographique du genre *Limnocnida* (Limnomedusae). *Ann. Soc. Roy. Zool. Belg. for 1956-1957. 87:* 254-500.

2. BRANDWEIN, P. 1937. The culture of some miscellaneous small invertebrates. In *Culture Methods for Invertebrate Animals.* Ed. P. S. Galtsoff et al. Comstock Publishing Company, Ithaca. pp. 143-144.

3. BROWNE, E. T. 1906. On the freshwater medusa liberated by *Microhydra ryderi* Potts, and a comparison with *Limnocodium. Quart. J. Microscop. Sci. 50* (N.S.): 635-645.

4. BURNETT, A. L. 1959. Histophysiology of growth in hydra. *J. Exp. Zool. 140:* 281-342.

5. CROWELL, S. 1957. Differential responses of growth zones to nutritive level, age, and temperature in the colonial hydroid *Campanularia. J. Exp. Zool. 134:* 63-90.

6. DEJDAR, E. 1934. Die Süsswassermeduse *Craspedacusta sowerbii* Lankester in monographischer Darstellung. *Z. Morph. Ökol. Tiere 28:* 595-691.

7. DUNHAM, D. W. 1941. Studies on the ecology and physiology of the freshwater jellyfish, *Craspedacusta sowerbii.* Ph.D. Thesis, Ohio State University, Columbus.

8. FOWLER, G. H. 1890. Notes on the hydroid phase of *Limnocodium sowerbyi. Quart. J. Microscop. Sci. 30:* 507-513.

9. GOETTE, A. 1909. *Microhydra ryderi* in Deutschland. *Zool. Anz. 34:* 89-90.

10. GOETTE, A. 1920. Über die ungeschlechtliche Fortpflanzung von *Microhydra ryderi. Zool. Anz. 51:* 71-77.

11. Hauenschild, C. 1954. Genetische und entwicklungsphysiologische Untersuchungen an Kulturen von *Hydractinia echinata* Flemm. zur Frage der Sexualität und Stockdifferenzierung. *Zool. Jahrb., Abt. allg. Zool. Physiol. 64:* 1-13.

12. Kuhl, G. 1947. Zeitrafferfilm-untersuchungen über den Polypen von *Craspedacusta sowerbii* (Ungeschlechtliche Fortpflanzung, Ökologie, und Regeneration). *Abhandl. Senckenbergischen Naturforschenden Ges. 473:* 1-72.

13. Lytle, C. F. 1959. The records of freshwater medusae in Indiana. *Proc. Indiana Acad. Sci. 67:* 304-308.

14. McClary, A. 1959. The effect of temperature on growth and reproduction in *Craspedacusta sowerbii. Ecology 40:* 158-162.

15. Moser, J. 1930. *Microhydra* E. Potts. *Sitsber. Ges. naturf. Freunde,* Berlin. pp. 283-303.

16. Payne, F. 1924. A study of the freshwater medusa, *Craspedacusta ryderi. J. Morph. 38:* 387-430.

17. Persch, H. 1933. Untersuchungen über *Microhydra germanica* Roch. *Z. wiss. Zool. 144:* 163-210.

18. Potts, E. 1897. A North American freshwater jelly-fish. *Amer. Nat. 31:* 1032-1035.

19. Potts, E. 1906. On the medusa of *Microhydra ryderi* and on the forms of medusae inhabiting fresh water. *Quart. J. Microscop. Sci. 50*(N.S.): 623-633.

20. Reisinger, E. 1934. Die Süsswassermeduse *Craspedacusta sowerbii* Lankester und ihr Vorkommen in Flussgebiet von Rhein und Maas. *Natur am Niederrhein 10:* 33-43.

21. Reisinger, E. 1957. Zur Entwicklungsgeschichte und Entwicklungsmechanik von *Craspedacusta* (Hydrozoa, Limnotrachylina). *Z. Morph. Ökol. Tiere 45:* 656-698.

22. Ryder, T. A. 1885. The development and structure of *Microhydra ryderi. Amer. Nat. 29:* 1232-1236.

23. Semal-van Gansen, P. 1955. L'histophysiologie de l'endoderme de l'hydra d'eau douce. *Ann. Soc. Roy. Zool. Belg. for 1954. 85:* 217-278.

DISCUSSION

FULTON: I noticed that the patterns were the same, but the absolute numbers were very different when you grew them at 20° versus 19° to 23°. Was one of these in the light and the other in the dark, or anything like that?

LYTLE: No. The animals in these experiments were all grown in an aquarium room with several large windows. No attempt was made to alter the normal photoperiod of light and darkness.

FULTON: So far as you know the 19° to 23° versus the 20° are under otherwise identical conditions, but just the temperature varied?

LYTLE: No. Unfortunately the conditions in these two experiments were not precisely the same, but I do think we can say that temperature is the most important variable here. The 20° cultures were maintained in running water in a constant temperature bath controlled ± 1°. The 19-23° cultures, however, were maintained in running water on a water table at the temperature of the incoming water. During the course of this experiment the temperature rose gradually from an initial 19° to 23° and slowly returned to 19° at the end of 16 weeks. There was also a small diurnal variation in the temperature, in the order of about 1°. Furthermore, because of a technical difficulty there was some difference in the rate of flow between the 20° experiment and the 19-23° experiment, but I doubt that this had any great influence on our results. I believe that the gradual rise and decline of temperature was probably more important than the small difference in rate of flow or the actual difference in mean temperature between the two experiments, but this has to be investigated further.

FULTON: I see that your absolute numbers were a lot bigger there.

LYTLE: Definitely. The large colony with 22 hydranths which I showed at the beginning of my talk was grown on the water table with the rise and fall of temperature (19°-23°-19°). I have never gotten colonies this large in cultures grown under more closely controlled temperatures within this range.

HAND: If I understood your summary, it sounded to me as if you were saying something backwards. You showed that when hydranth production falls off, frustule production comes on; and when frustule production falls off, medusa production comes on. It sounded as if you were saying that there was a backward action, that the second phenomenon was somehow affecting the first one. What were you thinking about?

LYTLE: As I stated in my talk, there appears to be a definite hierarchy among the three budding processes. Hydranth budding has first priority, and it is only after hydranth production slows down that frustule production begins. Medusa budding does not begin for some time after hydranth budding has ceased or greatly slowed down. In the interim there is a maximum in the production of frustules.

It appears that whenever metabolic reserves are not being siphoned off by hydranth or medusa budding, they become available for the production of frustules. Possibly the reason for the decline in frustule production two or three weeks prior to the appearance of medusa buds is that some of the reserve materials are already going into the pathway leading to the production of medusa buds before the actual morphological appearance of buds. In other words, the biochemical machinery is being set in motion. Similar phenomena have been demonstrated in several other developmental systems where biochemical differentiation precedes morphological differentiation.

HAND: That's fine. But as I visualized what you were thinking about, it seemed to me that you were saying that there was a feedback, and there can't have been in time; I think time doesn't run backwards.

LYTLE: Not very well, but there is another experiment we have done which further illustrates this point. A group of animals was reared from frustules in the normal way to obtain colonies; then the feeding rate was suddenly doubled. In this case there was no significant effect on hydranth and medusa budding, but the production of frustules doubled. When the feeding rate was again doubled suddenly, frustule production once more doubled, while hydranth budding and medusa budding remained unaffected. Therefore, the additional food went only into the production of frustules.

LOOMIS: We have been growing *Cyanea artica* in known solution for about eight months and have observed a very similar situation to the one you have described in *Craspedacusta*. Thus, we find that they will bud indefinitely if fed every day with brine shrimp and then placed in clean water. They give no hint of forming medusae under these conditions. I left one culture in the ice box for a month, however, and then found that it had strobilized and was now giving off medusae. The thing that is pertinent to Dr. Hand's question, I believe, is that the new routine of starvation and stagnation without water change stops budding and induces medusa formation, probably by a feedback action by inducing partial anaerobiosis in the culture water. This problem is related to the sexual differentiation of *H. littoralis* which also appears on stagnation, for in both animals the partial anaerobiosis of stagnation induces a second pattern of differentiation to be expressed, much as the butterfly pattern in the caterpillar becomes expressed during metamorphosis.

LYTLE: We have done a similar experiment with the scyphistomae of *Aurelia,* although our experiments took a lot longer than yours. We placed scyphistomae in a 5° cold room and left them there for about six months with only an occasional feeding. Shortly after we brought them back up into the laboratory (at 18.5°), they strobilized. This was the only time we have obtained strobilae in the laboratory, although admittedly we haven't tried too seriously. We did try different rates of feeding without any success, but when we left them in the cold room they got dirty and eventually strobilized.

CROWELL: Something similar happened with specimens of *Aurelia* which we gave to students at Bellarmine College. They tried, without success, to induce strobilization. Then, by accident, one of the students who had quit working but had a few polyps stored in a refrigerator, got medusae. So we have three explanations. Starvation is important, cold is important, and neglect is important.

LOOMIS: Calculated neglect.

CROWELL: Not even calculated neglect.

Feedback Factors Affecting Sexual Differentiation in *Hydra littoralis*

W. F. Loomis
The Loomis Laboratory, Greenwich, Connecticut

We have been trying to induce sexual differentiation in *Hydra* for some years now, because this instance of cellular differentiation is controlled externally by the water in which these little animals live. This circumstance allows the investigator to analyze samples from cultures that have turned sexual, and then try his hand at recreating such water artificially. In this way, an approach to understanding the biochemical variables that control cellular differentiation becomes experimentally possible.

We have found *Hydra* to be nearly ideal for such a study. Thus, any desired level of population density within a culture may be maintained indefinitely by simply removing all the baby *Hydra* that are produced daily by budding, baby *Hydra* being distinguished from their parents by the fact that they do not yet possess buds of their own. Secondly, *Hydra* may be kept in simple saline 99% of the time, for they can feed on enough brine shrimp in fifteen minutes to supply their nutritional needs for the ensuing twenty-four hours. All the tedious routines of sterile tissue culture, therefore, become unnecessary when this instance of cellular differentiation is selected for study. Thirdly, the end result of cellular differentiation in this system is unusually clear-cut, for even an inexperienced observer can identify functional testes (or ova) on a *Hydra* if a dissecting microscope is available. Finally, since the differentiation of interstitial cells into gonadal tissue is an accessory pathway over and above their usual differentiation into nematocysts, the phenomenon is reversible and sexual *Hydra* may be obtained from asexual and *vice versa*. These various factors combined have made the following study experimentally feasible.

Since several years' work will be reviewed in the next half hour, permit me to use an analogy to illustrate some otherwise confusing relationships. The analogy concerns a man who wears a little woolly sweater. Inside his skin we know the temperature to be 98.6°F. while the temperature of the room is perhaps 50°F. Now the question is: What is the temperature to which his skin is exposed? Clearly the sweater markedly affects the answer, so that the air in contact with his skin is nearer 98.6° the thicker, and more impermeable the sweater. How does this relate to *Hydra*?

Figure 1 is a photograph of some *Hydra* in a Petri dish in which a pH sensitive dye (brom cresol purple) is present as well as 0.5% agar. This is a small amount of agar, enough to increase the viscosity of the culture solution[1] without making it actually gel. Observe that each *Hydra* is surrounded by a halo of its own making, an area of increased acidity due to the increased pCO_2 adjacent to its body surface. Each *Hydra*, in other words, is inside a little woolly sweater, where the partial pressure or pCO_2 of carbon dioxide is neither as high as it is in his tissues proper, nor as low as it is in the general macroenvironment of the Petri dish. This "halo zone" corresponds then to the area inside the man's sweater. It is the zone of partial anaerobiosis where the pCO_2 and pNH_3 are increased and the pO_2 and pH are decreased in a microenvironment that is chemically quite different from that of the macroenvironment of the Petri dish proper.

Note that the halo zone around each individual *Hydra* varies with the size of the *Hydra*, so that larger and older *Hydra* are exposed to greater degrees of anaerobiosis than smaller and younger ones. In addition, group effects are present around *Hydra* that happen to lie close together so that their halo zones overlap and mutually reinforce each other. This group effect is clearly visible

[1]BVC solution composed of 100 mg./1. $NaHCO_3$, 50 mg./1. disodium ethylenediamine tetraacetate ("Versene") and 100 mg./1. $CaCl_2$, dissolved in deionized water from a Barnstead Bantam Demineralizer equipped with a red-cap Mixed Resin cartridge.

in Figure 1. It corresponds in our temperature analogy to the warmth generated by a group of baby birds that huddle together in the nest so that they create a microenvironment far warmer than the surrounding air.

Figure 2 represents Rachevsky's formulation of such a halo zone (25). He postulated that if a spherical cell of radius r should give off any metabolite such as CO_2 at a rate q, then the concentra-

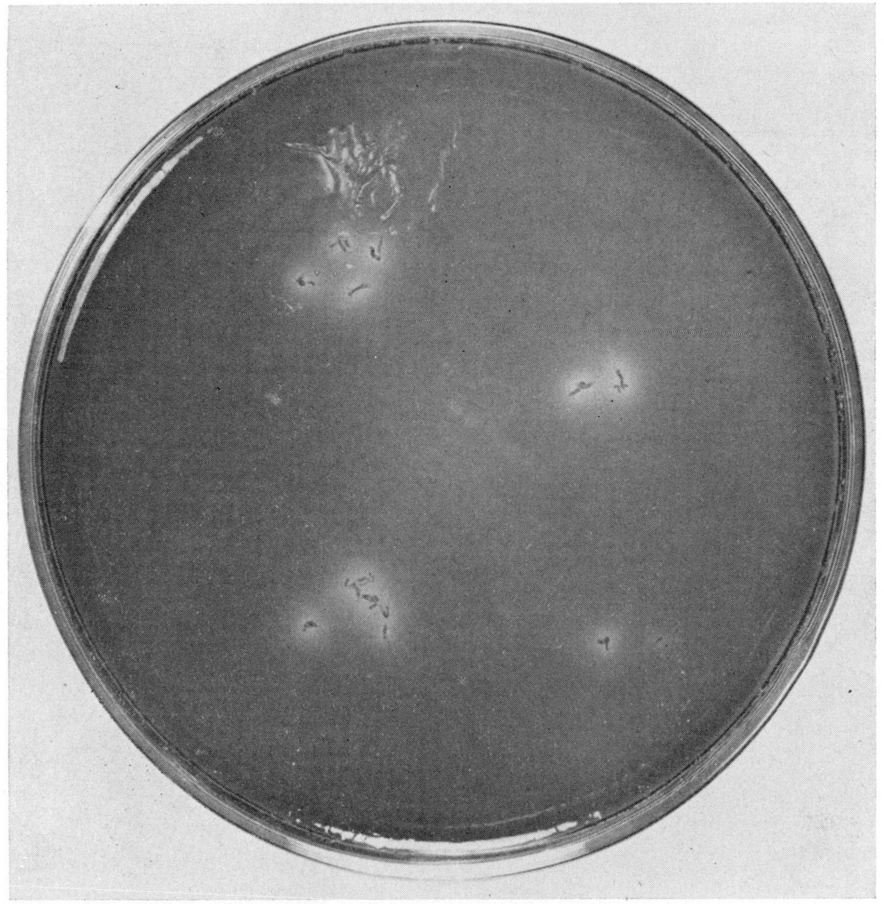

Fig. 1. Halo zones of partial anaerobiosis around single *Hydra*. These vary in size with the size of the *Hydra* as well as with the closeness of adjacent *Hydra*. See text for details.

tion of this metabolite at the center of the cell would be the sum of four factors.

At the bottom would be the macroenvironmental background, which in the case of pCO_2 is 0.03% atmosphere (0.22 mm. Hg) in all samples of aerated water but 5.3% atm. in mammalian blood.

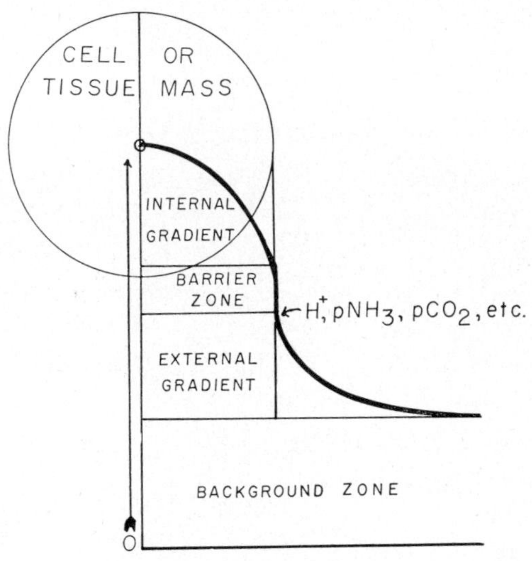

Fig. 2. Rachevsky's graph of the four zones that together determine the final degree of anaerobiosis to which the DNA in the nucleus of a cell will be exposed. This same analysis holds for a multicellular mass of cells such as a slime mold pseudoplasmodium, *Hydra,* or developing frog egg. See Rachevsky (25) for mathematical equation that determines the profile of this graph

Both of these backgrounds remain constant because the percentage CO_2 in the air (0.03%) is extremely constant while the pCO_2 of the blood is homeostatically regulated by the medullary center of the brain.

Above the background zone in Rachevsky's graph is seen the halo zone referred to above. This is the external gradient that forms around any respiring cell under stagnant conditions. It reflects both stagnation and crowding for the group effects mentioned above also increase as population density increases.

The third addition represents the cell membrane barrier, an addition that is very small in the case of CO_2 and NH_3 as the lipid cell membrane is known to be highly permeable to both these dissolved gases, (it is almost impermeable to the HCO_3^- and NH_4^+ ions that are fat insoluble) (10,27). For present purposes, this third or membrane effect may be neglected.

The fourth and final addition represents the intracellular pCO_2 gradient that varies both with q, the respiratory rate, and r the radius of the cell. Since cell division mechanisms keep r reasonably constant, we can experimentally control this fourth factor by controlling q with a thermostat, for it has been shown that the respiratory rate of *Hydra* varies logarithmically with the temperature, as well as also varying somewhat with the level of nutrition (11).

The main factors that control the pCO_2 in the center of a cell according to Rachevsky are then: 1) the external macroenvironmental background; 2) the "halo zone" microenvironment; 3) the barrier effect that is small if only a cell membrane is involved but can be very large if it involves an impermeable chitinous perisarc; and 4) the internal gradient.

This then was the thinking behind the various experiments reported below, experiments in which we studied the effects of temperature, rate of feeding, population density, stagnation, degree of aeration etc. on the sexual maturation of *Hydra.* It was our assumption that DNA in the nucleus of the interstitial cells in the hypostome can produce RNA and specific proteins such that gonadal tissues form whenever their "programming" is correct in respect to such feedback variables as pH, pO_2, pNH_3 and pCO_2 etc. Whenever the programming is not of this variety, then these same interstitial cells differentiate into nematocysts due to the intrinsic programming that, in this case, takes place wholly within the tissues of *Hydra.* Only in the case of sexual differentiation does the external halo, group, and background effects determine the outcome of the experiment. Only this case, therefore, can be experimentally manipulated by varying the external cultural conditions.

Let us examine the results of the experiment in Table 1 from this point of view. This experiment was originally performed in 1957 (16) but has been repeated eight times since then with entirely consistent results, an exceptional record it might be said in a field where over a score of operational factors have been shown to affect the results. In this experiment, ten male *Hydra littoralis* were grown in 15 ml. beakers in BVC solution[1] that had been aerated with oxygen in duplicate vessels 1 and 2, while vessels 3 to 8 received increasing amounts of BVC solution that had been equilibrated with oxygen containing 10% CO_2 gas. In all cases the *Hydra* were fed daily with an excess of brine shrimp and then rinsed and placed in clean BVC solution half an hour later when they had fed to repletion. In addition, each vessel was rinsed a second time about five hours later to remove any excreted material present at that time, the pCO_2 being readjusted each time the water was changed.

TABLE 1

Control of sexual differentiation in *Hydra* by pCO_2 (From ref. 16)

Vessel	1	2	3	4	5	6	7	8
Culture water shaken with 100 per cent O_2 (ml.)	15		14		10		5	
Culture water shaken with 10 percent CO_2 and 90 per cent O_2 (ml.)	0		1		5		10	
Initial pCO_2	0.0%		0.6%		2.8%		5.6%	
Day	Percentage of sexual forms							
1	0	0	0	0	0	0	0	0
2	0	0	0	0	0	0	0	0
3	0	0	0	0	0	0	0	0
4	0	0	0	0	0	0	0	0
5	0	0	0	0	0	0	0	0
6	0	0	0	0	0	0	0	0
7	0	0	0	0	0	0	0	0
8	0	0	0	0	0	0	0	0
9	0	0	10	30	70	70	70	60
10	0	0	60	50	100	100	100	100
11	0	0	70	60	100	100	100	100
12	0	0	100	60	100	100	100	100
13	0	0	100	70	100	100	100	100

[1] See p. 338.

All vessels were kept at 25° and all newly-detached buds were removed daily with a medicine dropper so as to maintain a constant population density within the culture. Population density, temperature, nutrition, stagnation, depth of water, surface/volume ratio, calcium, sodium and versene concentrations, sex and species were thus held constant.

This experiment demonstrates that under these exact conditions pCO_2 is a controlling factor in the sexual differentiation of these animals. The unusually high degree of repeatability of this experiment makes it significant, therefore, that a totally different result occurred when this experiment was repeated on a shaking machine that shook similar but closed vessels for a few seconds every twenty minutes day and night (Fig. 3). Under these shaken conditions, the same experiment failed to yield any sexually differentiated *Hydra.* In retrospect, this inhibitory effect of shaking is due to the breaking up of the halo zone by mixing the microenvironment with the macroenvironment every twenty minutes around the clock.

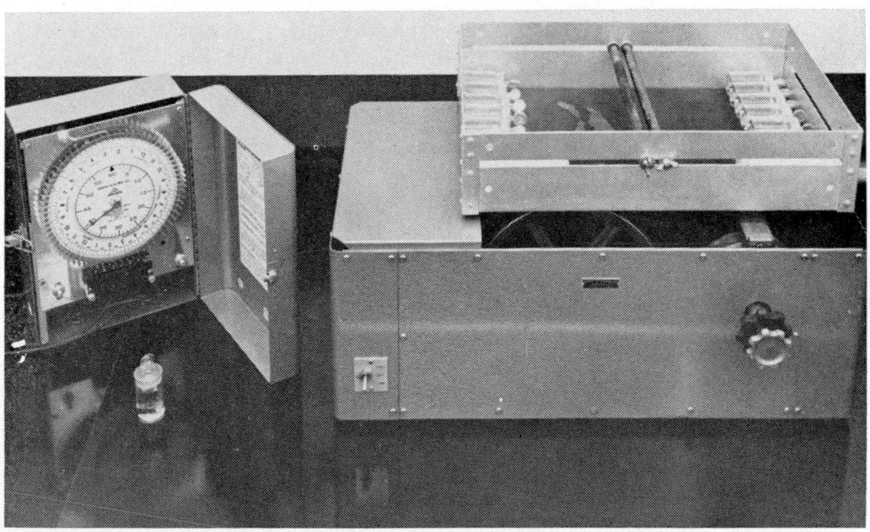

Fig. 3. Automatic shaker that is turned on for 5 seconds every twenty minutes to destroy the halo zone by mixing the microenvironment of the *Hydra* with the background macroenvironment.

Since the pCO_2 of the macroenvironment had been artificially increased in this negative experiment, it was concluded that high pCO_2 was not the sole factor needed to induce sexual differentiation in *Hydra littoralis* (19). The nature of the postulated second factor is still unknown; it does not appear to be simply lowered pO_2 or pH, or simply increased pNH_3 either, or all four factors combined, at least in any combination yet tried. Perhaps a fifth feedback factor exists, or even a sixth, but certainly some combination of known circumstances should be able to be brought together in the macroenvironment such that even shaken *Hydra* are exposed to conditions equivalent to that found within the halo zone of stagnant *Hydra.*

Before proceeding further, it is perhaps instructive to mention that a powerful group effect exists within this 1957 experiment, i.e. no sexual forms appear if one, rather than ten, *Hydra* are placed in each vessel. Here is an example of the crowding-effect referred to above in which several halo zones overlap to mutually reinforce one another.[2]

In contrast, single *Hydra* mature sexually when 0.1% agar is added to the BVC solution in which they are grown as in Figure 1, the viscosity being thus raised sufficiently to stop all thermal currents and hence allow extra large halo zones to form around even single *Hydra.* Perhaps it is for this very reason that Puck's sludgy-agar method enables single cells to grow in tissue culture when otherwise groups of fifty to one hundred cells are needed as inocula to obtain growth (24).

With the realization that feedback factors associated with halo zone anaerobiosis were active in this system, it became important to develop quantitative means of measuring them. Rapid micromethods were consequently devised for pO_2, pNH_3 and pCO_2, a Beckman micro glass electrode (Beckman 290-31 or 290-80) being already available for determining the pH of unaerated 0.5 ml. samples of water. All four methods are carried out in hypodermic

[2]Heisenberg's principle that the act of observing something alters the thing observed enters here, for high levels of pCO_2 were first tried on ten *Hydra* so as to be statistically significant. Only later did it become clear that the ten *Hydra* affected each other in a positive group effect so as to turn sexual when a lone *Hydra* would not, even though he was exposed to as high pCO_2 as were the ten.

syringes to protect the samples from equilibrating with the gases in the atmosphere. Furthermore, the tip of the needle of a syringe may be placed at the exact point from which it is desired to take the sample.

Our method of determining pO_2 has been described in detail elsewhere (13, 15). Basically, it consists of drawing 0.5 ml. of leuco indigo carmine reagent into a tuberculin syringe followed by 0.5 ml. of the water sample to be tested. After mixing, the red color that develops is measured at 586 mμ by placing the intact syringe within the light path of a Beckman spectrophotometer, thus avoiding all contamination of the reagent with atmospheric oxygen.

NH_3 is determined in our laboratory by mixing 0.5 ml. of water sample with 0.5 ml. of Nessler solution that has been diluted one to five. The resulting color in the syringe is measured at 480 mμ by the method described above for oxygen.

pCO_2 is measured directly by a method that has been published elsewhere (17). As originally described, this method required modification of a Henderson-Haldane apparatus, but this has since been found unnecessary, the standard apparatus (New York Laboratory Supply Co. 44250) being found sufficiently accurate for all practical purposes. One analysis takes about three minutes. It consists of 1) filling a 20 ml. syringe with 10 ml. of water sample and 10 ml. of air; 2) shaking the half-filled syringe for thirty seconds so as to enrich the gas phase with the CO_2 dissolved in the water phase; and 3) measuring the percentage CO_2 in the air phase volumetrically in the Henderson-Haldane apparatus by measuring its percentage shrinkage after exposure to NaOH.

Using these four methods, pH, pO_2, and pNH_3, pCO_2 may be determined in any given culture in less than ten minutes. Three of the methods require only 0.5 ml. water samples while even the fourth (the pCO_2 analysis) may be scaled down to 0.5 ml. if a Scholander burette is used in place of a Henderson-Haldane apparatus.[3] Alternatively, halo zone water may be prepared in large amounts by growing many *Hydra* in a closed vessel that is placed on the shaking machine described above so that the micro and macroenvironments are mixed every twenty minutes. Sexual dif-

[3]Personal communication from Dr. Leonard Muscatine.

ferentiation appears in such shaken cultures when the population density is around one *Hydra* per ml., all *Hydra* being fed and cleaned once per day.

This is our present approach to this fascinating problem. When completed it should be possible to place *Hydra* in a running stream of chemically treated water and have them turn sexual even though all feedback between them and their culture water has been eliminated. Figure 4 shows our apparatus for conducting such an experiment. It was used to show definitively that increased levels of pCO_2 alone were not sufficient to induce sexual differentiation in *Hydra littoralis,* the conclusion being that other feedback factors

Fig. 4. Set of six syphons that allow 1-5 *Hydra* (in small beakers at lower end of syphons) to be maintained in a flowing stream of chemically known water with all feedback effects removed. The rate of water flow is varied by the size of the hypodermic needle used as well as by the level of water within the large bottles. A liter of BVC culture solution is added to each bottle daily and the air space flushed out for five minutes with whatever CO_2-O_2-N_2 mixture one desires.

were also necessary (19). When these other factors have been identified, and their appropriate dosage determined, it should be possible to add the necessary components to the reservoirs of Figure 4 and have the constantly-washed *Hydra* in the syphoned beakers differentiate sexually because they "think" they are crowded, i.e. their ectoderm being exposed to the same conditions found within the halo zones of a crowded culture.

Since the present multi-factor approach has evolved gradually over several years, it may be worthwhile to review briefly the route by which this investigation has progressed since this provides a framework within which to discuss various important observations.

1) pO_2

Looking back, even our earliest observations suggested that sexual differentiation occurred under conditions of partial anaerobiosis (11). Thus, we found that 1) a score of *Hydra* turned sexual in a stagnant aquarium tank full of living *Daphnia;* 2) they reverted to the asexual state a few days after the aerator of the aquarium was turned on; 3) the shape of the container, and its surface/volume ratio, strongly influenced the reaction as seen in Table 2; 4) crowding *Hydra* almost automatically induced them to turn sexual in BVC while 5) stagnation constituted a reciprocal

TABLE 2

Percentage of sexual forms and oxygen tension in cultures of differing surface/volume ratio.

Depth (mm.)	Oxygen tension (mg./l.)	Percentage of sexual forms after 10 days
30	7.3	100
10	8.4	100
5	8.6	48
2.5	8.7	0

Each culture consisted of 25 *Hydra* in 25 ml. BVC solution contained in a 50 ml. beaker and three sizes of Petri dishes.

variable in that stagnant-but-not-crowded cultures would turn sexual just as would crowded-but-not-stagnant ones. Indeed this last observation explained why cultures of *Hydra* placed in an ice-box for several weeks sometimes turned sexual, a method often advocated by earlier workers who believed that they were mimicking the natural drop in temperature found in ponds in the fall of the year when *Hydra* often spontaneously turn sexual. Our observations suggested that it was the stagnation rather than the lowered temperature that induced sexuality, for we observed other experimental cultures turn sexual at 20°, 25° and 30° (14).

Analysis of over thirty spontaneously sexual cultures showed that the pO_2 was uniformly reduced from the 21% atm. of fully aerated water to about 15% atm. (70% saturation with air). When *Hydra* were grown in BVC solution whose pO_2 had been artificially lowered this amount (by aeration with a 15% O_2–85% N_2 gas mixture), no sexual differentiation took place. Closer analysis (Table 2) revealed that reduced pO_2 and sexual differentiation occurred simultaneously but not proportionately and it was concluded that lowered pO_2 was not the sole inductive stimulus if indeed it was not merely an unimportant accompanying factor (16).

2) *pCO_2*

Shortly after finding that lowered oxygen tension could not substitute for partial anaerobiosis, we began to investigate the possibility that an increase in the partial pressure – or pCO_2 – of carbon dioxide gas dissolved in the culture solution might be the inductive stimulus. This possibility was difficult to investigate at first because no accurate means of measuring pCO_2 existed. As with oxygen tension therefore, it was first necessary to develop an accurate and convenient determination, and as soon as this was available (17) it was found that spontaneously sexual cultures routinely showed an increase in pCO_2 from the 0.03% atm. of fully aerated water to around 0.60% atm. Indeed pCO_2 levels as high as 1.2% atm. were found in crowded cultures exposed to 100% oxygen rather than air, and a record level of 1.43% atm. was found to occur naturally in the hypolimnion of a neighboring fresh water pond in April (23).

The next step was to expose *Hydra* to BVC solutions whose pCO_2 had been raised artificially. Table 1 records the result of this 1957 experiment, an experiment that has been found to be highly repeatable as described above. Taking both the group and stagnation factors of this particular experiment into account, it is clear that pCO_2 strongly affects the reaction. Just as clear, however, is the fact that an increase in pCO_2 is not sufficient, for *Hydra* maintained in a flowing stream of BVC (Fig. 4) whose pCO_2 varied from 0.03% to 10% failed to differentiate sexually. Similar exposure of *Hydra* to conditions of both high pCO_2 and low pO_2 failed to induce sexual differentiation, and it was concluded that a third factor must be operative in the system (19).

3) pNH_3

Evidence that a third factor existed induced us to assay samples of "crowded water" for such metabolic gases as carbon monoxide, methane, ethylene, H_2S, SO_2 etc. Analysis by infra-red spectography, mass spectography and gas-liquid partition chromatography failed to show such gases to be present, only CO_2 and NH_3 being detectable beyond the gases found in normal air. Analysis for NH_3 by the 1 ml. syringe method showed that sexual cultures usually contained about 1 mg./l. NH_3 and that *Hydra* secreted large amounts of ammonia after being fed with brine shrimp. Since the toxic level of NH_3 varied with the pH, it was concluded that the active species was the NH_3 molecule rather than the NH_4^+ ion as only the former could penetrate the lipid cell membrane which is largely impermeable to polar solutes such as NH_4^+ (27).

Exposure of *Hydra* to increased levels of pNH_3 was accomplished by adding different amounts of NH_4OH to buffered culture solutions, and it was found that this variable alone and in various combinations with increased pCO_2 and decreased pO_2 was unable to induce sexuality in *Hydra* at least under the conditions tried to date. One insight came from these experiments, however: it became clear that *Hydra* release the salt ammonium bicarbonate into their halo zone and that this buffer is equivalent to $NaHCO_3$ which, as we will see below, strongly affects the system.

4) *pH*

Generally speaking, *Hydra* differentiate sexually above pH 7, the optimum being about pH 8. Since a pCO_2 of 0.5%–1% atm. is also required, the original pH of the unused culture solution must either be about pH 9 in weakly buffered solutions such as BVC, or else about pH 8 when strongly buffered with sodium bicarbonate, tris (hydroxmethyl) aminomethane, or Versene, which is a buffer as well as a chelating agent since it is an organic amine. In addition, we have seen that *Hydra* produce their own buffer – NH_4HCO_3 – in sufficient amounts to be very important. For example, the water from a dense culture of *Hydra* may contain as much as 5 mg./1. NH_3 (i.e. 10 mg./l. NH_4OH). At pH 8, this would be almost entirely in the form of ammonium bicarbonate, this concentration of ammonia having served to neutralize CO_2 that otherwise would have created a pCO_2 of 0.80% atm. Since this newly formed ammonium bicarbonate now serves as so much extra bicarbonate, it is clear that the liberation of NH_3 during digestion affects the pH, the bicarbonate concentration and both the pNH_3 and the pCO_2. Since all determinations of pCO_2 from pH depend on knowing the bicarbonate concentration (Henderson-Hasselbalch equation), it follows that all such measurements are suspect in crowded cultures since these can spontaneously increase their bicarbonate concentration through this mechanism. The direct method of measuring pCO_2 described above, of course, is not subject to this error.

The powerful effect of buffer concentration is seen in the fact that for an entire year we failed to produce any sexual *Hydra* when they were grown in 70 mg./1. $CaCl_2$; 350 mg/1. NaCl; and 10 mg./1. $NaHCO_3$ (12). When the $NaHCO_3$ was increased tenfold to 100 mg./1. (14), almost every culture in the laboratory turned sexual (21). In this connection, it is interesting that Dr. Park never observed any sexual *Hydra* over a period of six years while using an unbuffered culture solution composed of 0.4 mg./1. KCl; 10 mg./1. NaCl; and 4.8 mg./1. $CaCl_2$. We have confirmed her observations and also found that *Hydra* rapidly turn sexual when 100 mg./1. $NaHCO_3$ is added to her solution.

I would now like to describe in some detail a convenient method of growing *Hydra* (and other hydroids) under constant conditions of pH, pO_2, pNH_3 and pCO_2. In essence, the method consists of setting these variables in the water of uncrowded cultures twice a day. These twice-daily water changes are usually carried out thirty minutes and five hours after the cultures have been given their daily feeding of brine shrimp. In addition, the closed culture vessels are left on a shaking machine that shakes them strongly every twenty minutes (Fig. 3). Continuous mixing mechanisms, such as tissue culture roller tubes have been found to be either damaging to *Hydra* or not strong enough to break up the halo zone.

Figure 5 illustrates the method used in setting the pCO_2 of a series of *Hydra* cultures. Between one and ten *Hydra* are placed in a 30 ml. Pyrex weighing bottle with an interchangeable ground glass stopper within which are placed 25 ml. of culture solution which leaves 5 ml. of air space. Into such vessels are injected 1-10 ml. BVC culture solution whose pCO_2 has been set at 10% atm. by bubbling it for ten minutes with the gas from a Matheson tank of compressed air containing 10% CO_2. This bubbling is carried out about once a week, for the CO_2-enriched BVC solution can be stored in 100 ml. syringes as shown in Figure 5 since CO_2 does not escape from solutions stored in this fashion. Figure 5 also demonstrates the method of filling such 100 ml. syringes from the bottom of a 500 ml. graduate in which the bubbling is carried out.

The daily routine, therefore, consists of filling a 30 ml. dispensing syringe from the 100 ml. syringe-reservoir and injecting 0, 1, 2, 3, 4 ml. etc. of this solution through a long needle into the bottom of half filled culture vessels and then bringing their total fluid content to 25 ml. When these vessels are shaken, the gas and water phases equilibrate and then remain constant. The actual level of pCO_2 in the various cultures is determined the next morning by the direct method described above.

The great solubility of NH_3 makes pNH_3 easy to adjust for all that is necessary is to add varying amounts of NH_4OH to aliquots of the culture solution whose pH has been set with a buffer system. Culture solutions containing various concentrations of NH_4OH are thus prepared before the start of an experiment and then stored in capped gallon jugs. Whatever buffer is desired is also included in such solutions, provision being made for the change of pH that comes from the later injection of culture solution that has been enriched with dissolved CO_2 gas.

The final step in the twice daily setting of pH, pO_2, pNH_3 and pCO_2 involves setting the oxygen tension. Since oxygen is only

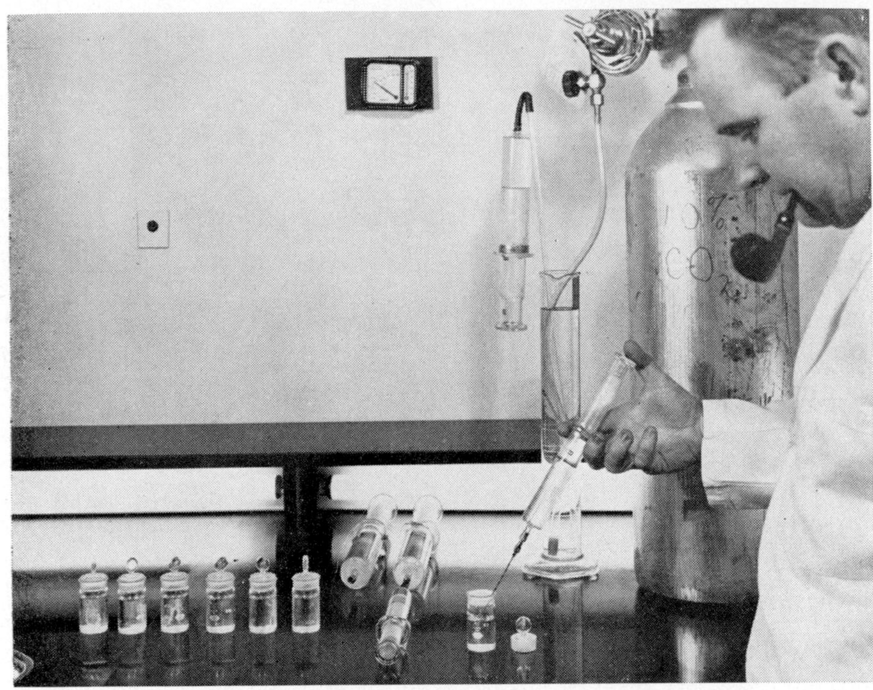

Fig. 5. The pCO_2 of a culture is adjusted by injecting a calculated amount of culture solution that has previously been bubbled for ten minutes with gas from a tank of compressed air containing 10% CO_2 (see tank behind technician). This CO_2-rich water is stored in the large 100 ml. syringes on the bench for later use. Such syringes are filled with a long glass tube from the bottom of the tall cylinder as illustrated.

slightly soluble in water, pO_2 is set by adjusting the air phase and then allowing the shaking machine to keep the air and water phase in equilibrium. In practice, a 100 ml. syringe is filled with N_2 from a tank and then partially emptied and refilled to 100 ml. with room air, the syringe thus containing whatever dilution of air in nitrogen that one desires. A needle is attached to the syringe and the tip of the needle slipped under the ground glass stopper of the culture vessel. Since the air space within the vessel is only 5 ml., it is clear that emptying the 100 ml. syringe into this space flushes it with twenty times its own volume and so sets the air phase to whatever percentage of oxygen one desires.

Summarizing then, buffer and ammonia concentration are arranged at the start of an experiment by preparing sufficient amounts of appropriate culture solution to last for the duration of the experiment. Then pCO_2-enriched water is injected at each water change from a syringe and the air space blown out with N_2-diluted air. The vessels are then left on a shaking machine that agitates them every twenty minutes.

Proof that pH, pO_2, pNH_3 and pCO_2 do not change is obtained by analysis. For this, the pH and pCO_2 are first determined and the results plotted on semi-log paper as in Figure 6. After this it is an easy matter to follow the cultures with a daily pH which yields their pCO_2 as taken from the logarithmic calibration curve.

The above system has been gradually evolved over several years. With its aid, we can now analyze and control most of the seemingly-magic variables that affect this system. How can the mere change of one Pyrex vessel for another completely alter the results (Table 2)? A second rinse? Leaving the cultures over the weekend? Changing the bicarbonate concentration? Aerating the cultures? These and many other operational variables are reflected in the changed values found in our four feedback variables. Some of them are listed in Table 3 where they are correlated with Rachevsky's four zones as well as with their equivalents in the analogy of the man in the little woolly sweater.

Perhaps further work will show that sexual differentiation can be chemically induced by appropriate levels of pH, pO_2, pNH_3 and pCO_2, i.e. that it is just a matter of finding correct dosage levels. Alternatively, it may be that further feedback variables are involved that will need identification, analytic quantitation and artificial application before *Hydra* will differentiate sexually in a no-feedback system. To date we have run experiments that apparently eliminate: carbon monoxide, ethylene, carbonic anhydrase, biotin, folic acid, lactic acid, as well as the possibility that a diurnal

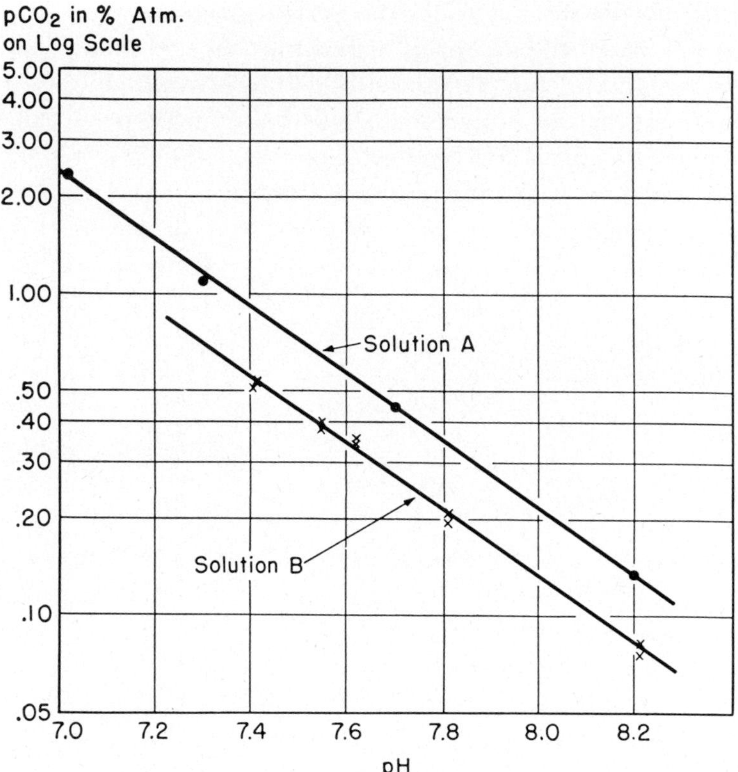

Fig. 6. Logarithmic calibration curves relating pH and pCO_2 in two solutions (25°): (1) 2 × 10^{-3} *M* $NaHCO_3$; 5 × 10^{-4} *M* $CaCl_2$, and (2) BVT solution prepared as described in Loomis and Lenhoff (21). Values of pCO_2 obtained by method of Loomis (17).

cycle of alternating high and low levels of pCO_2 is required for differentiation to occur.

Before concluding this presentation, I would like to broaden the discussion by suggesting that pH, pO_2, pNH_3 and pCO_2 affect many biological systems other than *Hydra*. Some of these systems have been mentioned in previous publications (14, 16, 18), but preliminary experimental work in this laboratory suggests that the following phenomena are controlled by one or more of these four feedback variables:

1. Tentacle number and rate of bud growth in *Hydra* (20).

2. Inhibition of *Tubularia* regeneration: Even an amputated hydranth can inhibit regeneration in adjacent *Tubularia* stems (5, 7, 28). This may result from the low intracellular pH that results from high background pCO_2 produced by bacterial decomposition (and possibly intrinsic respiration) of the amputated hydranth.

3. The Fulton effect in *Cordylophora:*
Fulton observed that *Cordylophora* "may be grown attached to microscope slides slanted in 100 ml. beakers. Such cultures may be grown to considerable density,

TABLE 3

Rachevsky zone (see Fig. 2)	Analogous zone	Factors affecting sexual differentiation in hydra
Internal gradient	Body temperature	Factors that affect the metabolic rate q: temperature, nutrition, etc. see (11) Factors affecting the radius r: size of individual hydra, which varies with age, also species of hydra
Barrier zone (Cell membrane, perisarc, etc.)	Permanent insulation such as fur	Genetic differences between strains, species, and genera of hydra and hydroids. May vary in thickness of perisarc, etc.
External gradient or Halo zone	Variable insulation such as a woolly sweater	Effect of stagnation shaking second water rinse crowding (population density) agar (viscosity) Fulton effect
Background zone	Room temperature	Effect of aeration shape of vessel surface/volume absolute depth other respiring life degree of stagnation bicarbonate concentration Versene concentration pH, pNH_3, pO_2 pCO_2 of culture water

whereas cultures grown in the bottoms of dishes quickly become necrotic." (6). This striking "position effect" in *Cordylophora* contrasts with *Hydra* which can grow equally well on the bottoms or sides of dishes. Preliminary results suggest that growth of *Cordylophora* is especially sensitive to the self-induced acidity present in the halo zone and that such zones are largely prevented from forming on slide-grown cultures by thermal currents (these can be made visible with methylene blue or other dyes). Experimental elevation of the pCO_2 in shaken cultures gradually inhibits *Cordylophora* growth whenever it is sufflcient to lower their pH below about 6.7, the actual pCO_2 varying with the buffering capacity of the solution employed.

4. Strobilization in *Cyanea arctica*.

   This organism buds indefinitely when fed and placed in clean water daily. One culture strobilized and produced many medusae after being left untouched for a month in an ice-box at 12°.

5. Spiral persons in *Hydractinia* and *Podocoryne*.

   Braverman has shown that spiral zooids of *Podocoryne* appear on the rim of hermit crab shells only if the shell is inhabited by a living hermit crab (4). He noted that spiral zooids never form on colonies grown on glass slides in the laboratory, an observation that we have confirmed on *Hydractinia*. Spiral zooids appear all over slide-grown *Hydractinia* cultures exposed to a pCO_2 of 2% atm.: a result that suggests that CO_2 coming from the respiration of the hermit crab is the stimulus that creates spiral zooids on lips of hermit crab shells.

6. Parthenogenetic reproduction in *Daphnia*.

   Both *Daphnia longispina* and *Daphnia magna* fail to reproduce parthenogenetically in aerated water while doing so in water whose pCO_2 is 1% atm. and whose pO_2 is 5% atm. *Daphnia* are thus neither aerobic nor anaerobic organisms, but like microaerophilic ("little air") bacteria, they require partial anaerobiosis to live. This fact explains their usual habitat which is the partially anaerobic environment of the hypolimnion (2) as well as their demand for the microaerophilic environment of a soil-manure culture (1).

7. Amoeboid motion.

Amoeba proteus and *Chaos chaos* are both far larger than the usual metazoan cell. Their central protoplasm would become extremely anaerobic if it did not liquify and then flow peripherally in long pseudopods with a high surface/volume ratio. The possibility that amoeboid motion results from this automatic gel-to-sol transformation under the high pCO_2 (and consequent low pH) existing in the center of these animals is supported by the experimental finding that a pCO_2 of 20% atm. "melts" their pseudopods back into their bodies so that they become spherical in form. With time, continued respiration would re-establish the inward-outward gradient of pCO_2, and hence normal amoeboid motion should recommence. In fact, it does just this, but only if oxygen is present. Furthermore, amoebae can crawl for days in the presence of 10^{-5} *M* dinitrophenol which is known to uncouple oxidation from phosphorylation at this concentration (22) and so suggests that it is the CO_2 from respiration rather than the ATP that is important in amoeboid motion. Finally, Pantin showed with neutral red that the anterior and sides of an advancing pseudopod were bright red (acid) and that the color was stronger the more active the pseudopod. This was especially the case with eruptive pseudopods.

8. The acrasin problem.

The slime molds grow as many separate amoebae and then aggregate by chemotaxis in response to the mutually-produced but unidentified chemical named "acrasin" by Bonner (3). Some preliminary experiments suggest that the highly labile stimulus may be simply pCO_2. With this goes the possibility that high levels of pCO_2 in the center of the multicellular pseudoplasmodium stimulate

> cellulose deposition and hence stalk formation in all cells that become buried in the central mass (see 26). Such a mechanism would explain how identical slime mold amoebae can differentiate into completely different types of cells once they have aggregated into a single multicellular mass whose central or medullary pCO_2 and pH are utterly different from what they are in the peripheral cortex.

Returning now to Rachevsky's formulation, we find that it applies to both isolated single cells (as he originally meant it to be) and to multicellular masses of cells such as hydroids and slime mold pseudoplasmodia. In fact, the great permeability of cell membranes to both NH_3 and CO_2 serves to unite such multicellular masses into one supercellular field or gradient of pCO_2 and pNH_3. Goldschmidt has stated (8) that "the most difficult and most neglected of all basic fields of morphogenesis is that of supercellular integration," and it is of interest therefore that Rachevsky's ideal formulation was developed for an isolated cell but fits the facts in differentiating metazoan tissues as well.

For example, Rachevsky's graph clearly brings out the great morphogenetic importance of a perisarc, that chitinous non-living envelope that surrounds the living coenosarc of some hydroids (29). In our analogy, a perisarc would correspond, not to a removable woolly sweater, but to a permanent coat of fur as seen in northern animals. Both types of insulation serve to build up the internal temperature gradient, but a perisarc is permanent while the halo zone "woolly sweater" is dependent on the presence of stagnant conditions.

In this connection, *Cordylophora* possess a perisarc and differentiate sexually in May and June even while growing in the fully aerated spillway of Nye's Pond near Woods Hole.[4] In this case, the perisarc probably insulates the animal sufficiently to allow partially anaerobic conditions to form inside its tissues as the temperature and food supply gradually increase their metabolic rate in late spring. In contrast to this, *Hydra* have no perisarc and turn sexual in the late fall when the temperature and food supply are

---

[4]Observed to be sexual in 1960 by C. Fulton and 1961 by W. F. Loomis.

dropping but when winter anaerobiosis in the pond is steadily increasing (9).

Seen from this angle, a *Hydra* is nearly as naked as a clone of cells growing in tissue culture. Having no perisarc, it is exposed to its external milieu in feedback fashion just as is a pseudoplasmodium or a developing frog egg. In each of these cases, morphogenetic gradients form and gradually shape the once-identical cells into diverse populations of differentiated cells. The purpose of this paper has been to show how these gradients may be approached both conceptually and experimentally.

REFERENCES

1. Banta, A. M. 1959. In *Culture Methods for Invertebrate Animals* by F. E. Lutz, P. L. Welch, P. S. Galtsoff and J. G. Needham. Dover Pubs., Inc., New York, page 207.
2. Birge, E. A. 1903. The thermocline and its significance. *Trans. Am. Micro. Soc., 25:* 5-33.
3. Bonner, J. T. 1960. Development in the cellular slime molds: The role of cell division, cell size and cell number. In *Developing Cell Systems,* 18th Growth Symposium, D. Rudnick, Ed., Ronald Press, New York.
4. Braverman, M. H. 1960. Differentiation and commensalism in *Podocoryne carnea. Am. Midland Naturalist, 63:* 223-225.
5. Fulton, C. 1959. Re-examination of an inhibitor of regeneration in *Tubularia. Biol. Bull., 116:* 232-238.
6. Fulton, C. 1960. Culture of a colonial hydroid under controlled conditions. *Science, 132:* 473-474.
7. Goldin, A. 1942. A quantitative study of the interrelationships of oxygen and hydrogen ion concentration in influencing *Tubularia* regeneration. *Biol. Bull., 82:* 340-346.
8. Goldschmidt, R. B. 1955. *Theoretical Genetics.* University of California Press, Berkeley, California.
9. Hutchinson, G. E. 1957. *A Treatise on Limnology.* Vol. *I.* Wiley & Sons. New York, page 627.
10. Jacobs, M. H. 1920. The production of intracellular acidity by neutral and alkaline solutions containing carbon dioxide. *Am. J. Physiol., 53:* 457-463.
11. Lenhoff, H. M. and W. F. Loomis. 1957. Environmental factors controlling respiration in hydra. *J. Exp. Zool. 134:* 171-182.
12. Loomis, W. F. 1953. The cultivation of hydra under controlled conditions. *Science, 117:* 565-566.
13. Loomis, W. F. 1954. Rapid microcolorimetric determination of dissolved oxygen. *Anal. Chem., 26:* 402-404.
14. Loomis, W. F. 1954. Reversible induction of sexual differentiation in *Hydra. Science, 120:* 145-146.
15. Loomis, W. F. 1956. Improved rapid colorimetric microdetermination of dissolved oxygen. *Anal. Chem., 28:* 1347-1349.

16. LOOMIS, W. F. 1957. Sexual differentiation in hydra: Control by carbon dioxide tension. *Science, 126:* 735-739.
17. LOOMIS, W. F. 1958. Direct method of determining carbon dioxide tension. *Anal. Chem., 30:* 1865-1868.
18. LOOMIS, W. F. 1959. Feedback control of growth and differentiation by carbon dioxide tension and related metabolic variables. Chapter 9 in *Cell, Organism and Milieu,* 17th Growth Symposium, D. Rudnick, Ed., Ronald Press, New York.
19. LOOMIS, W. F. 1959. Further studies on cellular differentiation in *Hydra. Fed. Proc., 18:* 1092.
20. LOOMIS, W. F. 1959. The sex gas of hydra. *Sc. Am. 200:* 145-156.
21. LOOMIS, W. F., and H. M. LENHOFF. 1956. Growth and sexual differentiation of hydra in mass culture. *J. Exp. Zool., 132:* 555-574.
22. LOOMIS, W. F., and F. LIPMANN. 1948. Reversible inhibition of the coupling between phosphorylation and oxidation. *J. Biol Chem., 173:* 807-808.
23. LOOMIS, W. F., and W. F. LOOMIS, JR. 1960. Constancy of the pCO_2 in the ocean. *Biol. Bull., 119*: 295.
24. PUCK, T. T., P. I. MARCUS, and S. J. CIECIURA. 1955. Clonal growth of mammalian cells *in vitro*: Growth characteristics of colonies from single HeLa cells with and without a "feeder" layer. *J. Exp. Med., 103:* 273-284.
25. RACHEVSKY, N. 1960. *Mathematical Biophysics, Physico-Mathematical Foundations of Biology.* Dover Publs., Inc., New York. Figure 1., page 32.
26. RAPER, K. B., and D. I. FENNELL. 1952. Stalk formation in *Dictyostelium. Bull., Torrey Botanical Club, 79:* 25-51.
27. ROBIN, E. D., D. M. TRAVIS, P. A. BROMBERG, and C. E. FORKNER, JR. 1959. Ammonia excretion by mammalian lung. *Science, 129:* 270-271.
28. TARDENT, P. E. 1960. Principles governing the process of regeneration in hydroids. Chapter 2, in *Developing Cell System,* 18th Growth Symposium, D. Rudnick, Ed. Ronald Press, New York.
29. WATERMAN, T. H. 1950. In *Selected Invertebrate Types.* F. A. Brown, Jr., Ed., Wiley & Sons, New York, page 89.

DISCUSSION

MUSCATINE: Have you ever turned green hydra sexual?

LOOMIS: Only once, even though I have grown them in "sludgy agar" and under the other conditions that make *H. littoralis* turn sexual. That one time was after they had been neglected in a stagnant aquarium for a week or so.

KLINE: Two questions. If you carry out the pCO_2 experiment in the low bicarbonate medium, what kind of results do you get? Also, I have heard discussion of a CO_2-bicarbonate equilibrium in which the two compounds were considered to be interchangeable. Will you comment on this?

LOOMIS: If the pCO_2 experiment is done in a low bicarbonate medium, the *Hydra* die for the pH becomes too acid. I do not have the full answer yet about just how much alkalinity, increased pCO_2, and the bicarbonate ion matters. Probably all three do, at least indirectly through the Henderson-Hasselbalch equation, but also perhaps each directly in its own right. An additional complication lies in the fact that crowded *Hydra* liberate ammonium bicarbonate in significant amounts and this salt can substitute for sodium bicarbonate as a pH buffer.

Now you asked about the pCO_2-bicarbonate equilibrium. Well, aerated bicarbonate-Versene-calcium solution does not work, hence the bicarbonate alone is not enough. What is needed in addition it seems is the CO_2 that comes from the respiration of crowded *Hydra.*

KLINE: Will there always be an equilibrium between the two?

LOOMIS: Yes, a three-way equilibrium between pH, pCO_2, and bicarbonate. You can set each one in an experiment and hold it constant while you vary the other two reciprocally, and you can do this for each of the three variables in turn. In this way, you can determine the role of each variable independently. I hope to do this as soon as I have the "halo zone" under control. The final answer will come when a solution can be prepared that will turn isolated single *Hydra* sexual without the need for any crowding or stagnation.

LENHOFF: I would like to propose a mechanism showing one way in which CO_2 can play a role in controlling sexual differentiation. This view emphasizes that CO_2 is an important metabolite needed for synthetic processes of the cell. First we must recognize that aside from producing CO_2 the Krebs cycle also serves at least two other major functions; it provides hydrogen atoms for energy production; and, of equal importance, it provides carbon skeletons for the synthesis of major portions of other molecules, such as some unessential amino acids and pyrimidines. Thus, when unusual demands are put on the cell's synthetic machinery, such as occurs during cellular differentiation, the keto acids may be pulled out of the Krebs cycle to give, for example, amino acids for protein synthesis. That is, α-ketoglutarate and oxaloacetate yield glutamate and aspartate on amination. When under these demands, the cell has to keep the Krebs cycle operating by replacing the di- or tricarboxyllic acids. This is usually taken care of by the Wood-Werkman, Utter, or malic enzyme pathways, all of which require a form of pyruvate and CO_2. In uncrowded cultures, however, hydra, as well as bacteria and tissue culture cells, probably lose much of their metabolic CO_2 to the environment. It would seem that these cells would have difficulty in resynthesizing the dicarboxyllic acids unless the partial pressure of CO_2 was increased either naturally, as in crowding, or artificially using known gas mixtures.

If this were true, then by exposing starved *H. littoralis* to $C^{14}O_2$, one might expect the C^{14} to be found mostly in glutamate and aspartate. This proved to be the case (Lenhoff, H., 1959, *Exptl. Cell Research 17*, 570-574). Alanine, which comes from pyruvate, and therefore would not be expected to incorporate $C^{14}O_2$, was not labeled. Furthermore, the C^{14} was localized in cnidoblasts, which are known to be active in the synthesis of nematocyst protein in the starved animal. The large amount of RNA-rich endoplasmic reticulum as shown in Slautterback's electron micrographs of cnidoblasts, is another indication of protein synthesis. Also, when we induced sexual differentiation in starved *Hydra* in the presence of $C^{14}O_2$, much of the C^{14} was concentrated in the testes and the ovaries of sexual *Hydra*.

Thus, the partial pressure of CO_2 may take on special importance in animals such as hydra that readily lose CO_2 to the environment. The increased pCO_2 would serve to drive the reactions forming the dicarboxyllic acids, thereby maintaining the continued operation of the Krebs cycle and thus regulating the activities of the cell.

LOOMIS: Yes, your radioautographs are very dramatic, showing how the C^{14} is concentrated in the growing testes and ovaries as well as in the cnidoblasts.

Added in proof: Two recent articles on pCO_2 are: Goddard, D. R. 1960. The biological role of carbon dioxide. *Anesthesiology, 21:* 587-596, and Loomis, W. F. 1961. Cell differentiation: a problem in selective gene activation through self-produced micro-environmental differences of carbon dioxide tension, in *Biological Structure and Function,* First IUB/IUBS Joint Symposium, O. Lindberg and T. W. Goodwin, eds., Academic Press, London (in press).

Apparent Rhythmicity in Sexual Differentiation of *Hydra littoralis*

HELEN D. PARK
Laboratory of Physical Biology, National Institute of Arthritis and Metabolic Diseases, National Institutes of Health, Bethesda 14, Maryland.

Hydra have been studied in our laboratory for many years, first by Dr. Harold Chalkley, then by Dr. George Daniel, and for the past seven years by myself. Dr. Loomis' early studies (3, 4, 5) on *Hydra littoralis*, which he has just reviewed for us, are especially interesting to me because Dr. Daniel and I maintained mass cultures of a clone of *Hydra littoralis* in our laboratory from 1950-1956 with only one three-week period in which any sexual *Hydra* were observed. These cultures were maintained in a solution containing 100 mg. NaCl, 4 mg. KCl, 48 mg. $CaCl_2$ per liter of double distilled H_2O, the last distillation being from glass. The cultures, unfortunately, were discarded in 1956.

In 1958, however, we obtained a culture of *H. littoralis* from Dr. Edward Kline of the Armed Forces Institute of Pathology. These were Loomis stock and had been cultured in BVT (100 mg. $NaHCO_3$ and 50 mg. Versene per liter of tap H_2O). We established a clone from a spermary-bearing individual and for three years have maintained in BVT mass cultures derived from this single male. Daily except Sundays we allow the cultures to feed on an excess of *Artemia* larvae for 30-60 minutes, rinse them with tap H_2O, and replenish the BVT. The laboratory temperature is $24° \pm 2°$.

Soon after setting up the clone, we noticed that on some days sexual forms were abundant; on other days they were difficult, if not impossible to find. This seemed interesting and puzzling enough to warrant quantitative investigation. Therefore, *Hydra* were picked at random from stock and placed in groups of 400 in finger bowls 10 cm. in diameter, containing 150 ml. of BVT. This gave a fluid depth of approximately 2 cm. These cultures were maintained as described above except that before each feeding we made total counts and counts of the sexual forms, and after each feeding we randomly discarded animals to keep the population at 400.

Figure 1 shows the percentages of sexual forms observed in a 400 *Hydra* culture over 200 days (Cf. 6). The ordinate value of each point is the average of four days' measurements. This culture was kept in the same bowl throughout. For the past 12 months, however, we have been changing all cultures to clean dishes and counting once a week. The percentages of sexual forms observed weekly have ranged between 10 and 55. I think you can see from Figure 1 why we began to think in terms of rhythmicity of sexual differentiation.

This type of curve is interesting, but tells us nothing about what

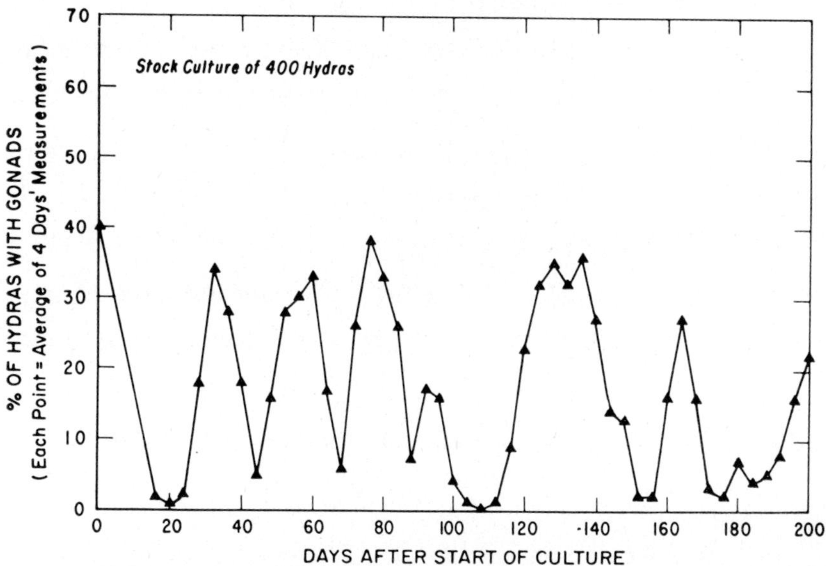

Fig. 1. Rhythmicity of sexual differentiation in a culture of Loomis stock *Hydra* maintained at constant population density for 200 days. Each ordinate represents the mean of four days observations.

an individual *Hydra* contributes to the curve. However, we now have records of some 40 to 50 individual, isolated *Hydra* for periods of 80-240 days (Cf. 7). *Hydra* bearing spermaries were selected from the stock cultures. Each *Hydra* was placed in 10 ml. of BVT in a 30 ml. beaker and maintained as described above except that buds were removed within 24 hours after separating from the parents.

Figure 2 shows the alternating sexual and asexual periods of 10 individuals left in their beakers throughout the observation period. *Hydra* #1, #4, and #5, whose records do not run 200 days, were discarded because they began to grow small and became transparent even though they appeared in ingest food and were producing buds. As can be seen, 6-10 days after isolation, each *Hydra* lost its spermaries. In the next 4-23 days each again differentiated sexually. This sexual period was followed by alternating

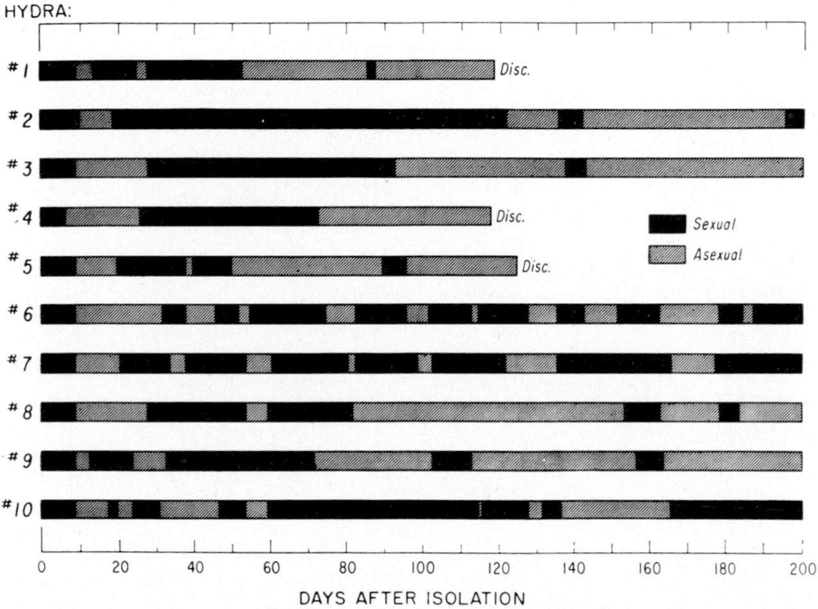

Fig. 2. Alternating sexual and asexual periods of 10 isolated, individual Loomis stock *Hydra* observed for 200 days. *Hydra* 1, 4 and 5 discarded because of unhealthy appearance. Solid sections of bars, sexual periods; hatched sections, asexual periods.

asexual and sexual periods varying greatly in length. Since my arrival here, Dr. Robert Bryden has called my attention to Itô's (2) observation of such alternating sexual periods in *Hydra magnipapilata.*

A striking characteristic of our isolated *Hydra* was the extreme variability in duration of sexual periods for a given *Hydra* and from *Hydra* to *Hydra.* For example, *Hydra* #6 went through 10 cycles while *Hydra* #2 went through only 3. *Hydra* #2 holds a record in our laboratory for sustained production of spermaries—103 days. I mention this in view of Brien's (1) statement that maintained sexuality results in death.

I would like, before we leave these isolated *Hydra,* to give you a bit of information which is not relevant to the main theme of this paper, but which I obtained in order to answer a recurring question, "Does sexuality have any effect on budding rate?" We now have an answer for 22 of these isolated *Hydra* involving a total of 69 sexual and 75 asexual periods after the initial sexual period. The budding rate per *Hydra* per day while sexual was 0.64 $\pm$ .08 and the rate while asexual was 0.78 $\pm$ .10. The difference is not statistically significant, and we conclude that sexuality does not affect budding rate.

We have known since we established our mass cultures that they are not sterile. We know that there are at least three kinds of protozoa, at least five kinds of bacteria; there are some molds. We have not attempted sterile techniques. Some time ago I was quite impressed by the possibility that the rhythmic nature of sexual differentiation might be related to a rhythm in some other organism or organisms in the cultures. We thought, therefore, that we would see if keeping individual, isolated *Hydra* "cleaner" would have any effect on the duration of sexual periods. Accordingly, we left half of the individuals in the same beakers for 100 days and changed the other half to clean beakers daily except Sunday. Other procedures were the same as those described above.

Figure 3 shows the results of two replicate experiments. Again, we found great variation in the lengths of sexual periods for a given *Hydra* and from *Hydra* to *Hydra.* The mean number of sexual days per *Hydra* in the changed group was 44 $\pm$12 and in the unchanged group, 50 $\pm$ 13. The difference is not statistically significant and indicates that the rhythm of sexual differentiation was not intimately related to the presence of other organisms in the dishes.

Before going on to describe some of our most recent work, I want to mention our experiences with clones of the Loomis stock

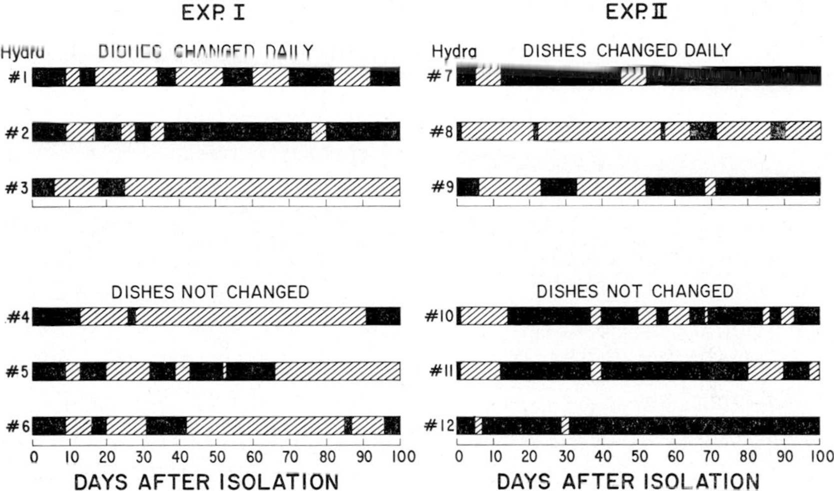

Fig. 3. Comparison of sexual periodicity in individual, isolated *Hydra* left in same dishes for 100 days with perodicity in comparable *Hydra* changed to clean dishes daily. Solid sections of bars, sexual periods; hatched sections, asexual periods.

transferred from BVT to Daniel-Park saline. Over the past three years we have started, at intervals, perhaps a dozen such clones. All have become sexual after 15-25 days. Our present clone has now been maintained for about two years and the weekly counts show that the percentages of sexual forms vary between 23 and 68, percentages that are quite comparable to those for the cultures in BVT. We are unable to explain the difference between the asexual clone of *Hydra littoralis* in Daniel-Park saline from 1950-1956 and the clone of Loomis stock over the past three years.

About five months ago I decided that we had worked exclusively with the Loomis stock of *Hydra* long enough. We, therefore, ordered a culture of *H. littoralis* from the Carolina Biological Supply Company, thinking that perhaps *H. littoralis* from another part of the country might be different from the Loomis stock in its patterns of sexual differentiation.

The Carolina *Hydra* arrived in pond water. We were immediately impressed by their large size when compared with the Loomis stock. They were, and have continued to be, three to four times larger. We need to have the hydra positively identified, but whether they are *H. littoralis* or not, we have learned something from them.

The *Hydra* were asexual when they arrived. We put 16 of them in 120 ml. of BVT in a small finger bowl giving a fluid depth of about 1.5 cm. This culture received the same care as the Loomis stock, except that no *Hydra* were discarded until the total reached 150 (on day 21). We saw the first sexual *Hydra* (a male) on day 10 when the population was 34. It was isolated for starting a clone. In the next 25 days, as many as 15 males and 2 females were seen at one time. On each of three days, one male was isolated. It is the four male clones I wish to describe now. Each male was put in a 30 ml. beaker as described for the isolation experiments but the population was allowed to increase. When each population reached 15 or 20 the clones were transferred to small finger bowls. When the populations reached 150 they were kept constant by daily random thinning. Two clones were aerated with room air; the other two were partially covered and were not aerated.

Figure 4 shows the rhythmic nature of sexual differentiation in the four clones. From 0-30 days (while the populations were small) the ordinate values are the total numbers of sexual *Hydra*. From day 31 on, the ordinates represent percentages. Again, as in the cultures of Loomis stock there was a rhythmicity in sexual differentiation. The four curves, on the basis of the number and height of the peaks, can be roughly divided into two pairs: the triangle and circle, and the square and inverted triangle. The triangle and circle show the percentages of sexual *Hydra* in the cultures that were aerated with room air; the other two show the percentages in the cultures that were not aerated.

In order that you join me in a state of confusion, I want to return to the 16 *Hydra* culture from which these four clones were started. The culture is now 125 days old. It is not a clone; it presumably contains both potential males and females. It has been sitting on the laboratory bench partially covered; the population density

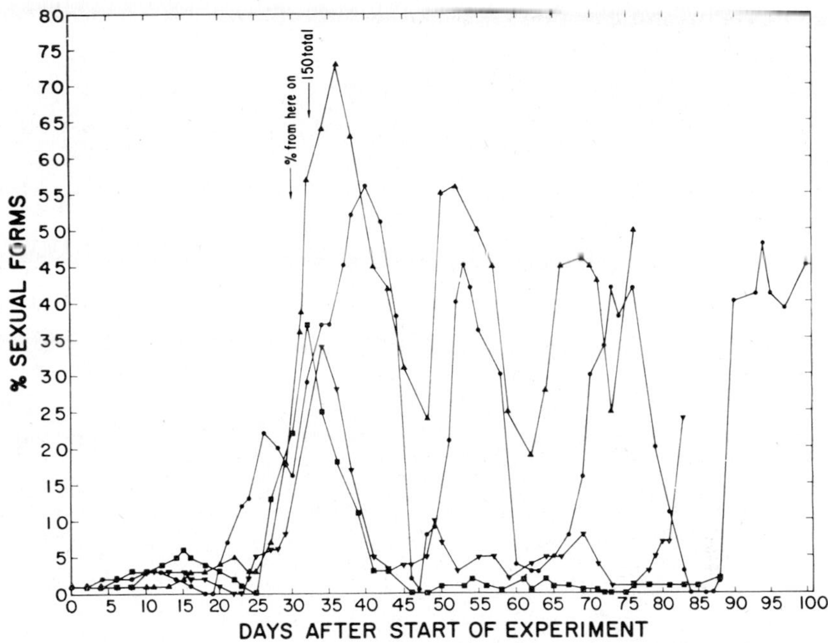

Fig. 4. Rhythmicity of sexual differentiation in four clones of Carolina stock *Hydra*. 0-30 days, ordinates represent total numbers of sexual *Hydra;* from day 31 on, ordinates represent percentages. ● and ▲, aerated with room air; ■ and ▼ not aerated.

has been the same as that of the clones (*viz.* 150); it has never been aerated. The maximum number of sexual forms (7%) was seen on day 34. Since then the culture has been almost free of sexual *Hydra;* four, four and five were found on each of three days. There have been long intervals (20 days) when no sexual forms could be found.

In summary, then, under the conditions in our laboratory, the Loomis stock *Hydra,* both in mass and isolation cultures, have undergone alternating sexual and asexual periods during the past three years. Furthermore, four clones of Carolina Biological Supply Company stock have shown a similar periodicity for four months. The original Carolina culture has remained relatively free of sexual *Hydra*.

At present we cannot explain the alternating periods we have observed. In our current approaches we are considering both environmental factors, and factors which may reside in each hydra itself.

REFERENCES

1. Brien, P. The fresh water hydra. *Amer. Scientist. 48:* 461-475.
2. Itô, T. 1952. Studies on the reproduction of hydra. III. Sexual periodicity found in the hydra, *Hydra magnipapillata* Itô. *Memoirs Ehime Univ., Sect. II (Sci.). 1:* 221-230.
3. Loomis, W. F. and H. M. Lenhoff. 1956. Growth and sexual differentiation of hydra in mass culture. *J. Exp. Zool. 132:* 555-574.
4. Loomis, W. F., 1957. Sexual differentiation in Hydra: Control by carbon dioxide tension. *Science 126:* 735-739.
5. Loomis, W. F., 1959. In *Cell, Organism and Milieu,* XVII Growth Symposium. The Ronald Press Company, New York, N. Y. pp. 253-294.
6. Park, H. D. 1959. Sexual cycles in *Hydra. Anat. Rec. 134:* 623.
7. Park, H. D., C. Mecca and A. Ortmeyer, 1961. Sexual differentiation in *Hydra* in relation to population density. *Nature* (in press).

DISCUSSION

FULTON: Did you run all of the isolation cultures simultaneously? Or when you were all through did you put them together as 200 days?

PARK: All of the isolation cultures in Figure 2 were run simultaneously. In Figure 4, I put all of the zero day clones back together. As you can tell by the ends of the lines, we can calculate how far apart in time they were started; I think not less than 3 days nor more than 10 days.

FULTON: Do these fit together better if you put them in chronological time? I think it would be good to look in terms of periods in the laboratory. In other words, what's happening on December 10th, and so forth, as opposed to time in culture?

PARK: I understand what you're asking, and I can't say that I know, because what we've seen is rather confusing. Sometimes they fit better if they are put together chronologically. For instance, if we take 10 *Hydra* plus another 10 which were run six months later, plus another, and put them all back to zero, the periodicity of the total disappears, this could be due to so many factors that I wouldn't even want to speculate.

FULTON: I have had Carolina *Hydra* for about a year, and as far as I know it is a strain of *H. littoralis.* Like the Loomis strain this *Hydra* becomes sexual following the surface/volume ratio experiments. That is to say, if you take the Carolina *Hydra* and put it in a beaker and in a flat Petri dish (I did just the two extremes), it will eventually become sexual in the beaker but not in the Petri dish. The only thing is that it takes about a month. It's fairly slow, but it does do it.

PARK: It is possible, of course, that the Carolina *Hydra* I received are different from those Dr. Fulton received more than a year earlier. Well, these are extremely interesting observations. Someday I hope we will be able to fit our observations with those of Dr. Fulton and Dr. Loomis.

LOOMIS: About seven years ago I asked Helen Forrest what made hydra turn sexual. She answered that they seem to turn sexual in the laboratory whenever they turned sexual in the neighboring ponds. Now this, of course, seems silly, but if one is using Versene-treated tap water, then it isn't as silly as all that. Tap water from a lake varies in pCO_2 and other factors from one season to the next. It is an interesting loophole in otherwise controlled experiments. It can be surmounted of course by using BVC solution made from deionized water. A Barnstead "red cap" mixed resin cartridge removes all CO_2 from tap water, which is not true of the standard cartridge.

LYTLE: This is both a comment and a plea. In the interesting report presented by Dr. Park, we have seen and heard evidence of the existence of physiological differences among different strains of a single morphological species of *Hydra.* I have recently become concerned about this matter of subspecific differences in hydroids since we now have evidence that such differences exist in *Hydra littoralis, Chlorohydra viridissima, Cordylophora lacustris,* and *Craspedacusta sowerbii.* No doubt in the next few years we will see similar differences in many more species of hydroids. I have just learned from Dr. Fulton at this symposium that he has observed a number of rather striking differences among several strains of

Cordylophora lacustris which he has isolated. In our laboratory we have also found morphological and physiological differences between different strains of *Cordylophora lacustris* and of *Craspedacusta sowerbii* which are both stable and transmissible. The extent and significance of these differences are not yet fully analyzed, but we are convinced that they do exist and that they are characteristic of our various strains.

Therefore, in view of the growing complexity of this situation, I should like to suggest that we establish some orderly and uniform system for designating these various strains of hydroids. The increasing number of investigators doing experimental work on hydroids and our frequent exchanges of stocks made it imperative that we take action on this matter.

There are already workable systems in operation for the identification of stocks of Protozoa, algae, *Drosophila,* and various other organisms important in research. Perhaps we should model our system after one of these existing schemes; at any rate, the important thing is that we establish a system for the identification of our stocks and that a central register be established for the purpose of listing them.

PARK: Some of us have been talking about this since we arrived. I don't know which laboratory could do it, but it seems to me that we need a type of collection of coelenterate strains, or at least of the ones that are being used in more than one laboratory.

Aging in Coelenterates

BERNARD L. STREHLER
Gerontology Branch, National Heart Institute, National Institutes of Health, PHS, Department of Health, Education & Welfare, Bethesda, and the Baltimore City Hospitals, Baltimore, Maryland.

Aging may be defined as the decrease in the functional capacity of an organism following its attainment of reproductive maturity (27). According to this definition, aging is not a continuation of development for aging generally expresses itself in a given species as an increase in the probability of death, whereas development leads to increased functional capacity.

Different species of animals and plants age in different ways (21). They age in accord with evolutionary forces, for length of life, like other features of organisms, is an adaptation, at least in part, to the niche which an organism occupies. Aging comparable to that occurring in man and other metazoans probably makes its first appearance in the coelenterates. There appeared to be controversy for some time regarding the presence or absence of aging processes in Hydrozoa, particularly in hydra (7). Boecker (4), Berninger (2) and Hertwig (19) found that their cultures of hydra underwent a depression with accompanying cytological changes. However, Goetsch (15) improved culture conditions and kept individuals of *Pelmatohydra oligactis* and another species alive for 27 months. He believed that hydra, as well as Actinians, were capable of maintaining themselves *in status quo* indefinitely. Gross (16), on the other hand, failed to keep any individual of *P. oligactis* alive for more than about a year and noted changes which he called "senile" beginning at about the fourth month of life. Pearl and Miner (23) used Hase's data (18) to construct a life table for hydra. David (11) kept records of *P. oligactis* and was convinced that the individual animals tended to die between 20 and 28 months. However,

Schlottke (25) made very careful cytological studies and, moreover, suggested that David's histological sections were heavily parasitized. Schlottke's observations can be summarized as follows. There appears to be an aging process in ectodermal cells which is characterized by nuclear changes, e.g., pyknosis. He noted that the cells move from the ectoderm into the endoderm after they degenerate and observed the appearance of what he called "guanine deposits" as the remains of cells which had been resorbed into the endoderm. Schlottke also noted that degenerating nematocysts tended to move into the endoderm.

Schlottke's early view is quite similar to that of Brien (5) who, in 1953, published evidence, based upon marking experiments, that there is a continual formation of new cells in the region around the hypostome and that this is followed by a continual, slow (but systematic) movement of cells down over the surface of the column of the hydra body to the foot where death and resorption take place. One of the reasons that coelenterates are valuable in aging studies arises from the fact that certain representatives of the phylum make it evident that there is no necessity for senescence in metazoa *per se*, just as certain immortal clones of protozoa demonstrate (26) that sexual reproduction is not necessary for clonal immortality.

A most charming description of a long-lived, and probably immortal coelenterate, was published by Ashworth and Annandale in 1904 (1): "We have, during the last two years, made a series of observations upon specimens of *Sagartia troglodytes* (later re-identified as *Cereus pedunculatus*) which are at least 50 years old and have thought it worthwhile to give a somewhat detailed account of these. So far as we can ascertain, there is only one other recorded case of longevity in coelenterates and very few in the whole of the invertebrates. These specimens of *Sagartia* were collected by Miss Ann Nelson (Mrs. George Brown) on the coast of Iran some few years previous to 1862 (the exact date has not been recorded) and were placed in bell jars containing sea water. In 1862, they were transferred to the care of Miss Jessie Nelson, in whose possession they still remain and to whom we are indebted for the opportunity of observing these interesting anemones. Sixteen of the original specimens are still living, so that they have lived in captivity for about 50 years. They are kept in a bell jar about 13 inches in diameter and 9 inches in depth. The original specimens are all together on a piece of stone which bears a number of deep depressions in which the anemones have ensconced themselves. These conditions closely resemble those in which *Sagartia troglodytes* are usually found, the specific name of this anemone being derived from its favorite habit of dwelling in holes and crevices of the rocks. These specimens have been under constant observation since 1862 and there can be no doubt that they are the original ones."

These animals were later transferred to the Edinburgh Zoo and lived until 1942 when all of them were simultaneously found dead one morning (7). I doubt that they died of "old age."

It certainly seems well established that a process of clonal aging, such as frequently occurs in protozoan cultures, is not a regular process among coelenterates (20). Lines of hydra in which the only means of propagation was asexual budding have been kept for decades without sexual crossing. In our own studies of *Campanularia flexuosa,* a colonial hydroid, (30, 31), we have kept a clone growing vigorously over the last three years on an artificial medium in the laboratory without sexual crossing. This strain was obtained earlier from Crowell (8, 9, 10) who had likewise kept it and perpetuated it as a clone for a number of years.

Although, in the opinion of most recent investigators, certain Hydrozoa such as hydra and probably many species of Anthozoa do not undergo individual aging, there are closely related species such as *Obelia commissuralis* and *Campanularia flexuosa* which do undergo a clear and most remarkable aging process. The details of the senescence and death of *Campanularia* hydranths is currently being investigated in our laboratory. The developmental history of clones of this species is approximately as follows. The animal grows by sending out a root-like structure called a stolon which grows on a hospitable substratum, either rock, piling or, even in some cases, an algal surface (e. g., *Fucus*). At periodic intervals, upright branches appear as shoots from the main stolonic growth. These proceed upwards for a certain distance, acquire a series of annulations, the most distal of which eventually enlarges into a bulblike structure. This primitive structure then elongates, acquires a rhythmic muscular contractility, lays down a protective covering shield or chitinous perisarc, develops tentacles at the upper end, hollows out and finally perforates a mouth in the center of the tentacles (see Fig. 1). For 4 or 5 days, this hydra-like animal, growing on a branched stalk, catches crustacea or other suitable prey with the batteries of nematocysts in its tentacles, ingests them, dissolves their contents which are taken up by a phagocytic process into the endodermal cell layer or transmitted back down along the branching root-like stolon to other individuals in the colony or to the region of apical growth.

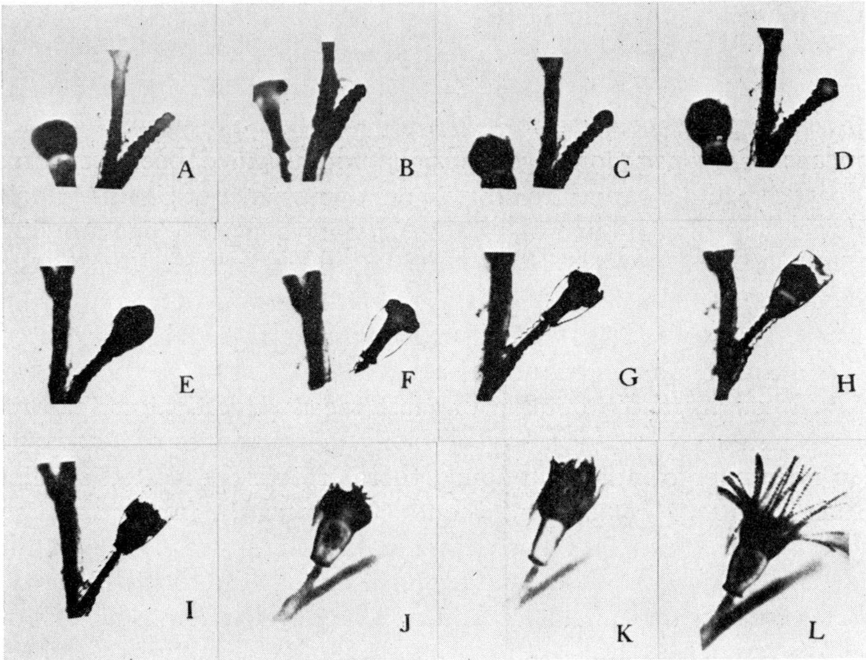

Fig. 1. Development of *Campanularia* hydranth. (Taken from time lapse sequence).

I would like to suggest that these contrasting species of coelenterates are useful in studies of the biological basis of senescence because they furnish us with exaggerated models of parallel systems we may observe within more highly evolved metazoa such as human

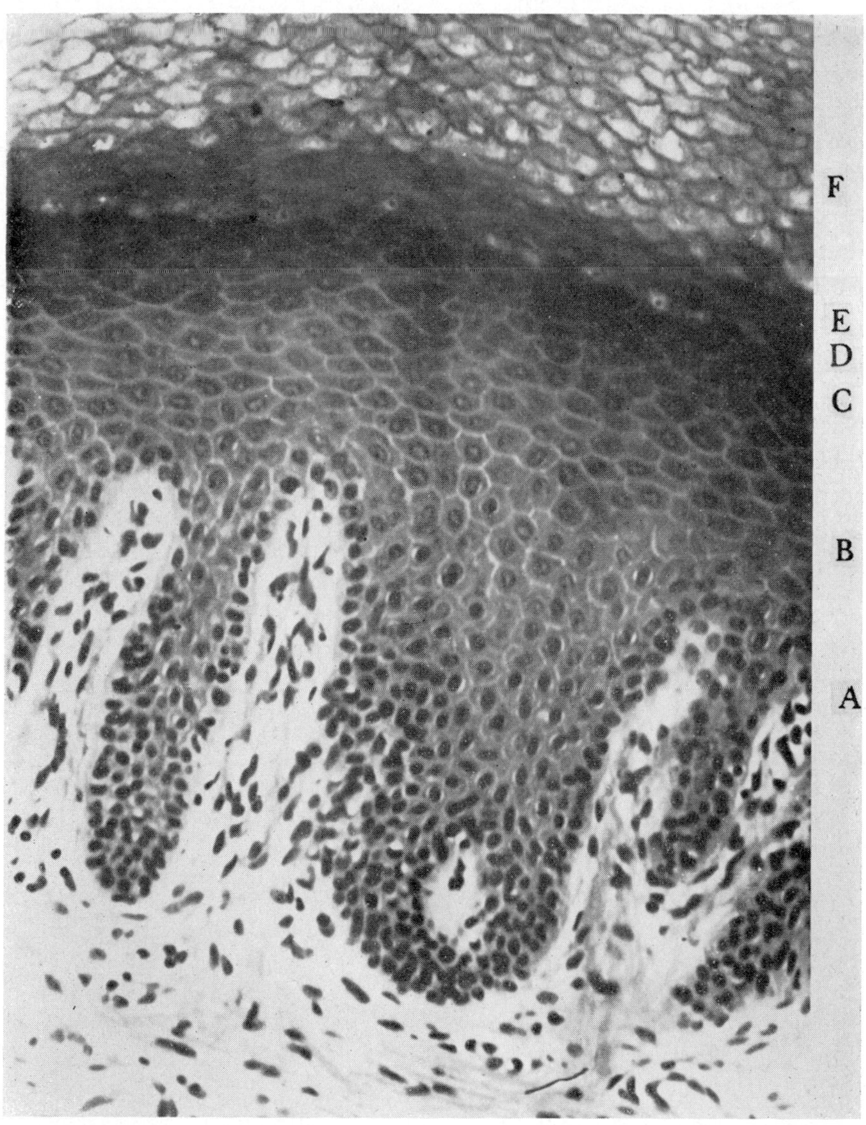

Fig. 2. Section of thick human skin showing sequence of cell growth (A), Differentiation (B, C), Death (D, E, F). A—germinal zone; B—prickle cell zone; C—zone of RNA granules (Granulosa); D—area of lysis (note nuclei in process of solution); E—area of cytoplasmic dissolution; F—keratinized zone.

beings. One such analogy is illustrated in Figure 2 which shows a section of thick human skin. You will notice that there is a generative zone, in which cell division and growth take place, and next to it the so-called prickle cells in the spinosa in the process of differentiating. Further toward the surface we see the granular layer. In addition to showing a strong basophilia, due to the presence of acidic substances which have been identified as RNA by Leuchtenberg (22), we observe in cells just distal to the granulated cells the complete disappearance of these acidic substances. I believe it is likely that this lysis is due to the action of lysosomes, bodies which DeDuve (12) identified some years ago as contaminants in mitochondrial fractions. Such structures occur in many cell types and, in the event that the cells are damaged, they are activated to break down cellular contents and thus clear the way for repair processes. In this present case, they appear to hydrolyze all of the cell contents except, presumably, keratin and a few other substances.

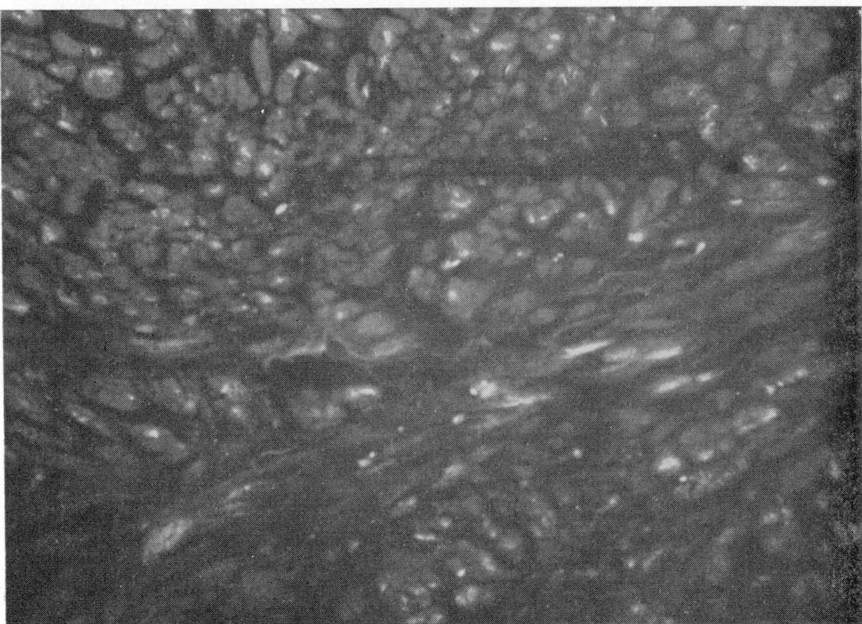

Fig. 3. Photomicrograph of old human myocardium (86 years old) taken by its own fluorescence in U.V. light. Bright spots are lipofuscin granules. 400X magnification.

The opposite extreme in cell types is illustrated in Figure 3 which shows a section from old human myocardium. These cells, in contrast to skin cells, do not die regularly, but rather live for the lifetime of the animal. A most interesting feature of such cells is the fact that they accumulate a fluorescent brown pigment known as lipofuscin (17). We are attempting to isolate and characterize this substance. The fluorescent component appears to be an auto-oxidized, unsaturated lipid. We have shown that this material accumulates linearly with time (32), at the rate of about three-tenths percent of the total heart volume per decade. Gedigk and Bontke (14) have demonstrated that these granules possess a number of lytic enzymes and may thus be a type of lysosome. Lipofuscin apparently accumulates in all non-dividing cell lines. On the other hand, it does not generally appear in dividing cell lines. I would like to suggest that the heart is analogous to *Campanularia* and that there exists an analogy between anemones or hydra and the regularly replenishing structure, skin. In the former case, there is no regular cell replacement since the cells of the nervous system and the heart are carried through the life of the individual. On the other hand, the skin is in a continual process of replacement just as is hydra with its growth in the hypostomal region and the death of cells at the base and probably at the ends of the tentacles.

In support of this thesis, I would like to concentrate on a comparison between certain histochemical properties of *H. littoralis* and *Campanularia* which are being studied in cooperation with Dr. Mary Anne Brock (6). In Figure 4 is illustrated the regression process in *Campanularia* as recorded in time lapse movies. *Campanularia* exhibits regular peristalsis very much as does *Cordylorphora*. The histological appearance of a young *Campanularia* is shown in Figure 5.

The first sign of the senescence of the individual hydranth is a slight shortening of the tentacles and the appearance of knobbiness accompanied by a change in refractive index on the end of them. The tentacles then begin slowly to shorten and draw in toward their bases. After the tentacles have contracted completely, there is a sudden release of something which breaks down the intercellular cement and, at the same time, results in cell autolysis. A hydranth in this stage is shown in Figure 6. Finally, the entire contents of the

Fig. 4. Regression of *Campanularia* hydranth. (Taken from time lapse sequence). Note thickening of tentacles prior to resorption. Entire sequence takes about 6 hours.

dead animal is passed back into the colony from whence it came, and all that is left as a reminder of the former inhabitant is the empty hydrotheca.

What is the mechanism of cell death underlying these changes? Is it similar to that which has been postulated or shown in other

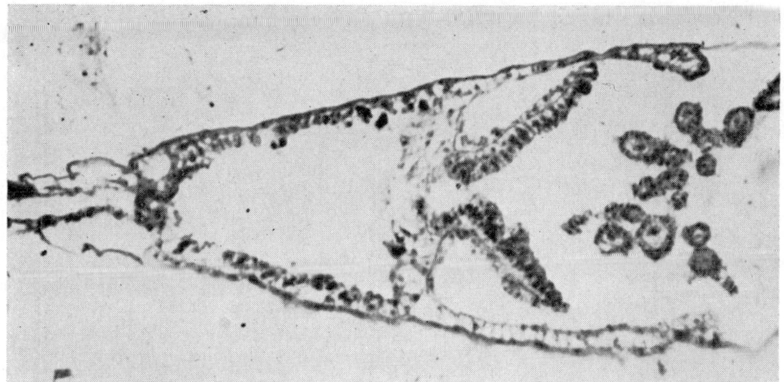

Fig. 5. Normal young *Campanularia* section. Magnification=500X.

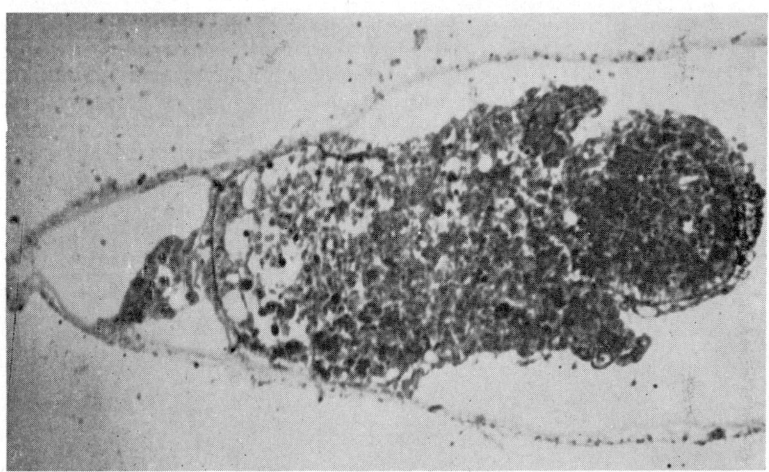

Fig. 6. Regressing *Campanularia* hydranth. Magnification=500X.

species? Might it be the activation of lysosomes? In order to test this thesis, we have compared *H. littoralis* of the Loomis strain with *Campanularia* for the presence and distribution of acid phosphatase positive granules. This is one of the simplest ways to localize presumptive lysosomes (13). Acid phosphatase is one of the enzymes which lysosomes generally contain.

Figure 7 illustrates a young *Campanularia,* stained for acid

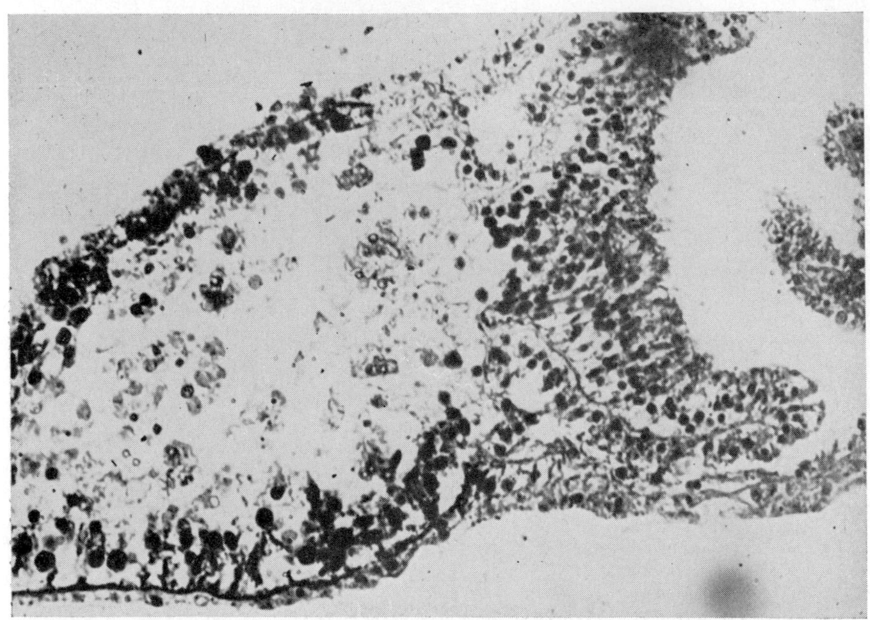

Fig. 7. One day old *Campanularia* hydranth. Gomori acid phosphatase stain. Note strong nuclear stain and essential absence of strongly positive small particles. Magnification=about 900X. (From Brock and Strehler, unpublished).

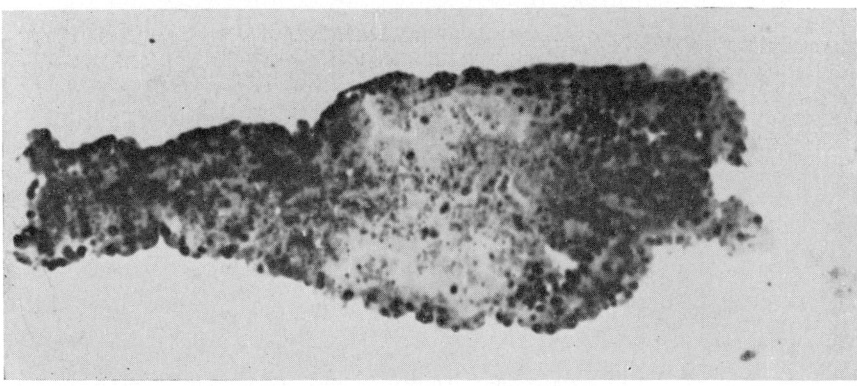

Fig. 8. Ten day old regressing hydranth of *Campanularia*. Gomori acid phosphatase stain. Both nuclei and a multitude of small cytoplasmic granules give positive stain. 500X magnification. (From Brock and Strehler, unpublished).

phosphatase by Gomori's method (24). Note that there is practically no acid phosphatase except in the nuclei, although there is an occasional granule here and there.

Compare the sparseness of acid phosphatase in the young animal with Figure 8 which shows a ten-day-old hydranth in early stages of regression. Particularly notice the enormous numbers of very small acid phosphatase-positive granules, which are nearly everywhere in the gastrodermal cells. Notice that the tentacles have

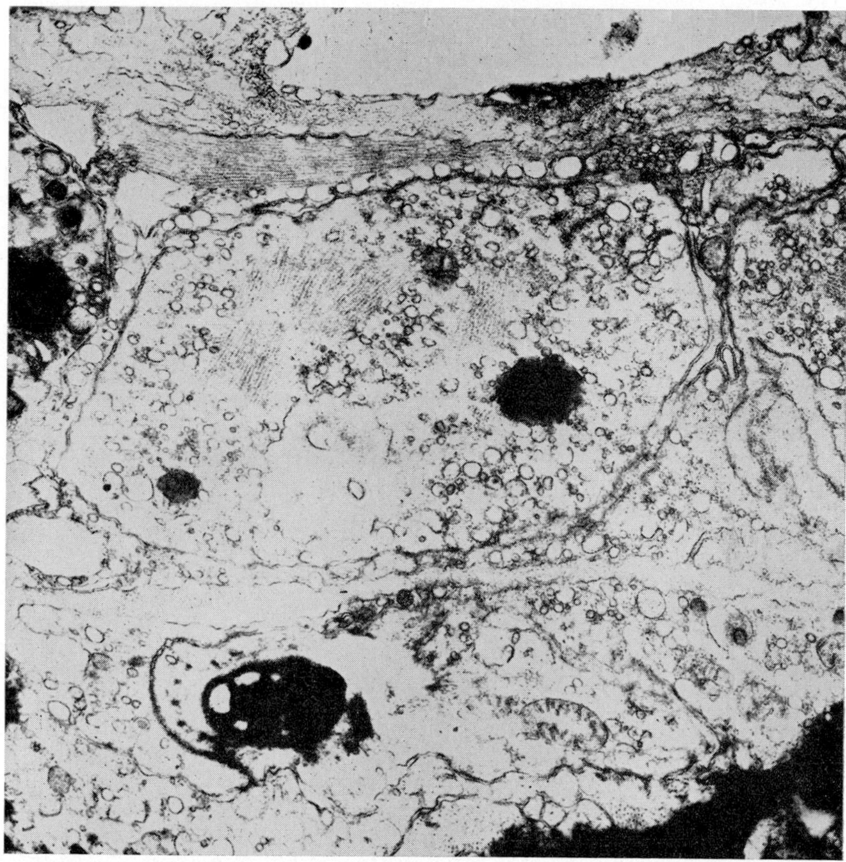

Fig. 9. Electron micrograph of regressing hydranth. Note cytoplasmic disorganization, vacuolization. Magnification about 24,000X. Taken in collaboration with Dr. D. Brandes, Pathology Department, Baltimore City Hospitals.

contracted somewhat. The huge vacuoles in the gastrodermal cells are diminished or absent. These acid phosphatase positive granules are of very uniform size.

Figure 9 is an electron micrograph of a regressing hydranth (taken in collaboration with Dr. David Brandes of the Pathology Department, Baltimore City Hospitals) and shows the complete intracellular disorganization which takes place during this process. An occasional mitochondrion still seems to have a few cristae intact but the high degree of vacuolization and lamination in this section is completely foreign to the normal anatomy of this organism.

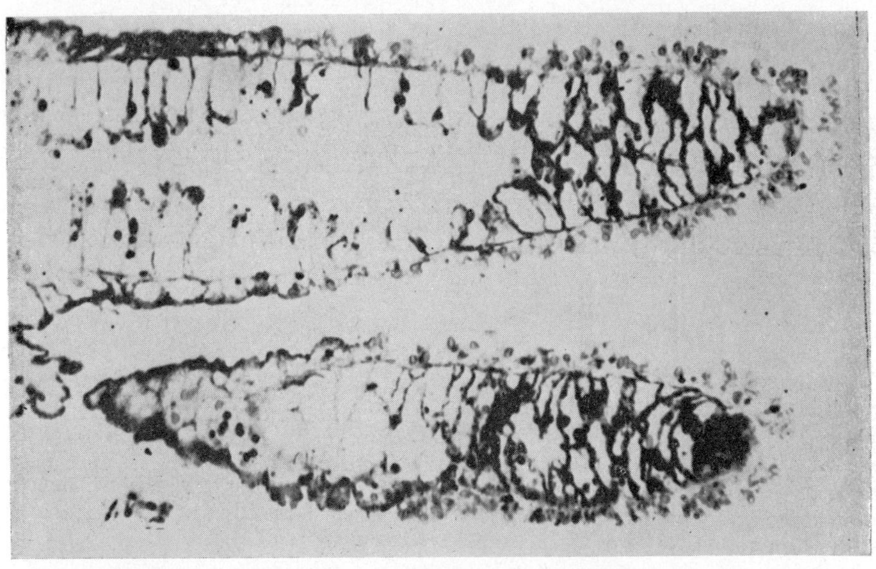

Fig. 10. Accumulation of acid phosphatase-positive granules in the tips of the tentacles of *Hydra*. Gomori stain. 500X. (From Brock and Strehler, unpublished).

For comparison in the succeeding figures, evidence of acid phosphatase activity in certain interesting regions of *Hydra* is presented. Note the gradient of increasing acid phosphatase activity as one moves toward the tips of the tentacles. This activity is confined to the gastrodermal cells of the tentacle tips (Fig. 10).

In the base, one also finds acid phosphatase activity in the precise area in which one would expect it (see Fig. 11). The enzymes (and lysosomes?) are localized in a pedal disc, although there is some accumulation even in cells that presumably are differentiating into lysosome-containing cells higher on the column. I think this would be interesting to study — the kinds of structures which contain the enzyme and whether they are similar to those which are present in other animals. Notice that acid phosphatase occurs both in the gastrodermal and ectodermal layer.

We were interested to see whether there are changes in the numbers of similar granules in *Campanularia*, particularly in the tentacular region where regression starts. In the young hydranth, there is very little acid phosphatase activity. By contrast, there are enormous numbers of very uniformly sized granules in the 10-day-old hydranth as was shown in Figure 8. Note the deposition of acid phosphatase positive material along the cytoplasmic septa separating the gastrodermal cells in the tentacles of a 9-day-old hydranth shown in Figure 12. These cells have huge vacuoles with an omentum-like cytoplasmic extension containing the nucleus hanging

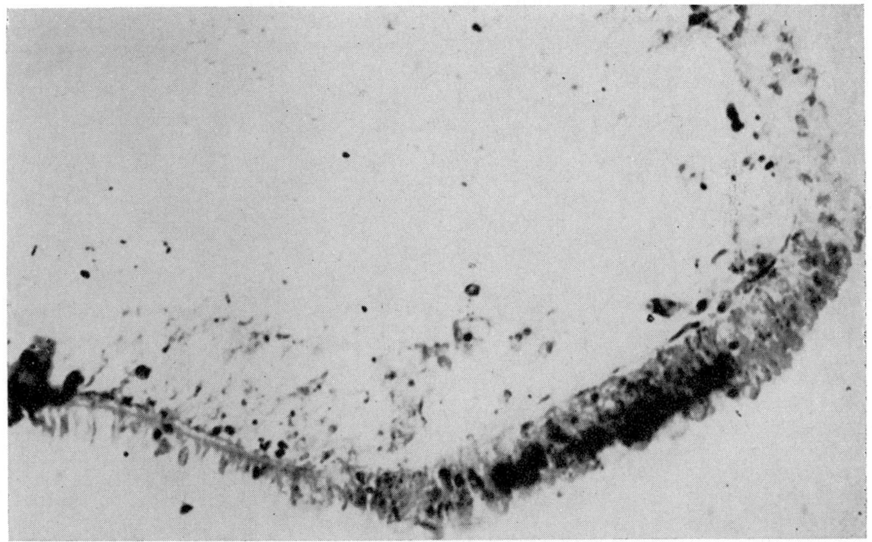

Fig. 11. Accumulation of acid phosphatase-positive granules in the pedal disc of *Hydra*. Gomori stain. 500X magnification. (From Brock and Strehler, unpublished).

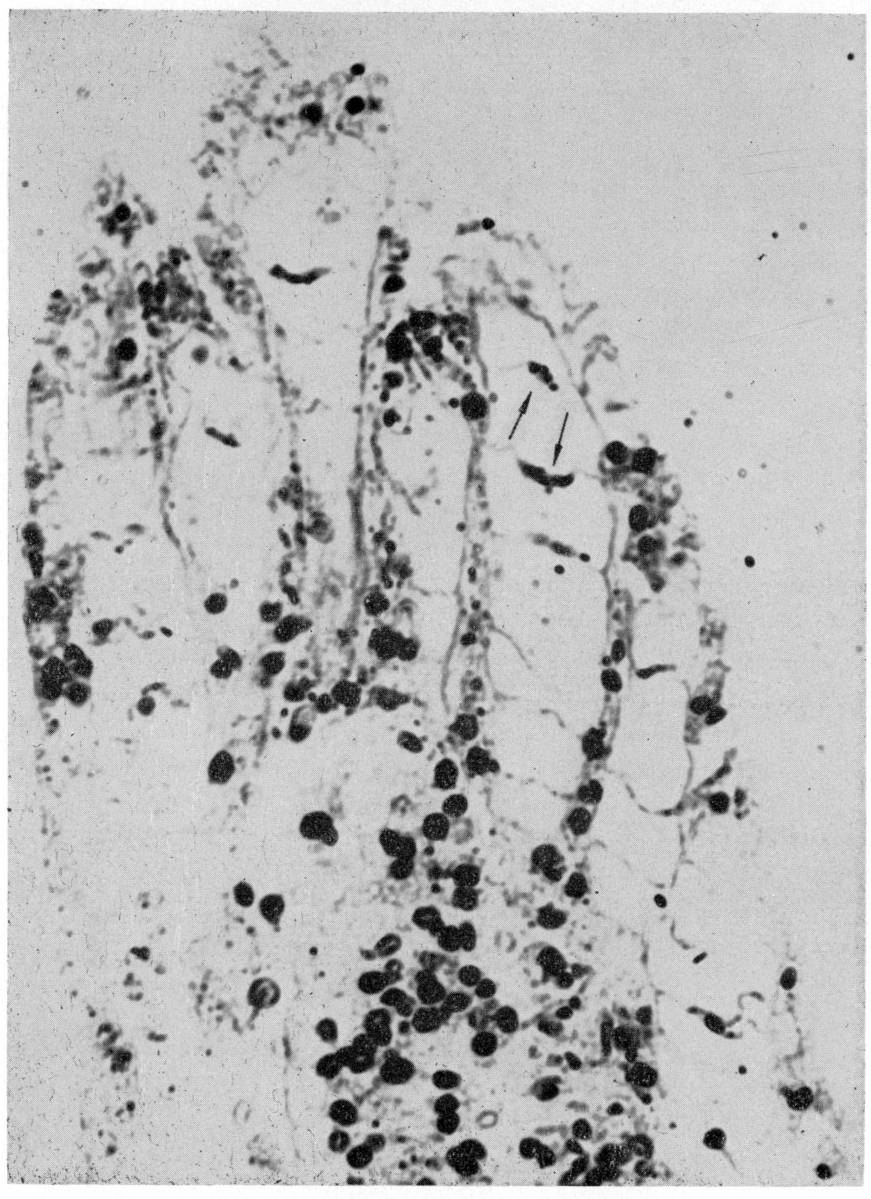

Fig. 12. Acid phosphatase-positive granules (arrows) in the tentacles of an 8 day old *Campanularia*. 1000X magnification. Gomori stain. (From Brock and Strehler, unpublished).

into them. After seeing the distribution of the acid phosphatase granules, we re-examined some electron micrographs that we had taken. We plan a much more systematic study of the degenerating hydranths to see whether they contain structures reminescent of lysosomes. In Figure 13, which illustrates a group of tentacles at their point of attachment to the body wall, are some objects which may be suitable candidates. They are certainly not mitochondria which are also located in these very thin walls.

Now, what can one say about the functional capacity of old

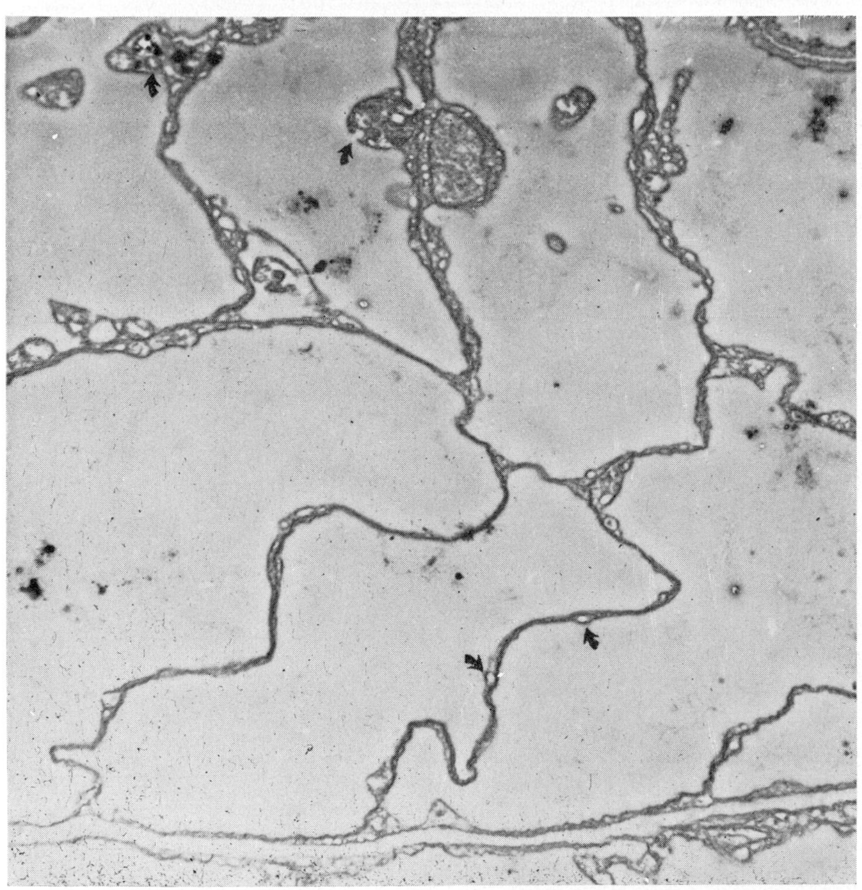

Fig. 13. Electron micrograph of a *Campularia* tentacle. Arrows indicate possible loci of acid phosphatase activity. Magnification=about 4000X. (From Strehler and Brandes, unpublished).

TABLE 1

Food catching ability vs. Age
Series I (about 2.0 *Artemia*/hydranth—fresh sea water)

Hydranth age (days)	1	2	3	4	5
No. of hydranths	10	5	14	14	3
No. of *Artemia* caught	13	7	19	13	4
Artemia caught/hydranth	1.3	1.4	1.35	0.93	1.33

Series II (about 0.5 *Artemia*/hydranth—artificial sea water)

Hydranth age (days)	1	2	3	4	5	6	7	8
No. of hydranths	299	224	187	150	104	63	35	10
No. of *Artemia* caught	73	47	47	32	51	21	6	3
Artemia caught/hydranth	.24	.21	.25	.21	.49	.33	.17	.30

TABLE 2

Ingestion time vs. Hydranth age

Age of hydranths	0	1	2	3	4
No. of hydranths tested	31	26	52	18	16
Average time for ingestion in seconds	257	256	300	295	237

Campanularia? How do they differ from young ones? Dr. Crowell (who did much of the basic work upon which this study is based) and I have measured a number of physiological capacities vs. age

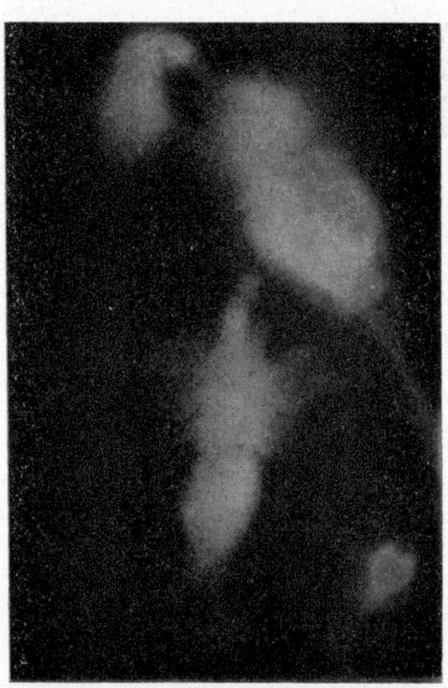

Fig. 14. Photomicrograph of *Campanularia* ingesting *Artemia* labeled with fluorescent dyes (0.1% acriflavine). From a time lapse sequence. Note appearance of fluorescent digest in upright proximal to upper hydranth.

(31). Some of these are shown in Tables 1 and 2. One of the things that we measured was the efficiency of catching *Artemia*. This did not seem to be altered between one and five days of age, which is about the greatest longevity of appreciable numbers of hydranths in Woods Hole at 17-18°. Similarly, the digestion time was measured by feeding fluorescent labeled *Artemia* to *Campanularia* and then measuring the time required for the first fluorescent digest to appear in the region proximal to the hydranth (see Fig. 14). As measured in this way, no differences between young and old were observable. Neither did the egestion time nor the maximum number of *Artemia* the hydranths can consume change with age.

In short, the only striking differences we have found between young and old *Campanularia*, other than the above-mentioned acid

TABLE 3

ATP content/hydranth vs. age

Stage	ATP/hydranth = (g × 10^{10})
Hydranth bud	15.0
Early differentiation	7.0
Complete differentiation but not extended	33.0
1 day old (young)	18.0
2-3 days old (middle-aged)	12.0
4-5 days old (old)	4.5

phosphatase accumulation, is a difference in the level of the adenosine triphosphate as measured by our firefly enzyme ATP assay method. We observed a decrease to about one-third of the total ATP level in passing from one to five days of age (see Table 3). This value was calculated per hydranth rather than on a dry weight basis and we do not know whether there is a change in the dry weight of *Campanularia* during this time interval. We can thus not say whether this ATP concentration drop is due to a decrease in the intracellular concentration or volume.

Complete lack of oxygen for a period of several hours does not produce degeneration of *Campanularia*, although we have obtained evidence from time lapse studies that partial anaerobiosis can rapidly induce degeneration. During the complete absence of oxygen for

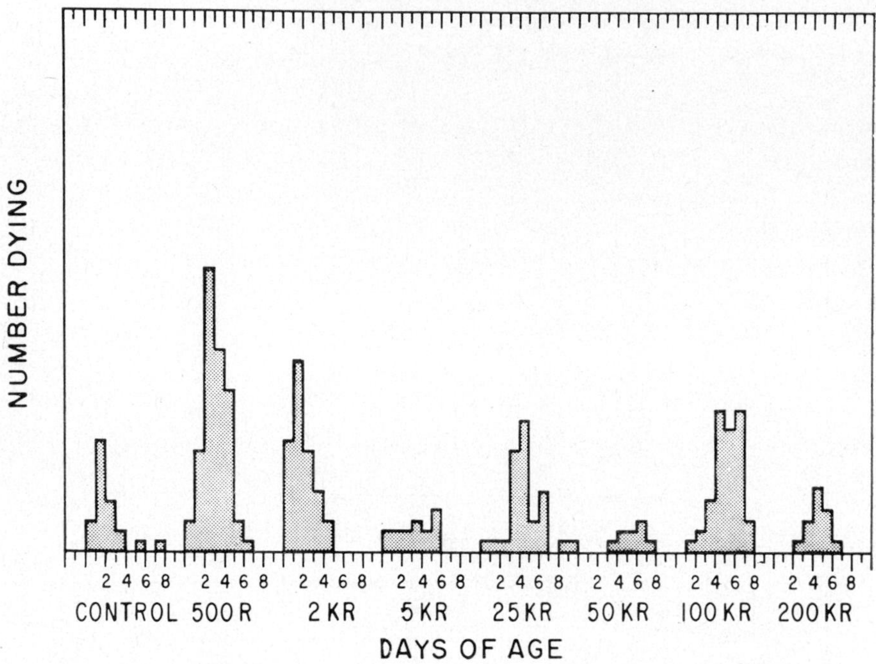

Fig. 15. Distribution of ages at death of *Campanularia* hydranths of various ages after exposure to various dosages of X-rays. The highest peak represents 23 hydranths.

the two hour period which we used, it may be that there is a complete arrest of metabolic activity including the synthesis of the lytic enzymes.

It was current doctrine about two years ago that high energy radiation is analogous to time in its effect on aging. We therefore undertook to see whether *Campanularia* is aged by high doses of radiation. We gave dosages up to 200,000 r and then followed the longevity of individual hydranths. Figure 15 shows the average life time at various dosages. The mean life time, under the control conditions, was about 2.7 days, whereas at 100,000 r the average life time was about 6.3 days. This radiation dose more than doubles the longevity of the hydranth!

Another remarkable fact is that hydranths continue to differentiate and be initiated even one week after exposure although the colony eventually dies. Figure 16 shows the survival curves of these

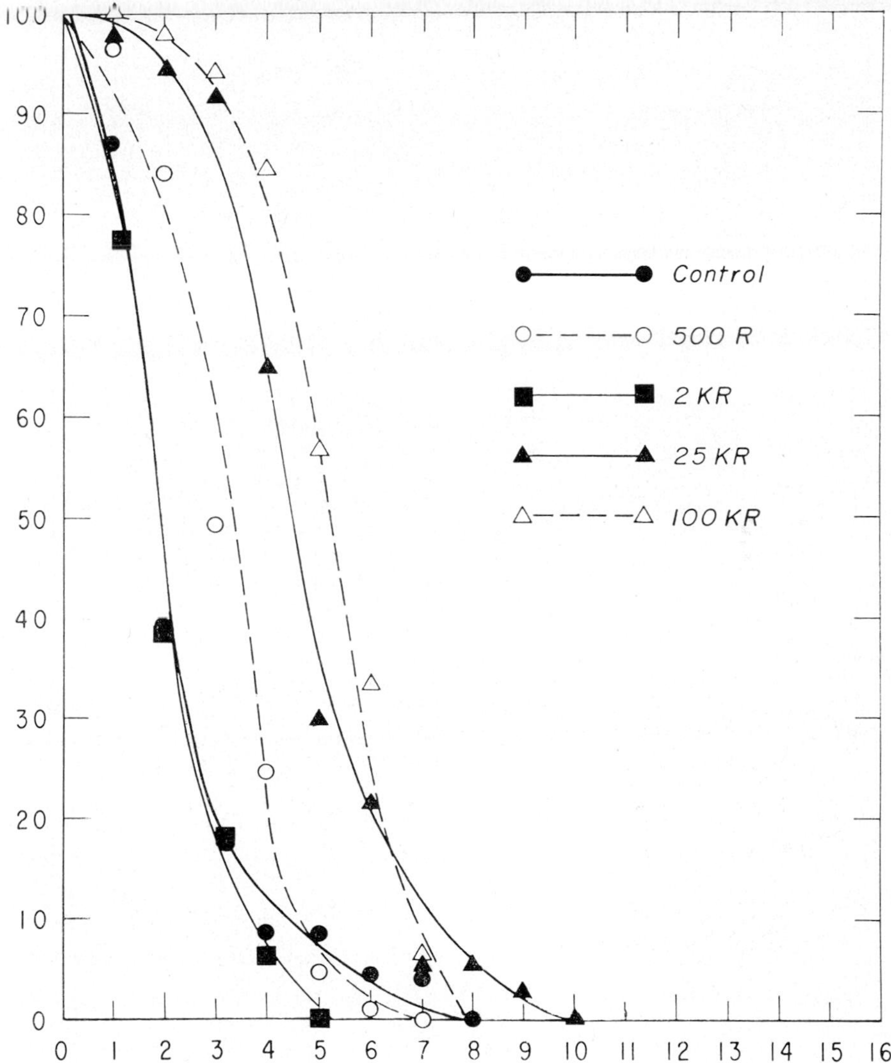

Fig. 16. Survivors (% remaining alive) at various ages following X-ray exposure.

animals plotted on a linear scale while Figures 17a and b show a control and irradiated colony at various times after exposure.

What relationship does aging in *Campanularia* have to aging in general? First, I believe it will turn out that the mechanism of cell

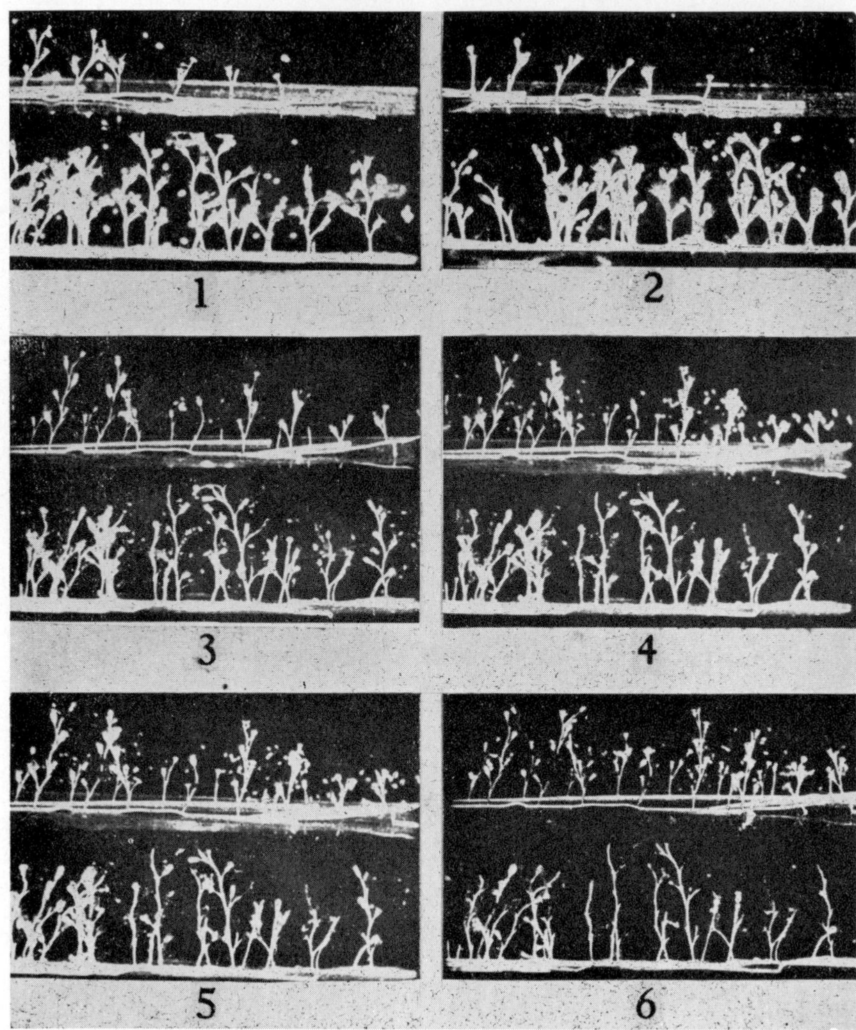

Fig. 17. Time lapse photographs of control (upper) and irradiated (lower) colonies of *Campanularia*—1, 36, 72, 108, 144, and 180 hours after receiving 100,000 r.

death in *Campanularia* and in hydra is probably quite similar to that which occurs in humans. Second, it is evident that mortality is an evolved character that may or may not express itself even in closely related species. Why should one strain of hydrozoan be essentially immortal and why should another strain be so highly mortal? In searching around for an answer to this, Dr. Crowell and I, in the absence of clear-cut functional differences between the young and old individuals, settled upon an interpretation which incorporates certain of his earlier studies on the response of the colony to restricted feeding (9). He noted, as he has mentioned at this meeting, that the individuals who have precedence in such a colony as *Campanularia* are those that are at the top of an upright, and that the lateral growth of the stolon and the growth of the apical hydranth are not so readily inhibited. This suggested to us that the colony distributes its feeding individuals on the periphery as a sort of umbrella during periods of poor food supply. They thus are in a position to intercept the greatest number of prey — an economically efficient distribution of a limited supply of protoplasm. Since these animals live under conditions of quite variable food supply, we postulated that their senescence is a built-in clock that forces the colony as a whole to evaluate on a very regular schedule the adequacy of its food supply. If the food supply is not adequate, then regeneration in the lower parts of the uprights does not take place. If there is a large amount of food available, then it is economically feasible to regenerate hydranths all up and down the upright and thus to survive.

In general terms, a paradox is apparent; namely, only those animals which have devised a means of replacing all of their cells on a regular schedule are able to live as individuals for indefinite periods. Part of this process of replacement involves, of necessity, a destruction of cells in a systematic, ordered way (28). If it takes place at the boundary of an animal or in a linear, ordered progression of some sort, then the animal, provided it has a germinal core of cells, is capable of continuing to exist indefinitely in a steady state. If it has no capacity for replacing its cells, or its cell parts, but rather accumulates damage, noxious substances or accidental by-products of metabolism, then it will eventually die. Hydra and the anemones are probably immortal because they have devised and maintained evolutionarily a systematic replacement scheme. We and *Campanularia* are mortal either because it is advantageous to the species' survival to be mortal or, either directly or as a by-product (3, 33) of some other advantageous genetic character, as appears more likely in our case, because selection pressure has not been sufficiently severe to provide a replacement regimen for those cells and tissues which are relatively well shielded from accidental damage or loss (29).

ACKNOWLEDGEMENTS

The author wishes to acknowledge the collaboration of Drs. David Brandes and Mary Ann Brock in many of these studies as well as the constant and invaluable assistance in all phases of this work by Mr. Malcolm Gee.

REFERENCES

1. Ashworth, J. H., and N. Annandale. 1904. Observations on some aged specimens of *Sagartia troglodytes* and on the duration of life in Coelenterates. *Proc. Roy. Soc. Edin., 25:* 295.
2. Berninger, J. 1910. Über Einwirkung des Hungers auf Hydra. *Zool. Anz., 36:* 271-279.
3. Bidder, G. P. 1925. The mortality of plaice. *Nature, London, 115:* 495.
4. Boecker, E. 1914. Depression und Missbildungen bei Hydra. *Zool. Anz., 44:* 75-80.
5. Brien, P. 1953. La Pérennité Somatique. *Biol. Rev., 28:* 308-349.
6. Brock, M. A., and B. L. Strehler. Unpublished.
7. Comfort, A. 1956. *The biology of senescence.* Rinehard & Co., New York, p. 257.
8. Crowell, S. 1953. The regression-replacement cycle of hydranths of *Obelia* and *Campanularia. Physiol. Zool., 26:* 319-327.
9. Crowell, S. 1957. Differential responses of growth zones to nutritive level, age and temperature in the colonial hydroid, *Campanularia. J. Exp. Zool., 134:* 63-90.
10. Crowell, S., and C. Wyttenbach. 1957. Factors affecting terminal growth in the hydroid, *Campanularia. Biol. Bull., 113:* 233-244.
11. David, K. 1925. Zur Frage der potentiellen Unsterblichkeit der Metazoen. *Zool. Anz., 64:* 126.
12. De Duve, C. 1957. The enzymatic heterogeneity of cell fractions isolated by differential centrifugation. *Symp. Soc. Exp. Biol., 10:* 50-61.
13. Essner, E., and A. Novikoff. 1960. Human hepatocellular pigments and lysosomes. *J. Ultrastruc. Res., 3:* 374-391.
14. Gedigk, P., and E. Bontke. 1956. Über den Nachweis von hydrolytischen Enzymen in Lipopigmenten. *Z. Zellforsch., 44:* 495-518.
15. Goetsch, W. 1922. Lebensdauer und Geschlechtige Fortpflauzung bei Hydra. *Biol. Zbl., 42:* 231.
16. Gross, J. 1925. Versuche und Beobachtungen über die Biologie der Hydriden. *Biol. Zbl., 45:* 385-417.

17. Hamperl, H. 1934. Die Fluorescenzmikoskopie Menschlicher, Gewebe. *Virchows Arch.*, 292: 1-51.
18. Hase, A. 1909. Über die deutschen Susswasser-polypen *Hydra fusca. Arch. für Rossen-und Gessellschaftsbiologie*, *6:* 721-753.
19. Hertwig, R. 1906. Über Knospung und Geschlectentwicklung von *Hydra fusca. Biol. Zbl.*, *26:* 489-508.
20. Huxley, J. B., and G. R. De Beer. 1923. Studies in dedifferentiation. IV. Resorption and differential inhibition in *Obelia* and *Campanularia. Quart. J. micr. Sci.*, *67:* 473.
21. Konigsberg, I. R. 1960. On the relationship between development and aging. *Newsletter (Geront. Soc.)*, *7:* (3), 33-34.
22. Leuchtenberger, C., and H. Z. Lund. 1951. The chemical nature of the so-called keratohyaline granules of the stratum granulosum of the skin. *Exp. cell Res.*, *2:* 150.
23. Pearl, R., and J. R. Miner. 1935. Experimental studies in the duration of life. XIV. The comparative mortality of certain lower organisms. *Quart. Rev. Biol.*, *10:* 60.
24. Pearse, A. G. E. 1960. *Histochemistry, theoretical and applied.* Little, Brown & Co., Boston, 2nd Ed., 998 pp.
25. Schlottke, E. 1930. Zellstudien an Hydra. I. Altern und abbau von Zellen und Kernen. *Z. Mikr. Anat. Forsch.*, *22:* 493-532.
26. Sonneborn, T. M. 1960. Enormous differences in length of life of closely related ciliates and their significance. In: B. L. Strehler et al. (Editors), *The Biology of Aging.* Amer. Inst. Biol. Sci., Washington, Pub. No. 6, p. 289.
27. Strehler, B. L. 1959. Origin and comparison of the effects of time and high-energy radiations on living systems. *Quart. Rev. Biol.*, *34:* 117-142.
28. Strehler, B. L. 1960. Dynamic theories of aging. In: N. W. Shock (Editor), *Aging—Some Social and Biological Aspects.* Amer. Assoc. Adv. Sci., Washington, Pub. No. 65, pp. 273-303.
29. Strehler, B. L. *Time, cells and aging.* Academic Press, New York, (in press).
30. Strehler, B. L. Unpublished.
31. Strehler, B. L., and S. Crowell. 1961. Studies on comparative physiology of aging. I. Function vs. age of *Campanularia flexuosa. Gerontologia*, *5:* 1-8.
32. Strehler, B. L., D. D. Mark, A. S. Mildvan, and Malcolm Gee. 1959. Rate and magnitude of age pigment accumulation in the human myocardium. *J. Geront.*, *14:* 430-439.
33. Williams, G. C. 1957. Pleiotropy, natural selection and the evolution of senescence. *Evolution*, *11:* 398-411.

DISCUSSION

MARTIN: By 100,000 r, do you mean tissue dose or dispensing dose?

STREHLER: Tissue dose.

MARTIN: You measure it underneath the water?

STREHLER: It was calculated for the chamber in which it was irradiated. Since it was a high energy photon I believe it was not attenuated much by the water.

GOREAU: Are there other criteria for measuring age? Two years ago we measured the effect of size on specific calcification rates on a free living coral where size was an indication of age. In this particular species, *Manicina areolata,* we found a progressive reduction in the calcification rate (per mg. of protein nitrogen) as the colonies got larger. The difference between the smallest (50 mg.) and the largest (149 g.) colonies tested was almost two orders of magnitude (Goreau, T., and N. Goreau. 1960. *Biol. Bull 118:*419). Now, it is interesting that these particular corals hardly ever grow beyond 500 grams. This may have some ecological significance for if the individuals get much larger and heavier than that they may sink into the sediments since most of them are not attached. However, many other species of corals do not show such a regulated growth pattern. I suspect that some species grow indefinitely.

STREHLER: The maximum ages for corals which are quoted in Comfort's excellent book (which I recommend to those of you who might be curious about senescence) is only about 28 or 30 years. Now this is based upon size estimates. I would be delighted to see somebody try to find a better index of age than simply size.

GOREAU: On the basis of some of the accretion data which I referred to in my talk on Thursday, I calculated that corals weighing about 200 tons may be as much as 800 years old.

STREHLER: You think these come from a single individual?

GOREAU: Not necessarily, but the specimens used in our experiments were clones descended from single planulae.

STREHLER: The difficulty here is that this is more like a hydra clone, it seems to me, than an individual animal.

GOREAU: Some corals, like the branching species, have an indeterminate growth pattern and can probably be considered immortal, because they can grow as long as there is room. This is probably not true of the massive ones in which the skeletal mass would increase much faster than surface area. These would col-

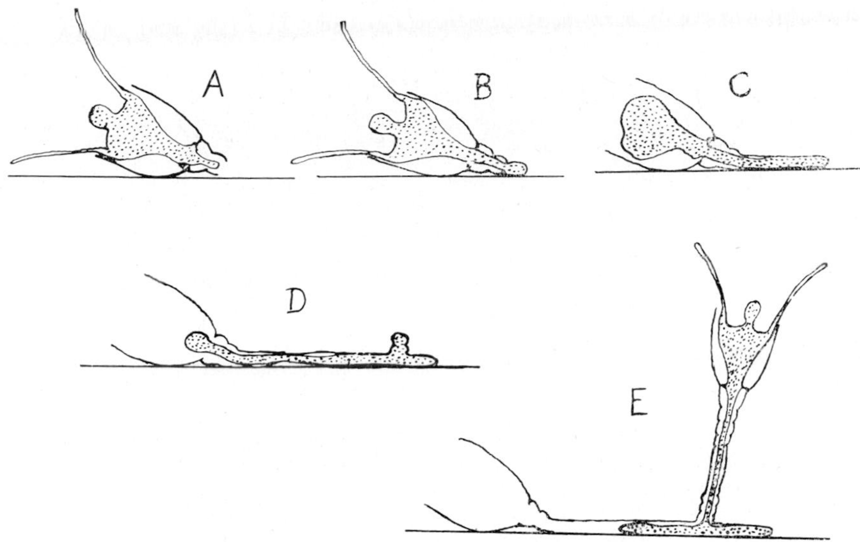

Fig. 1. Sketches to illustrate Nathanson's experiment. A. An isolated hydranth. B. The hydranth may produce a short stolon in a few hours. C. When regression of the hydranth occurs the stolon grows. D. A new upright has started to form; regression of the old hydranth is nearly complete. E. A new hydranth is produced.

lapse or become buried under the increased weight. However that may be, I believe all reef corals are clones.

STREHLER: Studies on the incorporation of tritiated thymidine into the DNA of *Metridium* or of other long-lived forms would be of interest in outling the pattern of cell division and replacement.

CROWELL: May I go back to what we were talking about this morning? How, and in what form, are materials moved to regions of growth? These sketches, Figure 1, show the results obtained by Nathanson (Nathanson, D. L. 1955. The relationship of regenerative ability to the regression of hydranths of *Campanularia. Biol. Bull. 109:* 350). He cut off single hydranths of *Campanularia,* placed them in stender dishes, but did not feed them. A hydranth merely sat for from one to four days. In some cases it produced a little bit of stolon, as shown in Figure 1B. When a hydranth began to regress the stolon elongated, as shown in C and D, then it sent up a new upright and produced a new little hydranth, Figure 1E. Presumably all of the new growth is made possible by utilizing the debris of the regressing hydranth and just a small quantity of good, new cells which at first were assembled at the base of the isolated hydranth. If so, this experiment of Nathanson points to a very rapid utilization and reorganization of this stuff in the building of new cells. No one has looked at such preparations with anything more powerful than a binocular microscope. This looks like a good place to make a start on the problem.

CHAPMAN: Do I understand you to indicate that you thought the dense particles in your electron micrographs indicated by the arrows were lysosome particles?

STREHLER: Possibly.

CHAPMAN: If you thought they were, I want to tell you I thought they weren't for two reasons. One, it seems to me they are too large to be lysosomes. Lysosomes fall in the range between the smallest mitochondria and the largest elements of the so-called microsome fraction. And two, they looked almost homogeneous to me and I would expect a more dense outer shell.

STREHLER: I think you are in error because lysosomes are quite variable in size. If you look at Essner and Novikoff's electron photomicrographs of liver lysosomes, the size variation occurs and they frequently appear with a moon shaped heavy border. This looks like a vesicle in this micrograph. But the acid phosphatase activity is actually usually associated with the dense staining portion. I don't think there is really enough structure in those particles to answer the question.

Studies on Chemical Inhibition of Regeneration in Hydra

ROBERT E. EAKIN
Clayton Foundation Biochemical Institute and the Department of Chemistry, The University of Texas, Austin, Texas.

First, I would like to express my disappointment that Dr. Ham and Dr. Spangenberg, former students of mine, were unable to get to the meeting to present their own contributions. They were responsible for developing the research program I shall discuss.

I would like to summarize the results of three phases of our investigations: first, factors influencing the regenerative response of hydra under normal conditions; second, the effects of chemical agents upon regenerative processes; and third, some biochemical observations on the effect of an agent which uniquely arrests regeneration – lipoic acid. (A fourth phase, histological studies on both normal and treated organisms, is included on pp. 413-423 of this volume.)

FACTORS INFLUENCING REGENERATION OF UNTREATED HYDRA

Seven years ago I would not have anticipated I would be at this late date reporting on the control of factors influencing normal regeneration. But we've had our troubles.

When Dr. Ham originally initiated the use of hydra in our laboratory, he did a thorough and comprehensive study on the environmental factors which influence the regeneration rate of *H. littoralis* (4). But over a period of several years' time, we encountered a considerable degree of inconsistency in the behavior of our stock clone when compared to previous responses which the organisms had given. Also, we were continually confronted with daily erratic behavior in *Hydra* taken from the same culture dish and treated in what we believed to be an identical fashion. And finally, it was found that our stock clones were uniformly parasitized by an intracellular protozoan, a species of Microsporidia. It was this point that we were ready to throw all our clones back into the lily pond from whence their great grandparent had come. In our earlier studies, we used one strain of *Hydra* and indeed were apprehensive about bringing into the laboratory any other strain of *Hydra littoralis,* lest there be mixing of stock clones. However, because of our difficulties we did bring other strains of *H. littoralis* into our laboratory – retreated, as it were, in our program–to re-examine more critically factors which could be causing variations in the response of "normal" untreated hydra.

Although it was a laborious undertaking, it proved worthwhile in that it not only pointed out the causes of the inconsistent results we had been getting, but also increased by a considerable extent our knowledge concerning both extrinsic and intrinsic factors which influence regeneration. This new data, in turn, led to histological studies giving valuable information concerning some of the basic factors influencing the rate and extent of regeneration and enabling us to develop a hypothesis for use in planning future investigations.

For the purpose of discussion, the factors studied can be classified as (A) intrinsic factors and (B) extrinsic factors.

In selecting criteria for measuring regenerative capacities of hydra, we have used two measurements which can be rapidly determined on a large number of organisms – namely, (a) the length:width ratio observed for the longest developing tentacle formed during the early stages (18th to 24th hour) of regeneration, and (b) the total number of tentacles observed after the regenerative process is well along (after the 44th hour). The early measurement of the extent of the growth of the future tentacle gives some indication of the rate at which morphological processes can be initiated. The total number of tentacles regenerated expresses roughly the total amount of morphogenic change. These two determinations obviously are a measure of the composite effects of many individual factors, but they have permitted us to run screening tests on thousands of organisms for the gross effects of a number of extrinsic and intrinsic factors which affect development. For example, information which we gained from later histological studies enables us now to look at gross regeneration data and make some educated guesses of interstitial cell patterns. Our ultimate goal is to relate the effect of physiological and chemical agents to much more specific phenomena — namely, changes induced in biochemical and structural patterns during the regenerative process, such as those described in the histological and enzymatic investigations I shall mention presently.

One intrinsic factor — the genetic differences in strains — is illustrated in the left half of the first figure (Table 1) which shows the differences in the gross macroscopic responses that have been studied in detail in seven strains of hydra (representing three different species), the experimental procedures being those reported in our previous publications (2, 3, 4).

Hydra littoralis — Strain I: These were *Hydra* derived from the clone initially used in this laboratory (1) and provisionally identified

TABLE 1

Effect of site of severance upon rate of regeneration

	Hypostomal cut Extent of Regeneration Hours					TN*	Mid-stomach cut Extent of Regeneration Hours					TN*
Organism	18	20	22	24	26		18	20	22	24	26	
	units**						units**					
Chlorohydra viridissima (green)	3.4	----	----	----	----	6.1	2.6	3.3	----	----	----	7.1
Chlorohydra viridissima (brown)	3.0	----	----	----	----	6.0	2.1	2.8	----	----	----	7.0
Strain I	1.8	2.6	3.2	----	----	6.3	.60	1.2	1.9	2.3	----	6.6
Strain II	.81	1.6	2.5	----	----	4.5	.09	.14	.26	.57	.89	3.0
Strain III	1.6	2.1	2.4	----	----	1.2	.22	.24	.28	----	.41	.33
Strain IV	1.4	2.5	3.0	----	----	6.2	.00	.00	.09	.22	.40	5.4
Hydra oligactis	.70	1.6	2.7	----	----	5.5	.00	.00	.00	.00	.11	1.4

Each value represents the average of 36 replicates.
*Tentacle number at 48 hours.
**Length:width ratio of the longest tentacle.

as *H. littoralis.* All organisms in the clone were found to be infected with Microsporidia, the parasitization occurring in both the epidermal and gastrodermal cells. Treatment of the *Hydra* with a fungicide, Fumidil B, apparently eradicated the parasite as clones of the treated *Hydra* have remained parasite-free for two years. These Microsporidia have been identified tentatively through the courtesy of Dr. R. R. Kudo as a species of *Plistophora* – a type of protozoal parasite causing fatal infections of silkworms and honeybees. Reported for the first time in *Hydra,* the infection in this organism is not fatal, nor does it interfere with normal asexual reproduction. Because of this, parasitized *Hydra* may provide a unique system for the study of the life cycle of Microsporidia (7).

Hydra littoralis – Strain II: These were from a clone generously furnished by Dr. Loomis and identified as *H. littoralis.*

Hydra littoralis – Strain III: In an effort to obtain a non-parasitized *Hydra* closely resembling Strain I, a sexual cross was made between an infected male of Strain I and a female of Strain II. The resulting offspring were parasite-free. These clones have been designated Strain III. (When the opposite cross was made, the eggs hatched only rarely and the offspring were infected.)

Hydra littoralis – Strain IV: Another clone, referred to as Strain IV, was developed from a *Hydra* found in a pond on the University of Texas campus and has been tentatively identified through the courtesy of Dr. L. H. Hyman as *H. littoralis.*

The two strains (I and IV) only tentatively identified as *H. littoralis* have been considered as members of this species in view of their close morphological resemblance to the positively identified Strain II and because of the readiness with which Strains I and IV cross sexually with Strain II to produce viable offspring which later become sexually reproductive. Although all four strains appear to be *Hydra littoralis,* there is variation in size, rate of regeneration, and physiological responses. Strains I, II, and III are all very much alike in appearance but Strain IV is a larger and a more slowly moving *Hydra.*

Hydra oligactis: These are from clones developed from an organism purchased from General Biological Supply Co., Chicago, Ill.

Chlorohydra viridissima (Green): This culture of *Chlorohydra* was derived from specimens found in a local pond.

Chlorohydra viridissima (Non-green): The non-green *Chlorohydra* were obtained by depriving green organisms of light for several weeks. Upon exposure to light, some soon regained their green color but the others, although subsequently grown in the light, have not regained their color after three years.

Not shown in this table is the growth rate by asexual budding. This can be most easily expressed in the time required for a doubling of the number of hydranths in optimally nourished clones. The fastest growing hydra are the *Chlorohydra,* both the green and the non-green strains doubling in about 1.3 days. *H. oligactis* and Strains I, II, and III of *H. littoralis* double in number in 2.0 to 2.4 days, but Strain IV is an unusually slower grower, having a doubling time exceeding 6 days. There is no apparent correlation between rate of asexual budding and the rate of tentacle regeneration in the different strains.

TABLE 2

Regenerative response of a "typical" and an "atypical" subclone of Strain II

Age of subclones days	Tentacle number at 48 hours*	
	Typical	Atypical
0	4.8	1.8
24		1.2
53	4.8	
57		1.4
68		2.0
123		1.6
151	4.8	
168		2.7
188		1.6

*Average of 18 replicates.

A *second intrinsic factor* influencing regeneration — inheritable variations arising within a clone — is illustrated in Table 2. Some of our erratic behavior finally was traced to the "area-of-the-dish" effect, that is, the regenerative response was related to the area of the culture dish from which an organism was taken. In determining the cause of this behavior, buds from parents used in tests were subcloned and their subsequent behavior determined. It was found that (a) some of the parent hydra regenerated fewer tentacles than others at 48 hours and that (b) the offspring in the subclones showed the same characteristics as their parents. Subclones selected on the basis of parents regenerating within 48 hours a normal number of tentacles – four to six – being designated "Typical" and those selected on the basis of parents regenerating fewer tentacles being designated "Atypical." After a week's time the two types of regenerates cannot be distinguished as the "atypical" hydra slowly regenerate a normal number of tentacles. Only by cutting and observing at 48 hours can we distinguish the typical from the atypical by gross observation. We do find differences in their interstitial cell patterns, though. These atypical subclones have maintained their "atypicalness" now for two years.

A *third intrinsic factor* studied – the aging of asexual clones – apparently has little effect on regenerative processes.

A *fourth intrinsic factor* – the effects of symbiotic relationships (this term is used in the broad sense, including the relationships of parasitism and mutualism) upon regeneration in hydra – was investigated when opportunities arose on two different occasions: (a) when the microsporidial infection of our Strain I (*H. littoralis*) clones was eradicated by the fungicide Fumidil in some of the subclones; and (b) when "non-green" clones of *Chlorohydra viridissima* were developed by culturing organisms in the absence of light for a period of time. One of the two symbiotic relationships studied (that in *Chlorohydra*) does not appear to affect the process; the other (microsporidial infection) does affect regeneration somewhat – the parasitized organisms regenerating more slowly than those which have been freed from parasites.

Three types of *extrinsic factors* – (a) mechanical, (b) environmental, and (c) chemical ("foreign agents") – were capable of having profound effects as measured by our gross observations.

One mechanical factor – the severance – was found to influence regeneration markedly, as the site of cutting determines to a greater or lesser degree the subsequent response to other variables. In standardizing his analytical procedures for measuring the regenerative response, Dr. Ham recognized the importance in severing the tentacles just below the hypostome. The importance of cutting close to the hypostome consistently cannot be overemphasized. In the course of later investigations, it was noted that marked variations occurred in rate of regeneration in hydra from a uniform subclone in the same dish of replicates. In an effort to trace the source of this variability, many factors were considered and examined. Among these was a comparison of the regeneration of some hydra that were cut while in the normally contracted state and others in the normally stretched state. It was found that the hydra cut in the contracted state regenerate at a slower rate than those cut while in a stretched state. To determine whether this was due to the removal of more tissue or to the occurrence of a larger wound in the hydra cut in the contracted state, some of the stretched hydra were cut just behind the hypostome and some at the mid-stomach region (midway between the hypostome and the budding region). Since the hydra were stretched while cut at both locations, the size of the wound was consistent but the amount of tissue removed varied. By referring to Table 1 again, we can see the differences that could result if the cutting were not accurately done – or if the organisms were not in a fully extended state at the time of cutting.

The variation in regeneration rate caused by cutting the different hydra groups at the two locations is not the same in all the hydra tested. The *Chlorohydra* and *Hydra* of Strain I were only slightly retarded in regeneration rate when cut at the mid-stomach region, whereas the regeneration rate in Strains II, III, and IV was quite retarded. The strains of hydra whose regeneration rate is decreased by cutting at the mid-stomach region also regenerated fewer tentacles than control hydra cut at the hypostomal region, a finding that can be explained by the observations made on interstitial cell differentiation and distribution to be discussed later.

As has been reported previously (2, 4), adding a foreign chemical or varying a natural environmental factor (pH, inorganic ion concentrations, osmolarity, temperature, or the adequacy of nutrition) can affect the regenerative response. In re-examining these factors in the present study, two new observations were made: (a) that often the qualitative effect of a physical or chemical agent will depend upon the exact site of severance; and (b) that, as is shown in Table 3, the temperature at which the stock clones have previously been maintained can affect the rate at which the experimental organisms later will respond under the standard tem-

TABLE 3

Effect of temperature on regeneration

Organisms	Tentacle Numbers at 48 hours	
	23-25°*	18-20°*
Strain II –Typical	5.2	6.0
Strain II –Atypical subclone No. 24	1.2	2.9
Strain II –Atypical subclone No. 8	1.1	3.5
Strain II –Atypical subclone No. 41	.76	4.1
Strain III	1.2	5.1

Each value represents the average of 18 replicates.
*Maintenance temperature of stock clones; temperature during period of regeneration was 27° for both groups.

perature (27°) used during the established regeneration testing procedure, a phenomenon subsequently shown to be related to differences in the interstitial cell patterns of the organisms maintained at the two temperatures.

The *effects of nutrition on regeneration rate* were pointed out by Ham (1) who found that even the elimination of one feeding has an adverse effect upon the regeneration rate for a few days thereafter. A more detailed study of this effect showed that: (a) one day's fasting markedly lowered the regenerative capacity of the organisms that were cut in the mid-stomach region, the regenerative ability being lowered, in fact, just as much by a 24 hour fast as is observed after three and five day periods of fasting; (b) but the regenerative ability of those cut just behind the hypostome was not significantly affected until the hydra had been starved for three or more days.

In studying *depressed organisms,* it was found that some "slightly depressed" and "moderately depressed" hydra are capable of regenerating as fast as, or faster than, the control hydra at 18 hours, and some are able to regenerate as *many* tentacles. Although not all the "depressed" and "slightly depressed" hydra regenerate as well as the controls, the fact that some are capable of doing so would indicate that depression in itself does not interfere significantly with the regeneration rate. Only severely depressed hydra are unable to regenerate. These hydra, however, are unable to eat so that their regenerative ability may be impaired according to the extent of fasting they have undergone. Also, since these are small contracted spherical hydra, it is very difficult to remove the tentacles and hypostomes accurately at the desired site.

Observations on all these and other variables impressed us even more emphatically with the fact that, before meaningful studies can be made on the action of any type of chemical or physical treatment "foreign" to the natural environment, one must have used extreme care in controlling all the factors just discussed. Also, postulates advanced concerning mechanisms controlling the rate and extent of regeneration should offer some explanation of these differences observed in the regenerative response.

CHEMICAL INHIBITION OF REGENERATION

The second aspect of our hydra research program which I wish to discuss concerns the effects of chemical agents upon the normal regenerative processes in well fed organisms. In order to find agents which would have selective action upon the regeneration process without materially affecting the normal maintenance and budding activities of the organism, hundreds of compounds having physiological or pharmacological effects on other types of life were screened, and from these a few compounds having marked effects were selected for more intensive study.

From the known physiological roles of the compounds that inhibit regeneration and alter tentacle number, the nature of a number of the processes involved in regeneration can be implied. In order to gain even more information concerning the mode of action of these compounds, the organisms were exposed to them for short intervals at different periods during the regenerative process. It was found that a four hour exposure at the proper time was adequate to obtain the effects of most of the compounds. We also found that different compounds acted at different times (Fig. 1).

The results of most of these studies were published several years ago along with a discussion of possible mechanisms involved (2). Most of these studies were completed before we realized the extent to which the factors just discussed were influencing the regenerative response. Another drawback, realized at the time these screening tests were made, was the fact that we were unable to determine the extent to which the agents being tested were actually absorbed into the hydra cells.

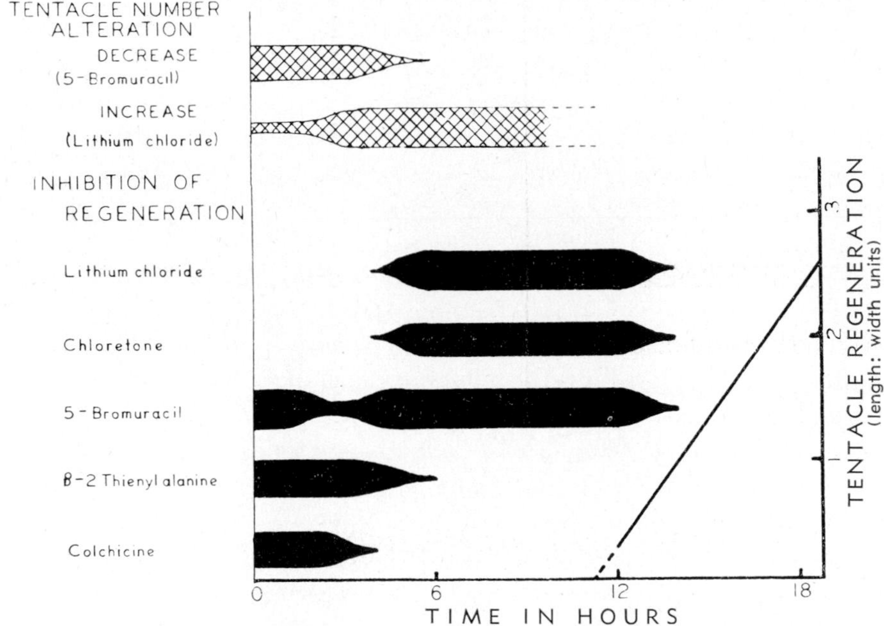

Fig. 1. Periods of sensitivity of hydra to regeneration-altering agents

The micro-injection technique perfected by Dr. Claybrook now makes it possible for us to introduce these inhibitors, metabolites, and drugs into the enteron in semi-solid agar where they will certainly be absorbed to a much greater degree than they would be from the environmental culture fluid. We are currently re-examining the effects of these agents with the refinements in our experimental techniques that we have developed since the initial chemical studies were made.

One of the most unique effects disclosed by the study of chemical agents was that encountered when one of the more recently discovered members of the B vitamin complex — lipoic acid —

was tested. A summary of a study we reported in detail several years ago (3) states:

1. Hydra treated with $10^{-5}M$ lipoic acid for short periods immediately after removal of their hypostomes and tentacles completely lose the capacity to regenerate those structures;

2. Removal of the non-regenerating tip of such blocked hydra leads to relatively normal regeneration;

3. The blockage of regeneration was found to be reversed in some cases by the action of agents known to interfere with normal nerve activity in more highly developed organisms.

At that time we postulated that the counteracting effect upon lipoic acid inhibition by certain agents known to depress neural activity in higher organisms was the result of interference with some nerve-mediated reaction which was a vital part of the overall regenerative process. This postulate seemed plausible because of the known involvement of nerves in regeneration of amphibian limbs. It was at this point that Dr. Spangenberg began her histological studies on hydra. In order to get a clear picture of the nerve pattern in untreated and lipoic acid treated hydra, she had to do considerable work in refining the methods then available for staining nerve cells (8). Her intensive and exhaustive studies failed to reveal any observable differences in the nerve cells of regenerating and inhibited organisms. However, her efforts were certainly not wasted because the study not only gave additional information concerning the epidermal nerve net in hydra, but disclosed that it was other type cells that were affected by the lipoic acid treatment. (Some of Dr. Spangenberg's histological and cytological investigations on the normal and abnormal regeneration of hydra are given on pp. 413-423.)

ENZYMATIC STUDIES ON A REGENERATION INHIBITOR

In order to determine whether or not specific phenomena observed in hydra were of general significance, we have used other more highly developed systems undergoing morphogenic changes in types of experiments suggested by the results obtained with the primitive hydra. We have made the most extensive investigations in this respect with regeneration in planaria (5). It has been most gratifying to find that many of the phenomena we have observed in hydra regeneration have analogous responses in the planaria. For example, exposure of a decapitated planaria to low concentrations of lipoic acid during the first part of the regenerative process results in arrest of regeneration and the development of an acephalic organism. These planaria appear to lead normal lives except they do not respond to the presence of food—they literally must be led to their piece of rat liver, but once they are on it they feed normally. Cutting again in the non-regenerating head area will initiate normal regeneration, a situation analogous to that observed in hydra.

Because planaria provide larger amounts of material with which to work, we are using this organism for enzymatic studies. Because the lipoic acid effect is so unique in regenerating hydra and planaria (and in a number of other organisms undergoing developmental changes), we have concentrated our efforts on determining the biochemical mechanisms which this compound must alter to produce the unusual morphogenic effects. It was found (a) that the presence of oxaloacetate (but not aspartate or α-ketoglutarate) during the exposure of regenerating systems to lipoic acid prevented the latter from arresting regeneration and (b) that lipoic acid inhibited certain enzymatic activities of planaria homogenates and preparations from mammalian tissues. Further investigation on enzymes related to oxalacetate metabolism showed the DPN-dependent malic dehydrogenase to be unusually sensitive to lipoic acid and to other related cyclic disulfides but not to the reduced (dithiol) derivatives. On the basis of several types of observations on a number of other enzymatic systems, we have concluded that the mechanism of action of these cyclic disulfides is unique for the DPN-malic dehydrogenases (6).

This was true not only in extracts prepared from planaria but was shown to be the case in highly refined porcine preparations obtained commercially. Subsequent tests with extracts of acetone powders prepared from hydra showed that their malic dehydrogenase activity was likewise inhibited by very dilute concentrations of lipoic acid and its homologs. In both planaria and hydra preparations the relative activity of enzymatic inhibition of a series of homologs strikingly paralleled their specific activity in arresting regeneration. On the basis of these results, we proposed that the primary action which eventually results in the inhibition of normal morphogenesis is the inhibition of this specific enzyme.

CONCLUSION

By the use of different strains subjected to various physical and chemical treatments one can produce a variety of different regeneration patterns that can be recognized by macroscopic observations. Treated and untreated organisms exhibiting these different responses can then be used for making comparative histological studies to determine the structural differences in the processes taking place in the different patterns of normal and altered regeneration. In these same organisms cytochemical, enzymatic, and related types of biochemical studies can likewise be used for comparative studies. The use of a particular agent, lipoic acid, is a beginning in this approach to establish correlation between the effect of an agent on gross development, its effect upon cellular patterns, and its effect upon specific biochemical reactions.

REFERENCES

1. Ham, R. G. 1957. Biochemical studies on regeneration of hydra. Doctoral Dissertation, The University of Texas.
2. Ham, R. G., and R. E. Eakin. 1958. Time sequence of certain physiological events during regeneration in hydra. *J. Exp. Zool. 139:* 33-54.
3. Ham, R. G., and R. E. Eakin. 1958. Loss of regenerative capacity in hydra treated with lipoic acid. *J. Exp. Zool. 139:* 55-68.
4. Ham, R. G., D. C. Fitzgerald, Jr., and R. E. Eakin. 1956. Effects of lithium ion on regeneration of hydra in a chemically defined environment. *J. Exp. Zool. 133:* 559-572.
5. Henderson, R. F., and R. E. Eakin. 1959. Alteration of regeneration in planaria treated with lipoic acid. *J. Exp. Zool. 141:* 175-190.
6. Henderson, R. F., and R. E. Eakin. 1960. Inhibition of malic dehydrogenase by cyclic disulfides. *Biochem. and Biophys. Res. Comm. 3:* 169-172.
7. Spangenberg, D. B., and D. L. Claybrook. 1961. Infection of hydra by Microsporidia. *J. Protozoology 8:* 151-152.
8. Spangenberg, D. B., and R. G. Ham. 1960. The epidermal nerve net of hydra. *J. Exp. Zool. 143:* 195-202.

DISCUSSION

EAKIN: When the use of oxaloacetate as a source of CO_2 was mentioned, during the previous discussion, the question came to my mind as to whether or not increased CO_2 tension would reverse the inhibition of regeneration caused by lipoic acid. I would be very chagrined if we found out that the effect of oxaloacetate was merely to build up the CO_2 level.

BURNETT: Were your normal hydra budding when you cut them through the middle?

EAKIN: Yes, we always use hydra that had one (or preferably two) buds in order to insure that our organisms were in an optimal state of nutrition. The use of the words "mid-stomach cut" was to indicate a severance in the region mid-way between the hypostome and the point of budding.

Perhaps I should explain how the differential counts on the developing interstitial cells were made. These counts were made on longitudinal sections through the center of the coelom. The ratio of interstitial cells (at the four stages of maturity) to total cells is a maximum at the hypostome and decreases as one progresses proximally until a minimum occurs just before reaching the budding area. Past this point the ratio increases markedly, the final stages of maturation into cnidoblasts being especially prominent. The counts were made in the area between the site of severance and the line demarcating the minimum concentration of interstitial cells, thus excluding the budding area.

A Study of Normal and Abnormal Regeneration of Hydra[1]

DOROTHY B. SPANGENBERG
Spangenberg Laboratories, Refugio, Texas

One of the most challenging fields of developmental research is the study of the regeneration of lost parts in lower animals. This area of investigation is of special interest because most of the processes involved in such regenerative phenomena (cell mitosis, cell differentiation, cell migration, the interaction of cells or tissues) are analagous to those taking place in most other forms of development, and because these processes in lower animals can be studied with relative ease.

Hydra are particularly suited for this purpose since they are able to regenerate lost parts rapidly and can be easily maintained in the laboratory. Previous investigators of hydra regeneration have placed a major emphasis on (a) the capacity of different hydra parts to regenerate, (b) histological changes during normal regeneration, (c) regulation following abnormal regeneration, and (d) metabolic gradients in regenerating hydra. Recent investigations made in this laboratory of the regenerative ability of hydra (as measured by the rate of regeneration of tentacles and the number of tentacles regenerated) revealed that normally this capacity varies even between strains of the same species of hydra and can be markedly influenced by environmental factors

[1] These investigations were carried out at the Clayton Foundation Biochemical Institute, The University of Texas, Austin, Texas.

such as the temperature at which the hydra are tested, the temperature at which they are maintained prior to severance, the site at which they are cut, their state of nutrition, and intracellular parasitism (4, 11).

A unique effect upon the regeneration of hypostomes and tentacles was demonstrated by Ham and Eakin (5) using lipoic acid, a cyclic disulfide which functions normally as a coenzymatic unit in the decarboxylation of α-keto acids. By exposing "decapitated" hydra to extremely dilute concentrations of this compound they were able to "permanently" inhibit regeneration of severed structures in *Hydra littoralis.* However, the "vitamin" was not otherwise toxic to the organisms, and such inhibited hydra regenerated normally if the non-regenerated tip was cut away after several days. Subsequent studies showed that alterations in the normal pattern of development induced by exposure to lipoic acid were not related to the compound's enzymatic functions but rather to a specific effect of the cyclic disulfide structure of the oxidized form of this vitamin. In *Chlorohydra* exposed to lipoic acid, the regeneration of tentacles and hypostomes is likewise retarded early in the regeneration period, but in this species abnormal regeneration subsequently occurs wherein large numbers of tentacles and extreme body deformity results (13). With the latter, higher amounts were needed.

Early studies on the action of chemical agents which counteracted the lipoic acid effect in *H. littoralis* (5) indicated that the disulfide might be affecting the nervous system of hydra. However, cytological studies of the nervous system of normally regenerating and inhibited hydra failed to reveal *morphological* evidence that the nervous system was altered in these treated hydra. Therefore, detailed studies of other processes either known to be or suspected to be involved in normal regeneration were carried out using both normal and lipoic acid treated hydra. The study of these processes (interstitial cell differentiation, cell mitosis, cell migration and the interaction of cell layers) led to the development of postulates concerning mechanisms involved in normal regeneration and to postulates explaining, at least in part, the effect of lipoic acid on hydra regeneration.

INTERSTITIAL CELL DIFFERENTIATION

The role of interstitial cells in hydra regeneration has been emphasized by many investigators (1, 7, 9, 10). While the ability of interstitial cells to differentiate into any other cell type in hydra is disputed, most authors agree that cnidoblasts arise from interstitial cell differentiation (2, 10, 14). The differentiation of interstitial cells into cnidoblasts (specifically those containing desmonemes) was selected as a process deserving study, since it can be directly related to the rate of normal and abnormal regeneration in hydra. Cell counts of differentiated stages of interstitial cells in the pre-tentacle area of non-regenerating hydra (severed and then immediately killed) revealed that those hydra whose tentacles and hypostomes had been removed close to the hypostomal area (while the hydra were in a stretched condition) contained more desmonemes and late-state interstitial cells than did hydra which had been cut in the mid-stomach region. This and other observations indicated that along the body of a hydra there is a qualitative gradient in the distribution of the various stages of interstitial cells, with the greatest concentration of desmonemes and late-stage interstitial cells at the base of the tentacles (11). Tardent (14), using *Chlorohydra*, reports a quantitative gradient in the distribution of all types of interstitial cells. The existence of a qualitative gradient explains the decreased regenerative ability observed in normal hydra severed at the mid-stomach region when compared to those severed at the hypostomal region, since in the former case most of the reserve of partially differentiated interstitial cells is removed at the time of the cutting. It is postulated, therefore, that any factor which is apt to interfere with normal differentiation of interstitial cells is a more effective inhibitor in hydra cut at the mid-stomach region than in those cut at the hypostomal region.

Some of these factors which have been observed to affect interstitial cell differentiation are a depletion of nutrients (fasting of the animal prior to testing), and the presence of intracellular parasites in hydra (11). Also, the inhibition produced by exposure to lipoic acid and to certain other chemical agents is much more effective in hydra cut in the mid-stomach region than in those cut at the hypostomal region.

Histological studies of lipoic acid treated hydra (*H. littoralis* and *Chlorohydra viridissima*) revealed that, at 20 hours after cutting, many undifferentiated interstitial cells were in the pretentacle area, whereas only a few late-stage interstitial cells and cnidoblasts containing desmonemes were present. This indicates that normal differentiation of interstitial cells does not take place in these hydra. Morphologically, however, the interstitial cells appear normal as compared to controls. It is questionable, therefore, whether the differentiation of the interstitial cells is inhibited by a direct action of lipoic acid on these cells or whether it is influenced by damage to another cell type which may normally contribute some substance to interstitial cell differentiation. Histological sections of lipoic acid treated *H. littoralis* and *C. viridissima* reveal that some of the gastrodermal cells are damaged. Whether or not this damage of gastrodermal cells is related to reduced interstitial cell differentiation in the epidermis is still to be determined. It is believed that many factors which influence the regenerative process do so by interfering with interstitial cell differentiation.

CELL MIGRATION

The importance of cell migration in morphogenesis has been emphasized both in embryonic development (16) and in the regenerative process (15).

Grafting segments of *Chlorohydra* from a normal clone (containing green algae in their gastrodermal cells) to segments of a modified clone (no visible green algae) revealed that during normal regeneration gastrodermal cells migrate from closely adjacent regions to participate in the regenerative reconstruction. Migration of gastrodermal cells was not impaired in lipoic acid treated *Chlorohydra,* and in fact, the extent of cell migration appeared to be increased (Fig. 1). It is possible that the increased migration of gastrodermal cells following lipoic acid treatment results from the need for replacement of the gastrodermal cells that are damaged by the chemical (13).

On the basis of many observations made of regeneration of

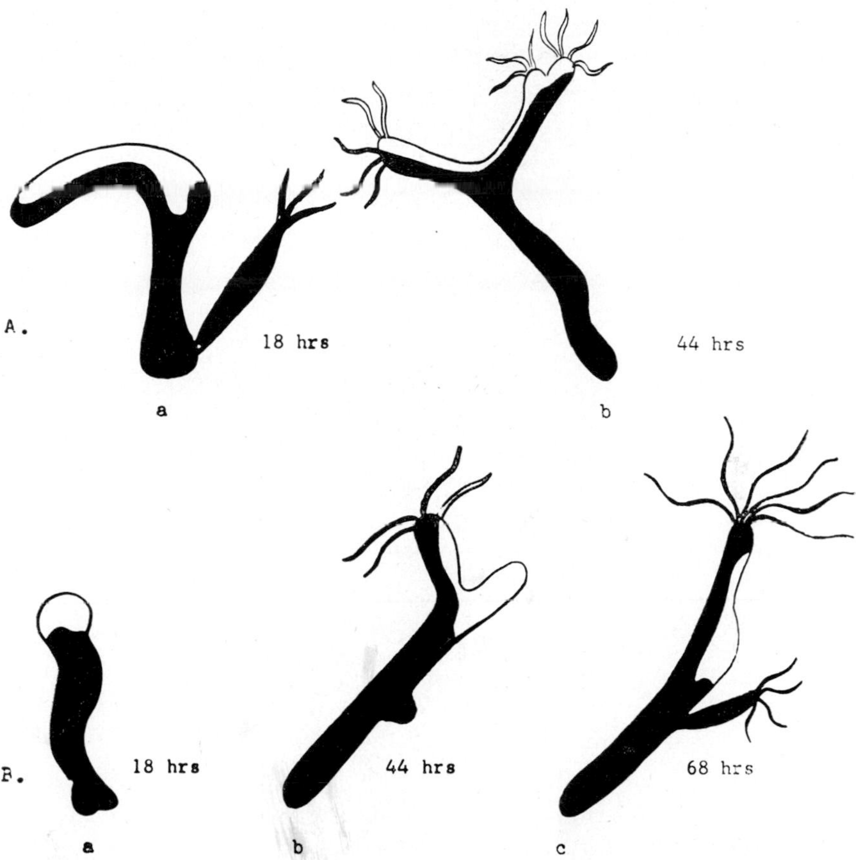

Fig. 1. Migration of gastrodermal cells in grafted *Chlorohydra* treated with lipoic acid.

new tentacles in *H. littoralis,* it is our opinion that some cnidoblasts migrate short distances to become incorporated into the new tentacle; however, most of the nematocysts for the new tentacles are formed after cutting from the differentiation of interstitial cells during the early part of the regeneration period. Histological sections of lipoic acid treated *Hydra* offered the best evidence of interstitial cell migration. In these organisms, where maturation of the interstitial cells is inhibited, large numbers of undifferentiated interstitial cells were seen at the pre-tentacle site twenty hours after cutting, whereas only a few cnidoblasts containing desmonemes were present. Although it was not possible to observe migration of the immature interstitial cells, their presence in such large numbers indicated that they had migrated. On the other hand, there was no such accumulation of desmoneme-containing cnidoblasts; hence, there could have been no significant amount of migration of these cells.

CELL MITOSIS

Cell mitosis during regeneration was studied by early investigators, many of whom did not regard this process as being immediately essential for tentacle formation. Rowley (10), while studying *C. viridissima,* concluded that the new cells are not formed at the cut surface alone and that the tentacles do not seem to be regenerated solely from new tissue. She felt that the new cells which appear during the regeneration of hydra are formed by division of the old cells throughout "the entire piece" (as in the normally growing animal) and that the tentacles are formed from old cells and from cells that have arisen by division of the already differentiated cells of the old part.

Except for a slight increase in mitosis noted by Ham and Eakin (5), reaching a maximum at 45 minutes near the site of the cut (a reaction possibly associated with wound healing), we have not observed any increase in mitotic activity during the remaining regeneration period. It is believed, therefore, that mitotic activity if diffuse throughout the body of the hydra and there is no increase in activity during normal regeneration or in hydra treated with lipoic acid. The presence of all stages of mitotic activity in lipoic acid treated hydra indicated that this process had not been altered by exposure to this disulfide.

Since interstitial cells are believed to be replaced through mitosis, there most likely is an increase in this activity after the regeneration period in order to replace those cells which differentiated into the necessary components of the new tentacles. Further research, however, will be necessary to determine the extent to which this occurs.

INTERACTION OF CELL LAYERS

The two cellular layers of hydra, the epidermis and gastrodermis are separated by a non-cellular substance, the mesogloea, which varies in thickness throughout the column of the hydra. The mesogloeal layer is extremely thin in normal hydra at the tentacle base and at the site of a newly forming bud. In regenerating hydra, the mesogloea is *not* replaced at the regenerating tip until the early tentacles have appeared and the hypostome has formed. In lipoic acid treated *Chlorohydra,* areas which are lumpy in form show a decrease or absence of mesogloea (13); and according to Chang, Hsieh, and Liu (3), in depressed hydra, prior to development of abnormal form, the mesogloea "dissolves." In all of these instances, in areas where there is active differentiation of interstitial cells prior to normal or abnormal growth of tissue, the mesogloea appears reduced or absent. Conversely, at the tentacle bases of fasted hydra and in the stalk region of normal hydra, where there is little interstitial cell differentiation taking place, the mesogloea appears to be relatively thick. In several hydra which have been permanently inhibited by lipoic acid, at 48 hours after cutting, the mesogloea has been restored although the hydra have not regenerated.

The foregoing does not imply that interstitial cell differentiation takes place only in areas where there is no visible mesogloea. A certain amount of interstitital cell differentiation is undoubtedly taking place continually in areas that contain visible mesogloea. However, we believe that the differentiation process is hastened in areas of active growth by a closer contract of the two tissue layers in the absence of visible mesogloea.

Whether the mesogloeal material is actually utilized in areas of active cellular differentiation is not known. If the mesogloea does contain collagen or a collagen-like material as postulated (12), then it is possible that this substance may be utilized in a manner analagous to its use in wound healing in higher animals. Whether or not such use is made remains to be determined.

Where the mesogloea is not seen in various areas of the hydra, however, the gastrodermis and epidermis appear to be in closer contact. Gastrodermis removal and fasting studies have indicated that a normal amount of gastrodermis and proper nutrition are necessary for normal regeneration. It is possible that a transfer of typical nutrients, or possibly some other specific substance necessary for epidermal interstitial cell differentiation, might be better facilitated when the two cellular layers are in closer contact. If this is the case, then variations in the amount of mesogloea might be an important factor in growth regulation of hydra by influencing the extent of interstitial cell differentiation.

Induction of the differentiation of one tissue by its close contact with another tissue has been studied extensively, but the exact mechanism is not known. Although it is interesting to compare the situation in hydra (wherein close contact of gastrodermis and epidermis occurs during active interstitial cell differentiation) to induction in embryological studies, there is no direct evidence that the mechanism is the same. However, Moore (8), working with the hydroid *Cordylophora lacustris*, noted that oral cone grafts will induce from mass tissue the development of hydranth regions basal to the oral cone. She observed that no induction was produced when an oral cone graft was separated from the host tissue by an agar or a cigarette paper barrier. "Direct close contact between the graft and the host appears to be necessary for induction to be produced."

The origin of mesogloeal material during regeneration is not known. In regenerating hydra, the mesogloea is restored in the hypostomal region, usually by 18 hours regeneration time, after interstitial cell differentiation has occurred. That the mechanisms involved in restoration of the mesogloea are not identical with those involved in interstitial cell differentiation is apparent in lipoic acid treated *Hydra littoralis,* wherein interstitial cell differentiation has not occurred normally by 18 hours, yet the mesogloea is restored at the same rate as in normally regenerating controls. If one considers that a normal balance must occur between the rate of interstitial cell differentiation and mesogloeal restoration, then a growth regulating mechanism can be postulated wherein alteration of either of these processes can cause a variation in the normal regeneration pattern.

RETARDED INTERSTITIAL CELL DIFFERENTIATION WITH NORMAL MESOGLOEAL RESTORATION

In normal regeneration, this relationship could account for variation in the regenerative ability of normal hydra. It has been demonstrated that the normal reserve of partially differentiated interstitial cells varies in different strains of hydra (11). The time required for the acquisition of the necessary number of differentiated interstitial cells is dependent upon the quantity of reserve differentiated cells already available. Variation in amount of such reserves and in the rate of differentiation producing new ones could account for variation in normal regenerative ability of hydra provided the mesogloeal material is restored in all hydra at the same rate.

In lipoic acid "inhibited regeneration" (*H. littoralis*), the differentiation of interstitial cells is definitely retarded, yet the mesogloeal material is restored at a normal rate. Once the mesogloeal material is restored, it appears that the interstitial cells do not differentiate sufficiently for regeneration to occur. However, if the non-regenerated tip (and consequently the mesogloeal layer) is removed several days hence (after cellular damage has been repaired) normal regeneration occurs.

RETARDED INTERSTITIAL CELL DIFFERENTIATION WITH RETARDED MESOGLOEAL RESTORATION

This condition is observed in lipoic acid treated *Chlorohydra* where the inhibitory effect expresses itself in one of two ways — (a) either permanent inhibition (as in *H. littoralis*) or (b) retardation with subsequent "wild" growth (13). In case (a), the restoration of the mesogloeal mechanism may occur before sufficient interstitial cell differentiation has occurred (as in lipoic acid treated *H. littoralis*), and the hydra would be permanently inhibited. In case (b), the restoration of the interstitial cell differentiation may occur prior to the restoration of the mesogloea, resulting in the differentiation of more interstitial cells than normally occurs, and the hydra exhibit the "wild" growths observed.

These postulated mechanisms are very speculative, but they do offer a basis for planning future investigations concerned with the mechanisms of *interstitial cell differentiation* and of *mesogloeal restoration* during regeneration and the interplay of these two factors as a growth controlling mechanism in regeneration.

CONCLUSIONS

Many factors (both intrinsic and extrinsic) influence the differentiation of interstitial cells to cnidoblasts during regeneration.

Other cell types must be considered as possible contributors to the process of interstitial cell differentiation.

The mesogloea is not visible in areas where intense interstitial cell differentiation is proceeding in normal hydra or severed hydra (both in untreated and lipoic acid treated organisms).

A growth regulating mechanism is proposed wherein a balance between the *quantity of mesogloea* present in an area of the hydra and the extent of cell differentiation (apparently brought about by the close contact of the gastrodermis and the epidermis) must be achieved for normal regeneration to occur.

Although the emphasis has been placed upon the importance of cell migration, cell differentiation and the interaction of cell layers during the regenerative process, other mechanisms (many of which are still unknown) must also contribute to this very complex process.

A knowledge of the interactions occurring throughout the whole animal, especially the interrelationship between different cells and cell layers through chemical and physical interchange, must be acquired before a true understanding of the overall process of regeneration will be achieved.

REFERENCES

1. Brien, P. and M. Reniers-Decoen, 1949, La croissance, la blastogenese, et l'ovogenese chez l'*Hydra fusca* (Pallas). *Bull. biol. France et Belg. 83:* 293-386.
2. Burnett, A. L. 1959. Histophysiology of growth in hydra. *J. Exp. Zool. 140:* 281-342.

3. CHANG, J. T., H. H. HSIEH, and D. D. LIU. 1952. Observations on hydra, with special reference to abnormal forms and bud formation. *Phys. Zool. 25:* 1-10.

4. HAM, R. G., D. C. FITZGERALD, and R. E. EAKIN. 1956. Effects of lithium ion on regeneration of hydra in a chemically defined environment. *J. Exp. Zool. 133:* 559-572.

5. HAM, R. G., and R. E. EAKIN. 1958. Loss of regenerative capacity in hydra treated with lipoic acid. *J. Exp. Zool. 139:* 55-68.

6. HAM, R. G. and R. E. EAKIN. 1958. Time sequence of certain physiological events during regeneration in *Hydra. J. Exp. Zool. 139:* 33-54.

7. KANAJEW, *J.* 1930. Zur Frage der Bedeutung der interstitiellen Zellen bei Hydra. *Roux. Arch. 122:* 736-759.

8. MOORE, J. 1951. Induction of regeneration in the hydroid *Cordylophora lacustris. J. Exp. Biol. 28:* 72-93.

9. MOORE, J. 1952. Interstitial cells in the regeneration of *Cordylophora lacustris. Quart. J. Microsc. Sci. 93:* 269-288.

10. ROWLEY, H. 1902. Histological changes in *Hydra viridis* during regeneration. *Amer. Naturalist 36:* 578-583.

11. SPANGENBERG, D. B., and R. E. EAKIN. 1961. A study of variation in the regeneration capacity of hydra. (Manuscript submitted).*

12. SPANGENBERG, D. B., and R. E. EAKIN. 1961. Histological studies of mechanisms involved in hydra regeneration. (Manuscript submitted).*

13. SPANGENBERG, D. B. and R. E. EAKIN. 1961. The effect of lipoic acid on regeneration of *Chlorohydra viridissima.* (Manuscript submitted).*

14. TARDENT, P. 1954. Axiale Verteilungs-Gradienten der Interstitiellen Zellen bei *Hydra* und *Tubularia* und ihre Bedeutung fur die Regeneration. *Roux Archiv. 146:* 593-649.

15. TARDENT, P. 1960. *Developing Cell Systems and Their Control.* 18th Growth Symposium, The Ronald Press Company, New York.

16. WAGNER, R. P., and H. K. MITCHELL. 1955. *Genetics and Metabolism.* John Wiley and Sons, Inc., New York.

---

*The investigations reported in these three manuscripts submitted to the *Journal of Experimental Zoology* have been published as a doctoral dissertation: A Study of Mechanisms Involved in Normal and Abnormal Regeneration of Hydra, 1960. The University of Texas.

Growth Factors in the Tissues of Hydra

Allison L. Burnett[1]
Universite libre de Bruxelles, Bruxelles, Belgium, and
The University of Virginia, Charlottesville, Virginia

THE METABOLIC GRADIENT OF HYDRA

The work of Child and Hyman (7) demonstrated that hydra possesses body regions which show a striking difference in metabolic activity. This finding was corroborated by Hinrichs (9), Weimer (20, 21, 22) and Child (5, 6). These investigations revealed in general that hydra possesses a primary apico-basal gradient with a secondary increase in metabolic activity in the budding region. The areas of the tentacles and peduncle were shown to have a low metabolic activity as compared to the hypostome and budding region, and the basal disk, while less active than the hypostome, was found to possess a metabolic activity higher than that of the gastric region and much higher than that of the tentacles and peduncle. Actually, it is unwise to state that hydra possesses a gradient at all, for it isn't a gradient in the true sense of the word. Hydra simply has three very active regions, the hypostome, budding region, and basal disk; one fairly active region, the gastric region; two regions of low metabolic activity, the peduncle and tentacles.

It is interesting to speculate on the factors which account for these differences in metabolic activity along the length of the body column. Burnett (3) has conducted a nutritional study on hydra during periods of rich feeding and prolonged starvation. He found

---

[1]Present address: Department of Biology, Western Reserve University, Cleveland, Ohio.

that the concentration of food reserves (glycogen, neutral fats, protein reserve droplets) along the body column is directly in proportion to the metabolic activity of a particular region. Areas of low metabolic activity contain few gastrodermal inclusions while areas which are capable of reducing methylene blue when applied to the living animal contain an excess of food reserves. Furthermore, a histological examination of different body regions in hydra has revealed that interstitial cells and gland cells are scarce or lacking altogether in regions of low metabolic activity and are abundant in regions of high activity.

A question which immediately comes to mind is reminiscent of the old "hen and egg" question, i.e. do regions of high metabolic activity possess this activity because of the presence of food inclusions and interstitial cells in this area, or do these areas contain these specific cells and food inclusions because of the general active metabolism of this area which is not directly related either to interstitial cells or specific food inclusions?

Nearly all workers in the field of metabolic gradient have stressed the fact that the "head" region (hypostome region), because of its high metabolic activity, in some manner supresses the formation of another head in its immediate vicinity. For this reason, a bud never forms directly beneath the head of the parent under normal conditions, but begins as an outpushing of the body roughly midway between the hypostome and basal disk. Such a hypothesis immediately suggests that the "head" region liberates an inhibitive substance which in some manner prevents the cells of the adjacent gastric region from entering the active cell divisions which would eventually lead to the formation of a bud. If this is indeed true, then it is first necessary to demonstrate that such an inhibitive principle exists, and secondly, if it does exist, it is necessary to determine why it doesn't affect cellular divisions in the head region itself.

Another series of questions are closely linked with this same problem. Brien (1) has shown that the sub-hypostomal region of hydra is an active growth center. Constant cell proliferation in this center forces cells distally towards the tentacle tips and proximally towards the basal disk where these "migrating" cells atrophy and are sloughed off the body column. Thus, by constant cell proliferation in the hypostomal region and constant cell death at the extremities, hydra is able to grow continually yet maintain its form.

Numerous grafting experiments conducted by several different investigators, notably Rand (15, 16, 17) Hefferman (8), Browne (2), Kolitz (11), Burt (4), Issajew (10), Rand, Bovard, and Minnich (18), Tripp (19), Mutz (14), Yao (23, 24, 25), demonstrated that the hypostomal region of hydra is the "dominant" center of the animal and will induce polyp formation at the site where it is grafted to the body column of another hydra. Similarly, it was shown by many of these workers that tissues of the developing bud will induce hydranth formation in another hydra at the graft site.

From the observations cited thus far in this paper, it would appear that the hypostomal region of the animal is one which is engaged in constant growth activities. In this highly metabolically active region a growth inhibitive principle is produced which passes down the stalk and inhibits cellular divisions in the adjacent gastric region. In the budding region of the hydra, the inhibitive principle presumably does not exert its affect and the cells in this area take on properties similar to those in the hypostomal growth region. In a sense, it may be stated that a new growth region is created in the budding region, for both the hypostomal and budding regions engage in cell divisions which lead to the formation of a new polyp. If this is correct, then it must be assumed that cells in the gastric region possess the potential of growth and rapid cell division, but that these cells are inhibited in some manner from performing these vital functions while they are located in the gastric region.

This paper will attempt to answer the following basic questions. What accounts for the high metabolic activity of a particular area? Does hydra possess a specific growth inhibitive principle which is produced in the hypostome? Does this principle become inactivated as it diffuses down the body column towards the budding region? Does this principle inhibit cellular divisions in the area in whch it is produced? Are there specific substances responsible for the growth and inductive potential of the hypostome?

None of the experiments designed to answer these basic questions will be described in detail in this paper. A long monograph describing the growth processes exhibited by hydra is now in press (*J. Exp. Zool.*). This monograph will describe in detail all of the experiments listed in the present paper.

THE GROWTH INHIBITING PRINCIPLE IN HYDRA

In order to demonstrate that hydra possesses a growth inhibiting principle in its tissues, and that this principle is produced in the hypostomal region, a simple experiment was conducted. It was assumed that if an inhibitive principle was produced in the hypostomal region and that if this principle diffused in some manner down the body column, it would be possible to induce head formation in the gastric region of the animal by simply preventing the flow of this principle. Such a manuever was accomplished by simply grafting the peduncle of one hydra between the hypostomal and gastric region of another animal. Burnett (3) has shown that the peduncular digestive cells are highly vacuolated and have a wasted, aged appearance. It was thought that perhaps these vacuolated cells might in some way impede the passage of a growth inhibitive principle proximally.

Thirty-nine grafts similar to that described in the preceding paragraph were performed. In 19 cases the hypostomal region plus the transplanted peduncle split from the gastric region and the original peduncle. After the split the gastric region grew a new "head" on its distal surface. However, in 20 cases, after a period of 1-2 days, tentacles formed in the gastric region just below the site of the transplanted peduncle. Eventually an entire hypostome was formed proximal to the grafted peduncle, and the outcome of this experiment was the formation of two completely normal hydra.

This experiment clearly indicates that cells in the gastric region, when removed from the direct influence of the hypostomal region, are stimulated to form a new "head" region. It may be possible that a growth inhibitive substance produced in the hypostomal region diffuses down the body column inhibiting substances which would normally promote growth in the gastric cells. Moreover, the inhibitive principle must pass down the column by diffusion from cell to cell since there was a direct connection between the head and gastric regions through the gastrovascular cavity.

Another series of experiments were undertaken to determine why the inhibitive principle is not effective in the budding region of the animal, and whether the inhibitive principle affects the dividing cells in the hypostomal region where it is produced.

It appeared possible that as the inhibitive principle diffused proximally along the gastric region that it might become more dilute or perhaps inactivated or broken down after it remained for a given period of time in the gastric region. If this hypothesis is correct, then it should be possible to suppress the asexual reproductive process by placing the growth region closer to the budding region than it is normally.

It was shown that if the gastric region of the hydra is removed, and the growth region grafted to the area adjacent to the budding region, budding will not occur until growth process in the hypostomal region have forced the "head" some distance away from the budding region. This distance is roughly porportional to the area occupied by the excised gastric region. However, it was also shown that if the head is transferred to a site adjacent to a budding region which has already begun bud formation, the bud goes on to form normally and is not inhibited by the transplanted head.

These experiments suggest that once a region is actively involved in growth processes it is not influenced by the growth inhibitive principle. This observation explains why the inhibitive principle is not effective in the area in which it is produced. It exerts its effect only on those cells which have been pushed proximally because of growth processes in the hypostomal region. However, these experiments also indicate that budding can be suppressed by the presence of a hypostomal region in the immediate vicinity if cell division which would eventually lead to the formation of a bud has not begun.

In view of these results it appears that once active cell division in the budding region begins this region is similar to the hypostomal growth region of the parent. Neither of these two regions are influenced by the inhibitive principle; both are, in a sense, forming an entirely new individual. Perhaps this analogy can be further extended, and it may be hypothesized that the developing bud liberates an inhibitive principle similar to that liberated from the head region of the parent.

Lenhoff (12) has demonstrated that, if the gastric region of a *H. littoralis* containing a bud is transected immediately above that bud, head formation of the parent is inhibited at the site of section even after the bud separates from the parent stalk. This observation strongly indicates that an inhibitive substance is released from the tissues of the bud. However, the answer is not as simple as that. If it is true that the inhibitive substance becomes more dilute as it diffuses along the column, the regeneration of the parent head should not be affected if the head is transected at the level of the sub-hypostomal growth region rather than through the gastric region as demonstrated by Lenhoff.

In order to test this hypothesis, parent hydra, bearing buds in all stages of development were transected either through the middle of the gastric region or through the sub-hypostomal growth region. Subsequent examination of these animals revealed that animals which had been excised through the growth region regenerated within twenty-four hours and were not affected by the presence of a bud on their column. However, animals which had been excised through the gastric region were inhibited in their regenerative processes and had not even begun tentacle formation after twenty-four hours. Interestingly enough, parent animals, excised through the gastric region and containing buds which had formed peduncles had begun tentacle formation after twenty-four hours. It will be remembered that the peduncular region is capable of inhibiting in some manner the passage of a growth inhibiting principle.

These results indicate that a developing bud does contain a growth inhibiting principle, and that this principle in some way is gradually rendered impotent as it diffuses from the bud along the length of the parent column.

Many aspects of hydra's biology can be tentatively explained in light of a growth inhibitive substance. For instance, many speculations have been made to explain why a hydra containing several buds always produces them successively, and why the buds, in addition to the fact that they are in different stages of development, are arranged in a helical pattern and are on essentially different sides of the stalk from one another.

The budding pattern may operate through the following mechanism. When a bud first begins its development an inhibitive principle is released. This principle does not permit the formation of another bud in adjacent regions of the parent column. As the bud continues to grow it forms tentacles and eventually a peduncle; at this time a second bud begins to form on the opposite side of the parent stalk. Presumably, the peduncle inhibits the flow of the inhibitive principle back to the parent stalk, also the principle which has previously diffused back into the parent before peduncle formation, is more concentrated on the side of the stalk adjacent to the bud than on the opposite side. The third bud will form on the opposite side of the stalk and above the second bud. Again, the formation of the third bud does not occur until much of the energy supply of the second bud in the form of food reserves is depleted, and the second bud has begun tentacle and peduncle formation. Such a mechanism makes it virtually impossible for two buds to compete for food materials from the same area of the parent column. However, the author has observed that under conditions of *extremely* rich feeding, it is not unusual for two buds to begin to form simultaneously from the same level of the parent stalk and directly opposite one another. Since both buds have begun to form simultaneously, their inhibitive principles will have no effect upon one another.

Furthermore, the presence of an inhibitive principle explains why cells which pass from the budding region down into the peduncle have a low metabolic activity, are highly vacuolated, and contain few food reserves. First, most of the food reserves which were originally in these cells have been utilized during bud formation. Secondly, subsequent ingestion of food by the hydra will not nourish the peduncular cells because they are under the direct growth inhibiting action of the neighboring budding region and do not require large amounts of food for the upkeep of this metabolically inactive region. If the peduncle is excised from the body column it will never completely regenerate into a normal hydra because of a lack of energy reserves. An excised peduncle is capable of forming only 2 or 3 tentacles when excised from the inhibiting action of the budding region.

GROWTH STIMULATING PRINCIPLE IN HYDRA

It is interesting at this time to consider the factors which stimulate growth in hydra and which are under the direct control in certain body regions of growth inhibiting principles. In order to demonstrate the existence of a growth principle in hydra it is first necessary to define the action of this principle. It has been previously stated that hydra possesses two "growth" regions in its body, the hypostomal growth region and the budding region. It is well known that if the hypostome is removed from a hydra, a new hypostome is always formed on the distal portion of the excised body column. The formation of a new hypostome may be interpreted as follows: after the excision of the hypostome, the gastric region is no longer under the influence of the growth inhibiting principle which normally diffuses proximally from the hypostomal region. Therefore, growth substances present in the gastric region are activated and a new growth center is established. On the other hand, if an animal is excised through the gastric region, the proximal portion of the region containing the hypostome always forms a new gastric region, peduncle, and base — never another hypostomal region. Again we may say that a growth inhibiting principle from the hypostome is inhibiting head formation in the proximal region.

If the foregoing analysis is correct, it should be possible to initiate head formation in the proximal portion of an excised gastric region by supplying additional amounts of the growth principle to this area. Presumably an excess of a growth stimulating principle would overcome the influence of the growth inhibiting principle.

In order to demonstrate that a growth principle exists in metabolically active regions of the hydra, and that this principle is capable of diffusing from these regions and stimulating cell growth and division in adjacent regions, the following experiments were conducted.

Two different species of hydra were employed in these experiments. One species was the common brown *Pelmatohydra oligactis*; the other was a new species, *Hydra pirardi,* recently discovered in Belgium by Dr. Paul Brien. When these two species are grafted to one another there is no cellular exchange whatsoever between the species, except that the nematocysts of one species are able to be incorporated into the tissues of the other species.

Twenty *Pelmatohydra oligactis* were excised through the middle of the gastric region, and the distal excised portions which contained the head region were grafted to the growth regions of a similar number of *Hydra pirardi* whose hypostomes and tentacles had been excised. After a period of 2-3 days the distal regions of the *H. pirardi* portions began to form new tentacles and hypostomes. The following day, tentacle growth invariably began on the proximal region of the *H. oligactis* portions. Ultimately, new head regions were formed on either side of the junction of the grafted portions and the grafted animals separated from one another. A true reversal of polarity had thus been effected in *P. oligactis,* and this had been accomplished without any exchange of cellular material from *H. pirardi* with the possible exception of cnidoblast cells which would presumably not be directly involved in growth processes.

These results indicate that a growth stimulating principle is present in the hypostomal region of *H. pirardi* and that this principle is capable of passing into the tissues of *Pelmatohydra oligactis* and stimulating head formation.

A further series of experiments were conducted to further confirm the presence of the potential of the growth stimulating principle. It will be recalled that cells of the peduncular region of hydra are highly vacuolated, contain few food inclusions, are metabolically inactive, and are destined to die and be sloughed off the basal disk. Furthermore, the epithelio-muscular cells of his region contain very little cytoplasmic RNA, and this area is characterized by the fact that it contains few or no interstitial cells and no glandular cells in its proximal regions.

Thus, it was desirable to determine whether a growth stimulating principle, after being introduced into the peduncular region, would be capable of "rejuvenating" this senescent region.

Fifty peduncular regions of *Pelmatohydra oligactis* were grafted to the growth regions of a similar number of *Hydra pirardi* as in the previous experiment. In 47 cases the peduncles of the *P. oligactis* portions formed a basal disk and separated from the *H. pirardi* portions before the latter had begun head formation. However, in

3 striking instances *H. pirardi* portions began tentacle formation before the *H. oligactis* portions had detached. In these 3 cases the results were most interesting. Small tentacles began to form from the peduncles of *P. oligactis* a day after tentacle formation. had begun on *H. pirardi*. When the grafts were fed with brine shrimp, it was noticed that the bulk of ingested food materials were taken into the digestive cells of the peduncle of *P. oligactis*. Such a phenomenon never occurs under normal conditions.

Three days after feeding the 3 animals were sectioned for histological study. It was found that the normally wasted peduncular digestive cells of *P. oligactis* were full of protein reserve droplets. Interstitial cells had invaded this area and appeared in concentrations comparable to the normal growth region of the hydra. Several dozen interstitial cells had transformed into gland and mucous cells, and in the lower regions of the peduncle where a basal disk would normally be expected to form, a new hypostome was nearly completely elaborated.

Thus, it appears that *P. oligactis* does contain specific growth stimulating principles within its tissues. When these principles (or principle) are present in a body region in sufficient concentrations, this region will take in large amounts of food after each feeding and will subsequently be invaded by interstitial cells. It is hypothesized that the metabolic activity of a given region of hydra is dependent upon the amount of growth stimulating principle which is present and which is not being affected by a growth inhibiting factor.

Unfortunately little is known at the present time concerning the nature of either the growth stimulating or inhibitive principle. A method has recently been devised whereby it is possible to collect the stimulating principle in agar blocks and introduce it into any desired body region of another hydra. Burnett and Schwager are in the process of elucidating the chemical nature of this principle.

The growth inhibiting principle has not been isolated from the tissues of the hydra at the present time. It will be interesting to determine whether the inhibitive principle which acts in the tissues of the hydra by diffusing proximally from the growth region is the same as that found by Lenhoff and Loomis (13) which can limit the asexual reproductive process of a colony of *H. littoralis*. The inhibitive principle described by Lenhoff and Loomis is heat-labile, dialyzable, non-gaseous, and absorbed on the cation-exchange reagent permutit. They have extracted this principle from the culture medium in which *H. littoralis* have been crowded.

REFERENCES

1. Brien, P., and M. Reniers-Decoen, 1949. La croissance, la blastogénèse, l'ovogénèse chez *Hydra fusca* (Pallas). *Bull. Biol. France et Belg., 82:* 293-386.
2. Browne, E. 1909. The production of new hydranths in hydra by the insertion of small grafts. *J. Exp. Zool. 7:* 1-23.
3. Burnett, A. 1959. Histophysiology of growth in hydra. *J. Exp. Zool. 140:* 281-342.
4. Burt, D. R. 1925. The head and foot of *Pelmatohydra oligactis* as unipotent systems. *Arch. für Entwick. mech. 104:* 421-433.
5. Child, C. M. 1934. Differential reduction of methylene blue by living organisms. *Proc. Soc. Exp. Biol. and Med. 32:* 34-36.
6. Child, C. M. 1947. Oxidation and reduction of indicators by hydra. *J. Exp. Zool. 104:* 154-195.
7. Child, C. M., and L. H. Hyman, 1919. Axial gradients in the hydrazoa. I. *Biol. Bull. 36:* 183-221.
8. Hefferman, M. 1901. Experiments in grafting hydra. *Arch. für Entwick. mech. 13:* 567-587.
9. Hinrichs, M. N. 1924. A demonstration of axial gradient by means of photolysis. *J. Exp. Zool. 41:* 21-32.
10. Issajew, W. 1925. Studien an organischen Regulationen (Experimentelle Untersuchungen an *Hydren*). *Arch. für Entwick. mech. 108:* 1-67.
11. Koelitz, W. 1911. Morphologische and experimentelle Untersuchungen an *Hydra. Arch. für Entwick. mech. 31:* 423-455.
12. Lenhoff, H. 1957. The induction of a new center of polarity in regenerating *Hydra littoralis. Anat. Rec. 127:* 325.
13. Lenhoff, H., and Loomis W., 1957. The control of clonal growth of *Hydra* by the self inhibition of tentacle differentiation. *Anat. Rec. 127:* 429.
14. Mutz, E. 1930. Transplantationsversuche an Hydra mit besonderer Berucksichtigung der Induction, Regionalität, und Polarität. *Roux' Arch. für. Entwick. mech. 121:* 210-271.
15. Rand, H. W. 1899. The regulation of graft abnormalities in hydra. *Arch. für Entwick. mech. 9:* 161-214.
16. Rand, H. W. 1899. Regeneration and Regulation in *Hydra viridis. Ibid. 8:* 1-34.
17. Rand, H. W. 1911. The problem of form in Hydra. *Science 33:* 391.
18. Rand, H. W., Bovard, J. F., and D. E. Minnich, 1926. Location of formation agencies in hydra. *Proc. Nat. Acad. Sci. U.S.A. 12:* 565-570.
19. Tripp, K. 1928. Regenerationsfahigkeit von Hydren in den verschiedenen Korperregionen nach Regenerations und Transplantationsversuchen. *Zschr. Wiss. Zool.* (Korshelt Festband), *132:* 476-525.
20. Weimer, B. R. 1928. The physiological gradient of hydra. *Physiol. Zool. 1:* 183-230.
21. Weimer, B. R. 1932. The physiological gradient of hydra. *J. Exp. Zool. 62:* 93-107.

22. WEIMER, B. R. 1934. The physiological gradient of hydra. *Physiol. Zool. 7:* 212-225.
23. YAO, T. 1945. Studies on the organizer problem in *P. oligactis. J. Exp. Biol. 21:* 147-150.
24. YAO, T. 1945. Effect of some respiratory inhibitors and stimulants and of oxygen deficiency on the induction potency of the hypostome. *J. Exp. Biol. 21:* 150-155.
25. YAO, T. 1945. Bud induction by developing hypostome. *J. Exp. Biol. 21:* 155-160.

DISCUSSION

STREHLER: How was it determined that cells move up into the tentacles and die at the tips?

BURNETT: Semal-Van Gansen (1951) vitally stained limited areas of the tentacles and watched the stain migrate distally.

STREHLER: Do both the gastrodermal and ectrodermal layers move towards the tip of the tentacle?

BURNETT: Yes, both move. In 1926 Issajew observed that if a fork forms in the tentacle of a hydra, the fork will move distally becoming progressively smaller until it gradually disappears at the tentacle tip. We have observed this many times. Such a phenomenon would not occur unless both cell layers were migrating. Moreover, cnidoblasts are steadily pushed into the tentacles through such growth processes from the sub-hypostomal growth region.

STREHLER: Then the cnidoblasts don't migrate as free cells?

BURNETT: In *Pelmatohydra oligactis,* there are always free nematocysts in the enteron and in the digestive cells of the tentacles. This can be demonstrated in the following experiments. The proximal portion of a methylene blue stained animal is grafted to the distal portion of an unstained animal. Under conditions of normal feeding, stained nematocysts are not found in the epidermal batteries, but only in the gastrodermal cells of the tentacles. However, if the nematocyst supply in the tentacle batteries is depleted, then stained nematocysts are transferred from the digestive cells of the tentacle to the epidermal batteries. It is impossible for stained nematocysts to reach the tentacle through growth processes because the stained nematocysts are all proximal to the growth region, and growth would serve only to push the nematocysts towards the base of the animal.

CROWELL: If you cut the tentacles off, nematocysts first form in the column, and then move into the tentacles from the lower region. How do they get there?

BURNETT: They are simply forced distally by an active cell proliferation in the growth region of the hypostome.

CROWELL: No, I'm not talking about the ones that grow normally, but when one cuts the tentacles off and mobilizes nematocyst formation elsewhere, how do these cnidoblasts move?

BURNETT: The answer is still the same. Cnidoblasts of a newly regenerated tentacle are pushed there by sub-hypostomal growth processes. Some cnidoblasts are pushed into the peduncle. Others pass into the enteron where they are swept to the tentacles; many are ingested by digestive cells in this area. However, in *Pelmatohydra oligactis* these ingested cnidoblasts will be transferred to an adjacent tentacle battery only if that battery's supply of nematocysts is depleted.

CROWELL: They are transported in the gastro-vascular cavity?

BURNETT: That's right.

LOOMIS: There is another piece of evidence suggesting that nematocysts reach the tentacles through the gastro-vascular cavity. This is the well-known fact that when the worm *Microstomum* eats hydra, the undischarged nematocysts migrate through the worm's tissues until they are in position in the ectoderm and ready to be used by him. In other words, if nematocysts can travel through the endoderm to the ectoderm of a flatworm, then almost certainly they can do the same through the tissues of a hydra. This would explain how a hydra can arm its tentacles within twenty four hours after being fed even though it takes about a week for new cells to grow out from the hypostome to the end of a tentacle.

BURNETT: Also, I believe that the nematocysts in the worm *Microstomum* are moved passively through the tissues of the worm. I think the nematocyst is phagocytized by a worm mesodermal cell and is transported to the epidermis. I do not think that the hydra cnidoblast is active in the process.

FULTON: What do you find in the gastrovascular cavity? Are these nematocysts or cnidoblasts?

BURNETT: In the worm the nematocyst is naked, as I understand it. In the hydra the nematocyst is always inside a cnidoblast.

SLAUTTERBACK: We have sought an answer to that question with the electron microscope and have never seen a nematocyst in the tentacles of hydra which was not still within the cnidoblast which produced it. It seems fair to assume that if the nematocyst migrates it does so within its own cnidoblast.

Also we have seen a cnidoblast migrating through the mesoglea only once. It seems rather unlikely to me that very many cnidoblasts can pass through the mesoglea and be repeatedly missed by us. We have studied *H. littoralis, P. oligactis* and *C. viridissima.*

BURNETT: This is interesting. *H. pirardi* appears to have a cnidoblast migration pathway different from that of *P. oligactis.* I have examined Dr. Brien's slides of *H. pirardi* and have observed that the digestive cells in the base of the tentacle contain many ingested nematocysts. Some of these nematocysts, in section, can even be seen traversing the mesoglea towards the tentacle battery.

SLAUTTERBACK: When nematocysts are seen in the gastroderm one must be very careful to determine that they are not degenerating and that they are still within a living cnidoblast. Many of these may appear to be variable even when examined quite critically with the light microscope but at higher magnifications there are often signs of cytoplasmic degeneration in the cnidoblasts and deterioration of the nematocysts themselves.

BURNETT: Yes, we have made the same observation. However, many of the cnidoblasts plus the enclosed nematocyst in the digestive cells of the gastrodermis are normal. We have shown that when a proximal portion of *P. oligactis* is grafted to the distal region of *H. pirardi,* nematocysts characteristic of *H. oligactis* pass into the enteron of *H. pirardi* where they are ingested. If this ingestion takes place in the tentacles, the nematocysts of *P. oligactis* are passed on to the epidermal batteries of *H. pirardi* where they are still capable of discharging.

CROWELL: I'm sure cnidoblasts have to migrate and I'm pretty sure we're not yet clear on how they do it. Now another aspect of the same thing. You spoke of inducing interstitial cells in the basal region. Were these cells there, or did they move in?

BURNETT: The interstitial cells migrated from more distal regions of the animal. I am almost certain of that.

CROWELL: Did they invade by way of the gastrovascular tract, or did they creep? What happens when they get there?

BURNETT: I don't think interstitial cells ever migrate via the gastrovascular cavity. Brien has studied interstitial cell migration from a small portion of normal hydra grafted to a hydra whose interstitial cells were killed through X-irradiation. He observed an epidermal migration of interstitial cells. We have noted a similar phenomenon in our induction experiments.

CROWELL: Were they creeping? Are they wriggling between epidermal cells?

BURNETT: I've never seen them creep. I suppose they migrate in an amoeboid fashion. I have never seen interstitial cells in the gastrodermis at any stage during the induction phenomenon.

CROWELL: I think Nelson Spratt has seen migrating cells working their way along. Were they interstitial cells?

FULTON: No, they were nematoblasts, but Dr. Spratt made his observations on *Tubularia*.

BURNETT: I'm not sure that undifferentiated cells are capable of migrating. I am referring to the small basophilic cells seen in nests along the length of the epidermis. Each time that I observe a "migrating cell" it is much larger than the cells found in these epidermal nests. Perhaps a "migrating cell" is a partially differentiated interstitial cell.

FAWCETT: It seems to me that these cells can only migrate at either end of this differentiation sequence. They could migrate as an individual interstitial cell or after the cluster has completed its differentiation and separates again into individual cells. It would be quite impossible for a syncytial cluster of 8 or 16 cells connected by these bridges, which I believe in very firmly, to insinuate themselves between other cells in the column or to cross the mesoglea and get into the gastrovascular cavity and re-invade at a higher level. I think this syncytial relationship almost excludes any migration in the interim period. They will either have to migrate as undifferentiated individual interstitial cells, or as cnidoblasts that have matured nematocysts within them.

STREHLER: I wonder whether you've ever seen migration of any nematocysts or cnidoblasts into the tentacles of *Campanularia*. In this case they could not move through the gastrovascular cavity because the tentacles have no cavity. Also, I would like to ask why you call that pigment lipofuscin.

BURNETT: The inclusions found in *Hydra pirardi* fed on *Artemia* are not carotenoids and are not dissolved by lipid solvents. They are dense bodies, often found in clusters, and as I remember, they stain only after they have been oxidized by permangenate or a similar oxidizing agent.

STREHLER: If it was not extractable with organic solvents, then perhaps you should call it "hydrafuscin." What were those slides stained with?

BURNETT: Methylene blue.

STREHLER: Was that the natural color of those granules?

BURNETT: Yes, the methylene blue didn't go into the granules.

STREHLER: Do you find them down toward the base?

BURNETT: Yes, like the carotenoids in hydra, they are especially concentrated in the hypostome, budding region and basal disk. They probably represent some type of excretory crystal. They persist for a greater length of time during starvation. I am not qualified to comment any further on their nature or function.

Nucleic Acid and Protein Changes in Budding *Hydra littoralis*

YU-YING FU LI

AND

HOWARD M. LENHOFF

Laboratories of Biochemistry, Howard Hughes Medical Institute, and Departments of Biochemistry and Zoology, University of Miami, Miami, Florida

Budding in hydra has excited biologists since it was first discovered over 250 years ago by Leeuwenhoek and Trembley. As one step toward understanding the mechanisms involved in the initiation and growth of a bud, we have been searching for means to characterize chemical differences between parent and bud tissues (2). Some of our preliminary observations concern changes in the amount and distribution of DNA, RNA, and protein in budding *Hydra*.

Experiments involving the chemical analyses of cellular components required large number of *Hydra* in the same stages of budding. These were obtained by carefully controlling the time at which they were fed, while keeping all other growth conditions constant. In these experiments, *Hydra* having one bud were removed from a mass culture (3). The animals were then allowed to starve 4-6 days, during which time the original bud and one or two latent buds completed their development, detached, and were discarded. On the sixth day of starvation the animals were fed once with excess *Artemia* nauplii. As shown in Figure 1, nearly all of the *Hydra* initiated a small bud within the first day after feeding.

The developmental stages of the budding *Hydra* are presented in Figure 2. First, the 6-day starved animal enters the "small bud"

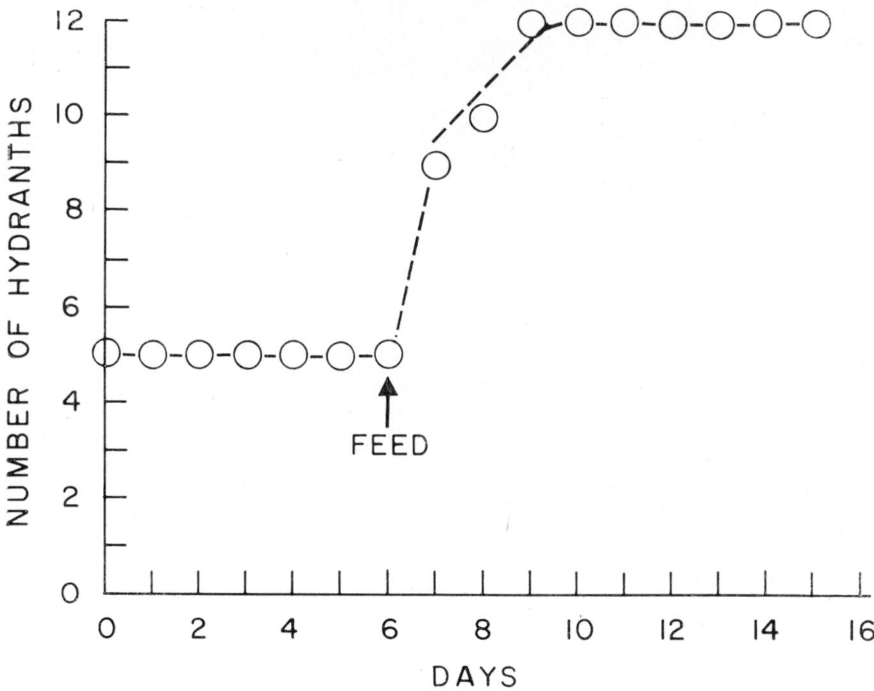

Fig. 1. Time of bud initiation in starved *Hydra* after one feeding. This is a representative experiment on 5 *Hydra*. Similar results were obtained using hundreds of *Hydra*.

stage 12 hours after one meal. Once the bud is initiated, it continues its development through the "medium bud" stage, the "short tentacled bud" stage, and the "long tentacled bud" stage. The gastrovascular cavity of each bud in the "long tentacled" stage are no longer connected to the parent's cavity, and the buds are now capable of detaching. After its detachment the new bud is then fed until it in turn begins to initiate its own bud. Throughout this entire process we followed the chemical changes occurring in two major phases: bud development initiated by one feeding, and the growth and development of the detached bud to the adult stage.

The protein, DNA, and RNA values of a six day starved *Hydra* following a single feeding and during the ensuing stages of budding are shown in Figure 3. It should be emphasized that all DNA

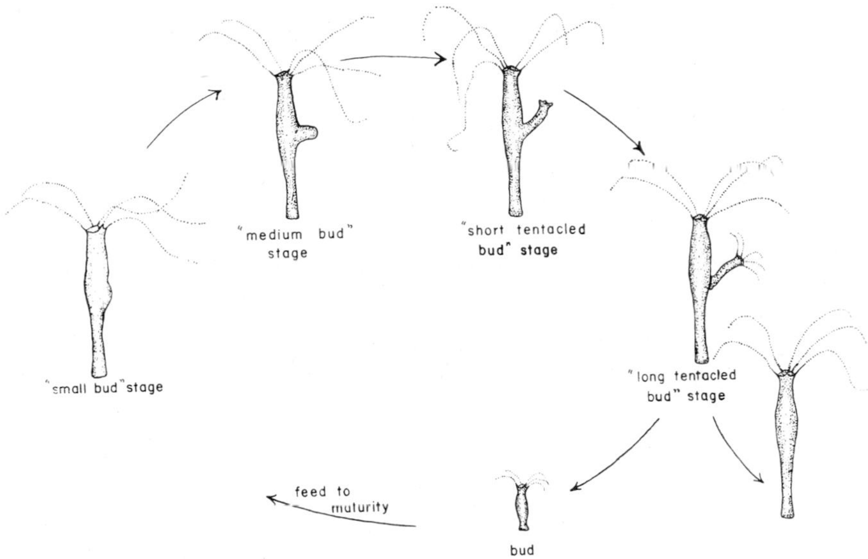

Fig. 2. Stages of budding *Hydra*.

and RNA measurements were made without separating these macromolecules from the rest of the cellular components. Thus, the DNA and RNA values also include the smaller species of these molecules. The DNA, RNA, and protein were assayed, using the diphenylamine (1), orcinol (5), and Lowry (4) methods respectively. The protein, DNA, and RNA values for *Hydra* before feeding (not shown on this figure) were about half that of their respective values at 12 hours. Thus, on feeding, a doubling in all of these components occurred because of the ingested protein, DNA, and RNA of the shrimp. During the next 72 hours, however, these macromolecular components decreased slowly, while the DNA/protein ratio remained relatively constant. The changes observed probably resulted from at least two factors: (a) degradation of the ingested food, and (b) the synthesis of *Hydra* cellular components.

In Figure 4 are shown the DNA/protein ratio of *Hydra* in the long-tentacled bud stage and that of the same animals 48 and 72 hours later when the buds have detached from the parent. (The protein content of the bud was about one third that of the parent.)

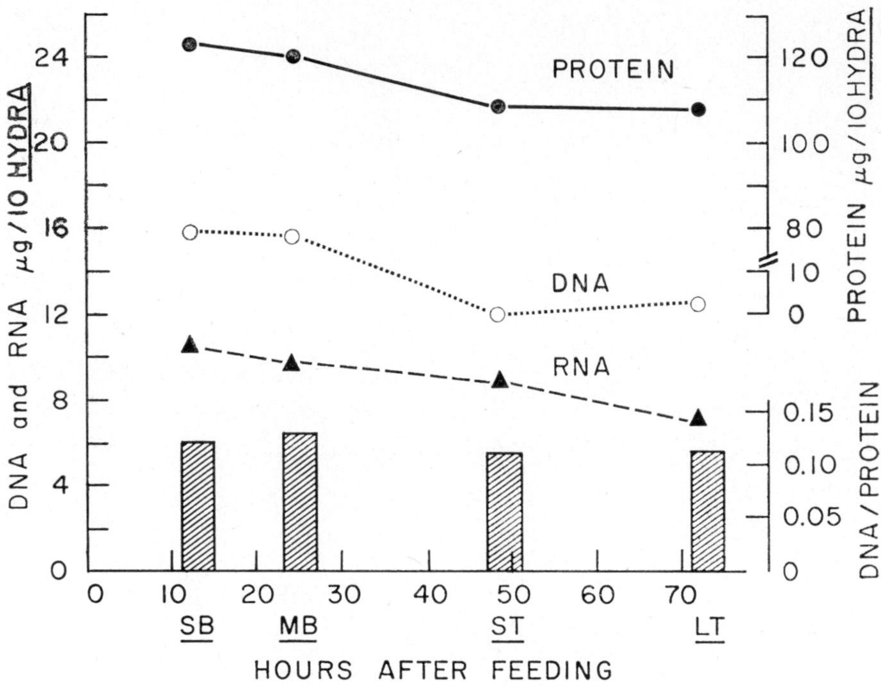

Fig. 3. DNA, RNA, and protein content of *Hydra* in different stages of budding. The symbols *SB, MB, ST,* and *LT* represent the small bud, medium bud, short tentacled, and long tentacled stage animals.

These data reveal the first major chemical difference between parent and bud tissues, the DNA/protein ratio of the bud being three times that of the parent *Hydra*.

Since the experiments in Figure 3 gave no indication of the bud possessing this high DNA/protein ratio, another type of experiment was carried out to determine whether this high ratio was already present in an early stage of bud tissue. In these experiments (Fig. 5), we excised only the bud portion of a "medium bud" stage *Hydra* and then determined the respective chemical composition of the dissected parents and buds. It can be seen that, although there is much less protein in the dissected bud than in the remaining parent, the DNA contents of both parts are nearly equal. More striking is the high DNA/protein ratio of the dissected bud. These results

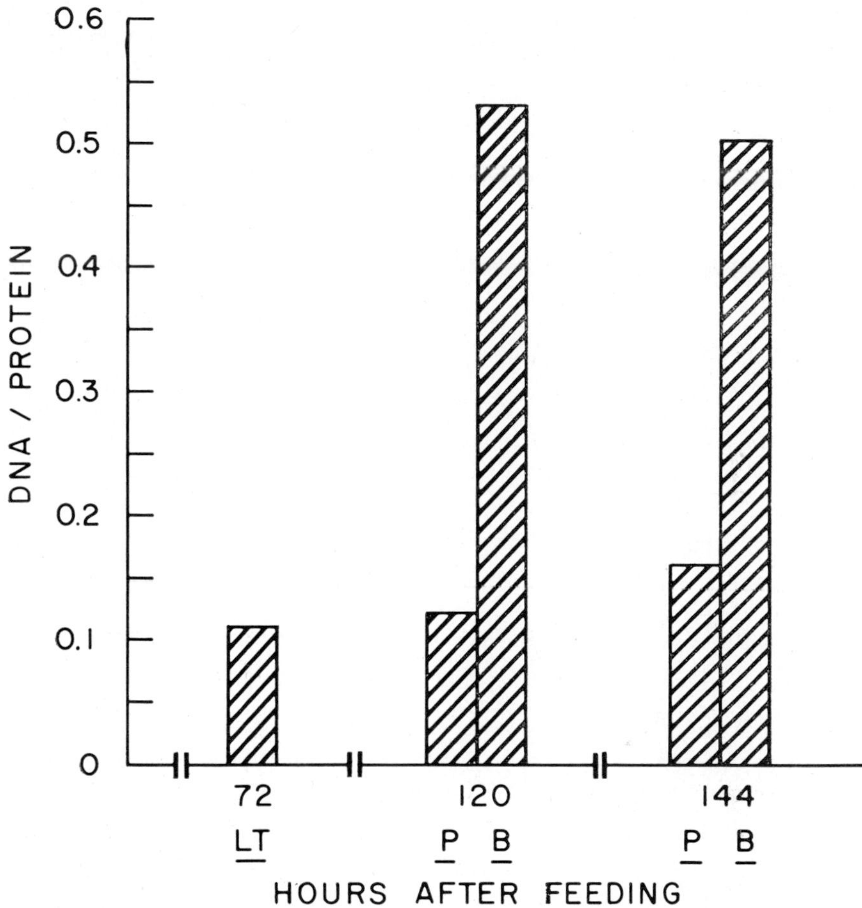

Fig. 4. DNA/protein ratio of long tentacled stage *Hydra (LT)* before and after the buds detached. *P* and *B* represent parents and buds. Ten animals are used in each experiment.

indicate that a high DNA/protein ratio is a property of bud tissue in its early development. It is also possible, although less likely, that the high DNA values in bud tissues actually represent large pools of diphenylamine-positive material which serve as precursors for DNA synthesis.

The chemical changes occurring in buds fed until they reach

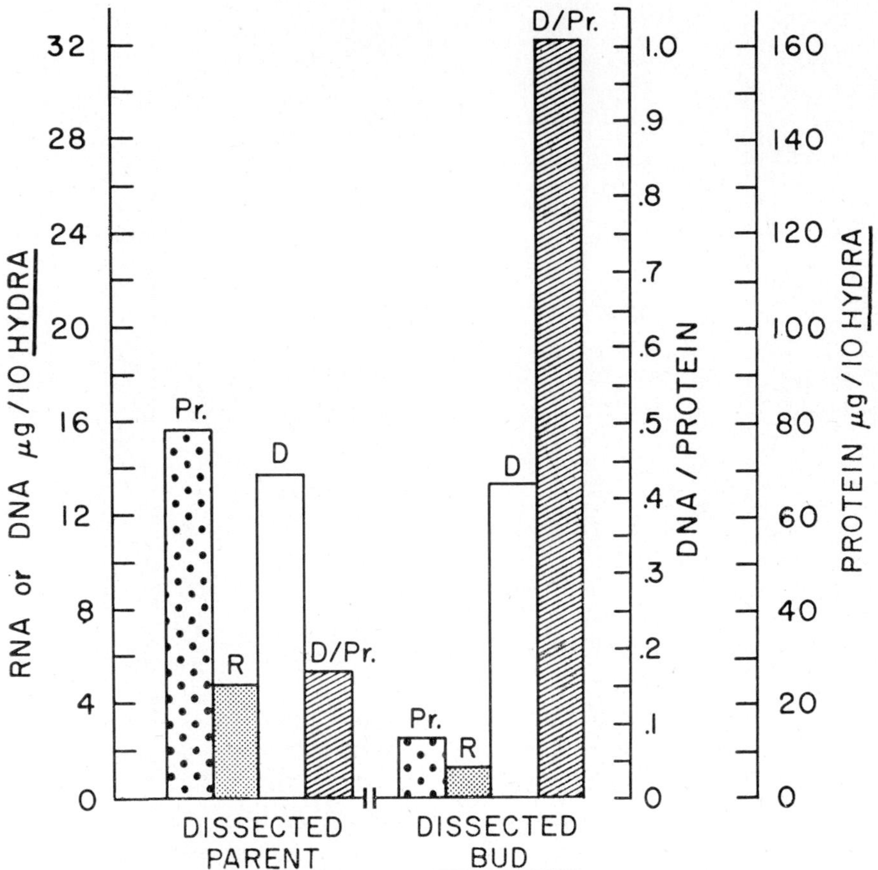

Fig. 5. DNA, RNA, and protein content of buds dissected from 10 medium bud stage *Hydra*, and of the parents remaining after dissection.

parent size is shown in Figure 6. The first sets of measurements were made before the animals were fed. The last measurement was made two days after the third feeding. The results show that the protein and RNA increased to that of the small bud stage *Hydra*. In contrast, the DNA, which was high initially, decreased slightly. Consequently, the DNA/protein ratio decreased until it approached that of the parent *Hydra* in the small bud stage.

The consistent finding of this study was the relatively high DNA/protein ratio of buds (Figs. 4, 5, 6). Consequent with growth,

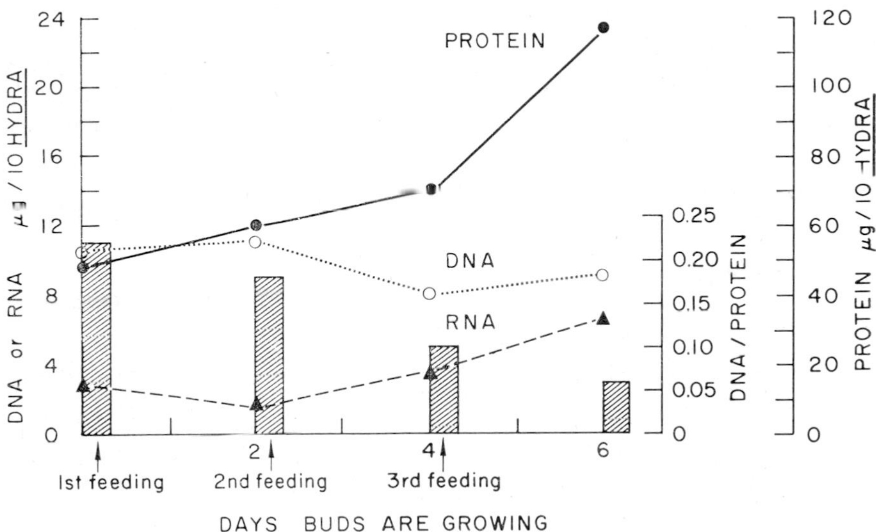

Fig. 6. DNA, RNA, and protein content of buds during growth to small bud stage *Hydra*.

owing to an increase in protein, the bud's DNA/protein ratio diminished to that of the parent (Fig. 6). These experiments suggest that in bud cells the amount of nuclear material is high relative to the cytoplasm, and that subsequent growth of the detached bud involves an increase in cytoplasmic components rather than mitosis.

REFERENCES

1. Burton, K. 1956. A study of the conditions and mechanism of diphenylamine reaction for the colorimetric estimation of deoxyribonucleic acid. *Biochem. J. 62:* 315-323.

2. Li, Y.-Y. F. and H. M. Lenhoff. 1960. Nucleic acid patterns of *Hydra* budding in synchrony. *Anat. Rec. 137:* 376.

3. Loomis, W. F. and H. M. Lenhoff. 1956. Growth and sexual differentiation of hydra in mass culture. *J. Exp. Zool. 132:* 555-574.

4. Lowry, O. H., N. J. Rosebrough, A. L. Farr and R. J. Randall. 1951. Protein measurement with the Folin phenol reagent. *J. Biol. Chem. 193:* 265-275.

5. Schneider, W. C. 1957. Determination of nucleic acids in tissues by pentose analysis. *Methods in Enzymology 3:* 680-691. Academic Press, Inc., New York.

DISCUSSION

BURNETT: I might mention that if the end of a bud is excised early in its development, the remaining part will regenerate while still attached to the tissues of the parent. This suggests that cellular divisions are occurring within the tissues of the bud proper. Moreover, we have been able to demonstrate that after the bud hypostome reaches a certain distance from the parent column, it develops a growth region of its own. The tentacles of the bud arise only when the tip of the bud has grown some distance from the parent. Tentacle formation is dependent upon cellular divisions in the budding tissue itself, and tentacular material is not furnished by the parent.

CLAYBROOK: I'd like to report an observation about which we have no further information. Occasionally, in cultures of *Hydra littoralis* growing at a minimal rate while being fed the heated *Artemia* diet which I reported on yesterday, we find buds that fail to form hypostomal tentacles or mouth. They may remain attached to the parent for days or weeks. Sometimes they detach after they have differentiated a basal disk, but some still do not produce any tentacles. Under these conditions, they cannot eat and eventually disintegrate.

Index